Disney

365
Stories

A story a day

PaRragon

Bath · New York · Cologne · Melbourne · Delhi
Hong Kong · Shenzhen · Singapore · Amsterdam

This edition published by Parragon Books Ltd in 2015

Parragon Books Ltd
Chartist House
15–17 Trim Street
Bath BA1 1HA, UK
www.parragon.com

ISBN 978-1-4723-7709-8

Printed in China

101 DALMATIANS

New Year's Day

It was the first day of the new year, and Pongo and Perdita were out for a walk with their pets, Roger and Anita. The morning fog was beginning to part, and the air was clear and cold. "Oh, Pongo," Perdita sighed happily. "What a wonderful year we've just had – 15 puppies to be thankful for!"

"Yes, darling, and think of all we have to look forward to this year," said Pongo.

"Can you believe they all stayed up till midnight last night to ring in the new year?" Perdita cried. "And still awake when we left! I do hope they don't tire out dear, poor Nanny."

"Yes, that was quite a party we had at the flat last night," Pongo agreed. "And Lucky would have spent the whole night watching television if we had allowed him to."

"Perhaps we should be getting home now," said Perdita. "I am so afraid that Cruella De Vil may come around while we're out. I dread the way she looks at our puppies."

"I suppose we should," said Pongo. "But I'm sure Nanny has been taking good care of them." Pongo and Perdita gently pulled on their leads to let Roger and Anita know it was time to go home. The four of them walked towards home just as a new sprinkling of rain began to gently fall.

"Nanny! Puppies! We're home!" called Roger as he and Anita took off their muddy boots and Pongo and Perdy brushed off their paws on the mat in the hall. But no one answered.

"Pongo!" exclaimed Perdita, her panic rising. "Where are the puppies?"

Pongo raced up the stairs and began searching the rooms one by one. Perdita went to check the kitchen. Roger and Anita exchanged concerned looks, but tried to remain calm.

Pongo hurried into the sitting room to rejoin Perdita, who was on the brink of tears. "Oh, Pongo!" she cried. "Where can …"

"Hush, darling," said Pongo, his ears pricked intently. The two dogs fell silent. Then they both heard it: a tiny snore coming from the direction of the couch. There, nestled among the cushions, the puppies were sound asleep!

"I found Nanny!" Roger called. "She fell asleep in her chair!"

Perdita was busy counting the sleeping puppies. "… 12, 13, 14 … Oh, Pongo! One of the puppies isn't here!"

But Pongo had trotted into the next room. "Here he is, darling!" he called. "It's Lucky, of course. He's watching the New Year's Day celebration on television."

The Arrival of a Space Ranger

Andy was a young boy with a big imagination. He loved playing with all his toys, but his all-time favourite was Woody, a pull-string cowboy doll.

"C'mon Woody!" Andy called. Andy took Woody everywhere. Just then, Andy's mother called out that his friends were about to arrive.

"It's party time!" Andy shouted happily. He dropped Woody off and headed downstairs. After Andy left, the room was quiet for a moment. Then, Woody sat up. "Okay everybody, coast is clear!" he shouted.

One by one, all the toys peeked out of the closet, from beneath the bed and out of the toy chest. Mr Potato Head, Hamm, Slinky, RC, Rex and Bo Beep all stretched and chatted as they came out – just as they did every time there were no humans around to see them.

Woody gathered the toys for a special meeting. First, he reminded them that only one week remained before Andy and his family would move to a new house. Then he blurted out the big news: "Andy's birthday party has been moved to today."

All the toys started squeaking and shouting! The toys dreaded Andy's birthday, because they feared some newer toy might replace them. This year, the party was being held earlier than usual because of the move.

"They're here!" Hamm shouted suddenly. Out the window, Andy's guests were arriving with lots of presents!

Woody sent the Green Army Men downstairs to spy on Andy's party. Using a jump rope, the soldiers scrambled down to the first floor, then set up a baby monitor inside a potted plant. Hidden, the soldiers described each present as it was unwrapped, sending the news back to Andy's room. Luckily, nothing sounded too threatening … until the last package. All the kids gasped as they saw –

Just then, the baby monitor cut out. The toys were frantic! What was that last present?

Suddenly, Andy and his friends burst into the bedroom. They ran around happily, then rushed out again – leaving the mystery toy on the bed. In the excitement, Woody had fallen on the floor. All the toys watched anxiously as he climbed back up onto the bed.

The new toy turned and blinked. He was white and green and stood with his hands on his hips.

"I am Buzz Lightyear, Space Ranger," he declared. He claimed to be a space hero who had just landed on Earth!

Woody sighed. He knew this newcomer was going to be trouble.

Relaxopolis

It was another cold blustery day in Monstropolis. Sulley and Mike were on their way to work. Mike sighed heavily.

"What's wrong, little buddy?" asked Sulley.

"I'm sick and tired of winter!" Mike replied. "It's cold, it's windy and it gets dark early." He thought for a moment. "Sulley, I think I have the winter blues!"

"Sure sounds like it," said Sulley. "Only a month or so to go, though."

Mike sighed again. A month or two more of winter sounded like an eternity! But a big smile spread across his face when he looked up and saw an advertising board. On it was a big pink monster sitting in a lounge chair on the beach, wearing sunglasses and sipping what looked like an ice-cold booberry slushie. In big letters it said: BEAT THOSE WINTER BLUES IN RELAXOPOLIS!

Mike stopped in his tracks and grabbed Sulley's furry arm. He pointed at the sign, too excited to say a word.

"That's a great idea!" Sulley cheered. "A week on a tropical island is just what we need!"

As soon as he and Sulley got to work, Mike filled in their holiday forms. They would be on their way to Relaxopolis first thing Saturday morning!

When they arrived, they didn't even unpack their bags. They went right to the beach where they each ordered an ice-cold booberry slushie.

As they lay down on their deck chairs on the sunniest part of the beach, Mike said, "This is the life!"

"You bet," said Sulley. "Do you think you need some of this Monster Tropic sunscream? You'd better be careful. You don't want to get too much sun on your first day!"

"I'll just soak up the rays for a little while first," said Mike happily. "My winter blues are just melting away." He slipped a big mirrored sunglass over his eye and put his arms behind his head. This was paradise!

After a while Sulley got bored with sunbathing and decided to go for a swim. Then he joined in a game of beach monsterball. Then he let some little monsters bury him in the sand up to his neck. A couple of hours later, he returned to the deck chairs, where Mike was sound asleep. Sulley took a closer look. His little green friend had not changed position since Sulley had left. Mike had burned himself in the sun!

Sulley covered Mike with a towel and ran over to get him a refreshing booberry slushie. When he returned to the deck chairs, Mike was just waking up.

"Hey, little buddy," said Sulley. "Guess you chased those winter blues away, huh?"

Mike just looked at Sulley sleepily.

"You aren't blue any more," Sulley explained. "Now you're bright red!"

Disney · PIXAR

FINDING NEMO

Marlin's Story

"P. Sherman, 42 Wallaby Way, Sydney ... P. Sherman, 42 Wallaby Way, Sydney." Dory kept muttering the address. She and Marlin were searching for Marlin's missing son, Nemo. They had just escaped an angry anglerfish, and now they were trying to find someone who could give them directions to Sydney. That's where Nemo probably was.

"P. Sherman, 42 Wallaby Way, Sydney ... P. Sherman, 42 Wallaby Way, Sydney," Dory continued to chant.

Marlin had the address memorized and thought he would go crazy if he had to hear it again. "Dory!" he said with a sigh. "I know you just want to be helpful, but do you really need to keep talking?"

"I love to talk," said Dory. "I'm pretty good at it. Hmm ... what were we talking about?"

"I just want to find Nemo," Marlin said.

"That's right, Chico," said Dory.

"One time, Nemo and I ..." Marlin began.

"Go on," Dory said. "Is this going to be exciting?"

"Yes, it's an exciting story," said Marlin, relieved that he had got her to stop reciting the address. "Well," Marlin began, "one time, I took Nemo to the other side of the reef, to visit a relative of mine who was known as the fastest swimmer of all the clownfish, in his day.

But when we visited him, he was getting on in years."

Dory yawned. "When's the good part?"

Marlin sighed. "I was just about to get to it!" he said. "So, anyway, on the way back home, guess what we ran into?"

"What?" asked Dory.

"A huge jellyfish! It was hovering in the water, blocking our way through two big tufts of sea grass."

"Uh-huh," said Dory. She seemed to be trying to remember something. "P. Sherman ..." she muttered softly.

"For a moment there I thought we were goners," said Marlin. "But then ... a huge sea turtle swam up and swallowed the jellyfish in one gulp!"

"Did you say thank you to the sea turtle?" asked Dory, who seemed back on track.

"Well, no," Marlin replied. "I was afraid he would eat us, too, so Nemo and I hurried on our way. But, ever since then, I have been fascinated with sea turtles. And I hope I never have to meet another jellyfish!"

"Say, I've got a story too!" said Dory excitedly. "It takes place at 42 Wallaby Way, Sydney. At P. Sherman. Now, at P. Sherman, 42 Wallaby Way, Sydney, there was this, um, fish ... and ... well ..."

Marlin just groaned and kept swimming.

Scaredy Cats

"Nala!" Simba whispered. "Are you awake?"

"Yes," Nala whispered back, stepping out of the dark cave where she slept with her mother. "Why are you here? You're gonna get us in trouble ... again."

Earlier, Simba and Nala had gone to explore the forbidden Elephant's Graveyard, where they'd been trapped by hyenas. Simba's father, Mufasa, had rescued them.

"Come on," Simba hissed. "Follow me."

Soon the two cubs were on the dark savannah near the base of Pride Rock.

"What do you want, anyway?" Nala asked.

"I just wanted to make sure you weren't still scared," Simba said.

Nala scowled at him. "Scared?" she exclaimed. "*I'm* not the one who was scared!"

"What?" Simba cried. "You're not saying *I* was scared, are you? Because there's no way I'd be scared of a few stupid hyenas. I wouldn't have been scared even if we ran into *10* hyenas."

"Well, I wouldn't have been scared even if we found *20* hyenas and an angry water buffalo," said Nala.

"Oh yeah?" Simba said. "Well, I wouldn't have been scared of *30* hyenas, an angry water buffalo and a – "

"FURIOUS HORNBILL?" a new voice squawked from the darkness.

"Ahhhhhh!" Simba and Nala cried, jumping straight up in the air.

Just then, a brightly coloured bird stepped out of the shadows. It was Zazu, Mufasa's most trusted adviser.

"Zazu!" Simba cried. "You scared us!"

"I wasn't scared," Nala put in indignantly.

"Me neither!" Simba added quickly.

Zazu glared at both of them over his long beak. "Not scared, were you?" he said drily. "That certainly explains the shrieking."

"You just startled us," Nala mumbled.

Zazu fluffed his feathers. "Listen up, you two," he said. "There's no shame in admitting you're scared. Even King Mufasa wouldn't deny that he was terrified when he found out you were missing. And, if it's good enough for him, it's good enough for a pair of scrawny cubs like you. Right?"

"I guess so," Simba said as Nala shrugged.

"Everyone gets scared," Zazu went on. "It's how you respond to it that counts. That's where *true* bravery lies. Get it?"

"Got it," Simba and Nala said.

"Good." Zazu marched towards Pride Rock. The sun was coming up and it was time for breakfast. "Now let's get you back home post-haste ... or I'll *really* give you something to be scared of!"

Red's Tune-Up Blues

One morning, Red the fire engine thought it was the perfect day to plant a garden. He started his engine. *Rrrrrr.* Red's engine sounded funny. *Pop! Pop! Pop!* Now loud noises were coming out of his exhaust pipe.

As his engine sputtered, Red tried to shrug it off. Hopefully, whatever was wrong would go away, because Red did not want to go to Doc's clinic. He sure didn't like the idea of being poked and prodded.

Instead, Red headed into town to work on his garden, and soon passed Lightning McQueen.

"Hey, Red!" Lightning greeted him. "How's it going?"

"Fine," Red replied shyly. *Bang! Bang!*

"Whoa!" exclaimed Lightning. "That can't feel good. You okay?"

"Mmm-hmm," said Red.

Pop! Red continued driving towards town. Lightning headed into town, too, to find his friends. They wouldn't want Red to be sick. Lightning found the others at Flo's V8 Café, filling up on breakfast.

"Red's not running right," Lightning explained as he pointed to the fire engine, who was starting to plant a garden across the street. "But he's afraid to go to the clinic."

"Aw, shucks," said Mater the tow truck. "I know how the poor fella feels. I was scared my first time, too! But Doc's a pro. He'll have Red fixed up before he knows what hit him!"

The friends tried to convince Red to visit Doc. Ramone offered a new coat of paint at his House of Body Art, but nothing would convince Red to go.

"We had better get over there," Lightning said to Sally, who had just rolled up. The two cars sped over. Mater, Luigi, Guido, Fillmore and Flo followed.

Bang! Pop, pop, pop! Red's engine gurgled and more loud noises came out of his exhaust pipe.

Sally inched forwards. "Listen, Red. We all know going to get a tune-up for the first time can be scary. But whatever is wrong could be easy to fix. If you don't go now, it could turn into a bigger problem later. None of us wants you to need a complete overhaul. We care too much about you."

Red looked back at his friends. He knew what Sally said was true. "Will you go with me?" he asked Sally.

"Of course I will," she replied.

Later that day, Red rolled out of the clinic and all his friends were waiting for him. Red revved his engine. *Vroom!* It sounded smooth as silk. It was great to be running on all cylinders again!

Dusty the Crop Duster

Dusty was a small-town crop-dusting plane, but he had a big dream. He wanted to be the fastest racing plane in the world! The problem was that nobody would take Dusty seriously as a racer.

So Dusty decided he was going to prove it by winning the biggest racing competition in the world – the Wings Around The Globe Rally.

Racing was all Dusty thought about day and night – even when he was at work.

"Pay attention!" said his boss, Leadbottom, interrupting Dusty's latest daydream where a crowd was cheering his name as he flew across the finish line.

Leadbottom was satisfied being a crop duster and thought Dusty should be, too. "Why would you give up crop dusting?" he asked. "Blue skies, no air traffic and that tangy scent of Vita-minamulch!"

But Dusty couldn't help himself. Every day after work, he practised racing in the skies above his home in Propwash Junction, soaring from one end of the town to the other. After all, the qualifying race for the rally was coming up soon! Dusty had to be in his best form ever to stand a chance against real racing planes.

Chug the fuel truck was Dusty's best buddy. He was also his racing coach and was helping to train him for the big rally. Using a radio on the ground, he talked Dusty through different moves – dipping, diving and looping through the air.

During one training session with Chug, Dusty got a bit carried away. He dipped up and down over the treetops and pushed his speed more than ever. Everything was going well, until he started leaking oil. That was never a good sign!

Dusty went to Dottie, the local mechanic, to be fixed. She'd been repairing him a lot lately and was starting to get concerned. Dottie asked Dusty if he had been racing again. Dusty got flustered and quickly denied it. He knew Dottie wouldn't approve. She didn't think he could be a real racing plane. But then Chug arrived and blurted out the truth!

"You're not built to race," Dottie told Dusty. She wanted to support Dusty, but she was afraid he was going to crash if he kept it up.

Dusty knew Dottie was trying to help, but racing was all he wanted to do – and he was going to fly in the Wings Around The Globe Rally as fast as his propeller would carry him!

A Visit in the Night

It's not easy to read with a broken arm! Alone in his room, young Carl was trying to turn a page without letting go of his torch.

Suddenly, he heard a gentle rubbing noise. Then a blue balloon forced its way through his bedroom curtains!

"Ouch!" cried Carl, as he knocked his plaster cast against the bedside table.

A merry little face, framed by a mop of red hair, appeared at the window and Carl let out a second cry.

"It's me! I thought you might need a little cheering up!" whispered Ellie, his new friend, before she leaped down onto the floor.

She slipped quickly under the cover that Carl had made into a tent.

"Look!" she said, showing him a small notebook. "I'm going to show you something I've never shown to anyone else. Swear you won't tell anyone; cross your heart!"

Carl promised and Ellie opened up the book. A photo of the explorer Charles Muntz had been stuck on the first page.

"It's my adventure book! When I grow up I'm going to be an explorer too. And I'll go to South America, to Paradise Falls!"

Carl looked admiringly at the beautiful waterfalls, next to which Ellie had drawn the little house where they'd met each other that same afternoon.

"Obviously it'll be tricky to move the clubhouse all that way!" said Ellie, who had noticed Carl's look of surprise.

The boy didn't say a word, but couldn't stop his eyes from looking up to the shelf where his collection of miniature airships stood, including a model of Muntz's *Spirit of Adventure*. Ellie immediately understood.

"But of course!" she cried out. "You can take us there in an airship! Promise me you'll do it! Promise!"

Carl promised. He could see no reason not to. Ellie was a true adventuress!

"See you tomorrow, right?" she said, getting up. "You're one hell of a chatterbox, you know?" she added, laughing, before straddling the window and disappearing into the night.

"Wow!" murmured Carl, totally bowled over by his new friend. Just 10 minutes in Ellie's company was one of the biggest adventures of his life!

That night, as he slept, he dreamed of a colourful little house perched at the top of Paradise Falls....

A Rookie Racecar

Rookie racer, Lightning McQueen, was waiting for the biggest race of the year to begin. The winner would receive the Piston Cup and a sponsorship deal with Dinoco.

"Speed. I am speed," Lightning repeated. When he roared onto the track, the crowd went wild!

Lightning was fast – but could he beat the King, who had won the most Piston Cups in history, or ruthless Chick Hicks, who always finished second?

The race was on! Lightning and Chick sped around the track side by side. Suddenly, Chick slammed into Lightning, sending him skidding off the track. Lightning raced to catch up.

"Dinoco is mine!" Chick shouted. He veered and caused a pile-up! In seconds, wrecked cars littered the track. Lightning dodged and leaped over wrecks. To Chick's fury, Lightning took the lead!

But then Lightning made a huge mistake. He refused to let his pit crew put on fresh tyres. On the last lap – *BANG! BANG!* – Lightning's old tyres blew out! As he limped towards the finish line, the King and Chick caught up. It was impossible to tell who had come in first.

"Ka-chow!" Lightning posed for reporters with cameras. "I'm a one-man show!"

"We quit!" His pit crew stormed away.

Lightning didn't care. He thought he could win without anyone's help. He was daydreaming about fame and fortune when, suddenly, he heard a loud announcement: The race was a three-way tie! A deciding race would be held in California in one week.

Lightning wanted to leave for California immediately. But his driver, Mack, reminded Lightning that he had to make an appearance for his sponsor, Rust-Eze. Lightning reluctantly greeted the old rusty cars that were his fans. As soon as he was finished, he raced into Mack's trailer. Mack was tired and needed to get some sleep, but Lightning insisted. "We're driving all night."

As Mack struggled to stay awake, four flashy cars pulled alongside and shoved him back and forth across the road. Startled, Mack swerved. Inside the trailer, a trophy fell and landed on the ramp button. The back of the trailer lowered, and a sleeping Lightning rolled out! Lightning woke up in the middle of oncoming traffic – with giant trucks coming straight at him!

Because he'd forced Mack to drive, even though he was too tired, Lightning was now lost in the middle of nowhere! Would the rookie ever learn to listen to his friends?

Dusty's First Race

One night, Dusty and Chug watched a show about racing-plane crashes. This was getting serious. Chug decided Dusty needed a plane, not a fuel truck, to coach him for the Wings Around The Globe Rally. The race was coming up soon and there was still a lot of work to do.

Suddenly, Chug had a great idea! He suggested the perfect coach for Dusty – Skipper, an old navy fighter.

Everyone in Propwash Junction had heard stories of the daring missions Skipper had flown with the Jolly Wrenches, his old navy squadron. But Dusty wasn't so sure. The grouchy warplane didn't even fly anymore. Sparky the tug pushed him everywhere. How could he help Dusty become a proper racing plane? Still, Dusty had to try.

Chug and Dusty went to Skipper's hangar. Dusty told Skipper about his love for flying and asked Skipper to coach him. "I figured with my guts and your glory…." he began.

"Go home," Skipper snarled before Dusty could finish. "You're in over your head, kid." Skipper slammed his hangar door.

Chug and Dusty were shocked and disappointed, so Chug continued to coach Dusty as best as he could. Soon it was time for the qualifying race in Lincoln, Nebraska.

At the airstrip, a three-time rally winner named Ripslinger made a grand entrance. His teammates, Ned and Zed, warmed up the crowd.

Dusty was so excited to see such a talented racing plane up close! "He's so good, he's pre-qualified!" Dusty said in amazement.

"Okay then, people!" called an official. "Today's qualifying round is one lap around the pylons. The top five finishers will qualify for the Rally."

One by one, the planes took to the air. Everyone was impressed by a racer named Fonzarelli. He had a great finish time.

Finally, it was Dusty's turn. As he rolled down the tarmac, Ripslinger, Ned and Zed insulted him. Soon the crowd started teasing Dusty, too.

Dusty was upset, but he tried to focus as he prepared for take-off. He needed to be fast enough for fifth place to qualify.

Everyone in the crowd watched in disbelief as the little small-town crop duster had an amazing run!

Dottie and Chug rushed over to congratulate Dusty. They were so proud of their friend!

Soon after, the official results were in. Dusty's finish time was a tiny bit slower than Fonzarelli's. Poor Dusty hadn't qualified for the rally! How would he ever achieve his dream now?

Disney

Lady and the TRAMP

Spaghetti and Meatballs

Tramp had just escaped from the dogcatcher – again. He'd taught that dogcatcher who was boss! Tramp could smell wood burning in fireplaces, dinner cooking … his stomach suddenly rumbled. Escaping from the dogcatcher always made him work up quite an appetite!

But where would he go for dinner tonight? He usually stopped by the Schultzes for some Wiener schnitzel on Monday, he had corned beef and cabbage with the O'Briens on Tuesday … but what he was really craving was some spaghetti and meatballs.

So, Tramp headed to Tony's Restaurant. He scratched at the back door, as was his custom.

"I'm coming! I'm coming!" Tony shouted. He appeared at the door wiping his hands on a towel. He pretended not to see Tramp, as he always did.

"Hey, nobody's here!" Tony shouted. "It must be April Fools' Day!" He pretended to think for a moment. "No, it's not the first! It's not even April! It's January!"

Tramp couldn't take it any more. He was so hungry! He barked.

"Oh, there you are, Butch my friend," said Tony. Tramp, aka Butch, jumped up and down. "I'll get your dinner," said Tony. "Relax, enjoy yourself."

Tramp sat down and looked around the cluttered alleyway. This was the life!

Just then Tony appeared with a plateful of pasta. He had given Tramp two, no make that *three* meatballs! This was quite a special night.

Tony stood and chatted with Tramp as he ate his meal, telling him about his day – the late delivery of fish, the customer who had complained that the tomato sauce was too garlicky, the trip that he and his wife were planning to take….

Tramp finished eating and gave the plate one last lick. It was sparkling clean.

"That reminds me," said Tony. "There's something I've been meaning to talk to you about. It's time you settled down and got a wife of your own."

Tramp gave Tony a horrified look and began to back out of the alleyway.

Tony laughed so hard his sides shook. "Goodbye, Butch!" he called. "But mark my words, one of these days, you're going to meet the dog you can't resist! And, when you do, I have a good idea – you bring her to Tony's for a nice romantic dinner!"

Tramp barked his thanks to Tony. He walked down the block, shaking his head. He was footloose and collar free! Settle down? That was never going to happen!

Peter Pan
A Never Land Story

It was a cold winter night, and John and Michael just couldn't get to sleep.

They climbed onto the bed of their older sister, Wendy.

"Oh, tell us a story, Wendy!" said Michael.

"Yes, please. A Peter Pan story!" pleaded John.

"Certainly," said Wendy. "Have I told you about the time that Peter Pan outsmarted the evil Captain Hook?"

"Yes!" said Michael eagerly. "And we want to hear it again!"

Wendy laughed and began her story. "Well, one night, Captain Hook moored his ship in a secret cove close to the island of Never Land. He and his men rowed ashore quietly, for he was intent on discovering the hiding place of Peter and the Lost Boys. Captain Hook hated Peter Pan because the boy had cut off his hand in a duel and fed it to a large crocodile. And now that crocodile was determined to swallow up the rest of him. Luckily for Captain Hook, however, this crocodile had also swallowed a clock, so the pirate would always be alerted to the crocodile's presence by the sound of the ticking clock.

"Fortunately for Peter Pan," Wendy continued, "his dear friend Tinker Bell learned of Captain Hook's evil plan ahead of time. She flew to Peter and warned him that the pirate was coming. 'Oh-ho!' laughed Peter. 'Well, we shall be ready for him then!' He found a clock just like the one the crocodile had swallowed. He whistled up into the trees, and a group of his monkey friends appeared. 'Here's a new toy for you!' Peter shouted, and tossed the clock up to them. 'Stay out of sight, now!' Peter told the monkeys, and then he and the Lost Boys hurried to their hiding places.

"When Hook came to the clearing, the first thing he heard was the ticking clock. The sound seemed to be coming at him from all sides! The monkeys were having a grand time, tossing the clock back and forth, and creeping up behind Hook. Seized with terror, Hook and his men raced to their boat and rowed madly back to their ship."

Just then, the Darling children's parents came in to check on them. "You're not telling more of these poppycock stories about Peter Pan, are you, Wendy?" their father asked.

"Peter Pan is real, Father!" cried the children. "We know he is!"

As the parents kissed their children goodnight, they didn't see that a boy in green was crouching just outside the nursery window. He had been listening to the story, and he would be back again – soon.

Dusty's Secret Fear

After Dusty's first race, he was so disappointed that he decided to give up racing forever. Maybe everyone else was right. After all, he was just a small-town crop duster – how could he ever expect to compete against real racing planes? He went sadly about his work, dusting the field and trying to forget about his dream.

Then one afternoon, a race official showed up in Propwash Junction. He had very special news for Dusty. He told Dusty that Fonzarelli, the racer who had been slightly faster than Dusty in the qualifier, had broken the rules and been disqualified! Now Dusty was in fifth place and was going to race in the Wings Around The Globe Rally after all! Chug, Dottie and Dusty celebrated the fantastic news.

Propwash Junction was buzzing with the story. Now that Dusty had proven he could race, Skipper was persuaded to take over as Dusty's coach. This was just what Dusty would need to take him to the next level!

Skipper was a tougher coach than Chug. He pushed his student to fly higher because the tailwinds above the clouds would give Dusty more speed. But Dusty preferred to stay nearer the ground. He made endless excuses why he couldn't fly higher.

"The Jolly Wrenches have a motto: 'Volo Pro Veritas'. It means 'I fly for truth'. Clearly you don't!" Skipper said. He couldn't understand why Dusty wasn't willing to try harder. It seemed to Skipper that Dusty didn't take his racing seriously after all. What was the matter with him?

Skipper was ready to quit as Dusty's coach, so Dusty knew he had to come clean. Finally he revealed a big secret.... He had always been too embarrassed to tell anyone, because surely no other plane in the world had a fear like this: Dusty was afraid of heights!

Skipper was surprised. He thought about it carefully and figured out a clever way to work around Dusty's fear. He taught Dusty how to race the shadow of a passenger plane that flew above Propwash Junction every day. That way, he could stay close to the ground, but he could challenge himself as if he was in a real race.

Day after day the passenger plane beat Dusty across the town. With Skipper's support, Dusty didn't give up. With hard work and determination, Dusty eventually beat it!

Dusty finally felt ready for the biggest race of his life.

Disney·PIXAR
MONSTERS, INC.

Monster Moneymaker

As Mike and Sulley walked through the lobby of Monsters, Inc., to the Scare Floor, they passed the Scarer of the Month photos of Sulley hanging on the wall.

Mike suddenly turned to his big blue friend. "Sulley," he said, "do you ever think that we deserve a little more?"

"More?" Sulley asked.

"Oh, you know," Mike continued. "You're the top Scarer month after month. All you get is a lousy picture in the hallway, and I get nothin'. We should be famous!"

"What have you got in mind?" Sulley asked.

"A marketing campaign," Mike told him.

"How would we do that?" Sulley asked.

"Well, for starters, we'll get you some new head shots, and not just any old head shots but autographed head shots. And we won't stop there." Mike was on a roll. "We'll make mugs, posters – T-shirts even – with all your best poses." Mike demonstrated a few of his friend's Scarer poses for Sulley, including Sulley's personal favourite – the ol' Waternoose Jump and Growl. "We can set up a gift shop right here in the building featuring 'Sulley the Super Scarer' memorabilia."

"Why would we want to bother with all that?" Sulley wondered.

"Money!" Mike exclaimed, rolling his eye.

"I don't know, Mike," Sulley said. "It just doesn't seem right, us making money off these things. But what if we ... that's it!" Sulley jumped up, nearly knocking Mike over. "We'll donate the money to charity!"

"Who said anything about donations?" Mike asked.

"That's a great idea!" Sulley said, ignoring Mike.

"How will we bask in any glory if we give the money away?" Mike asked.

"Well, we will, sort of," Sulley explained. "We'll make the donation on behalf of Monsters, Inc."

"I don't know about that," Mike said.

"It's a wonderful idea!" Sulley replied. "And when we help the company make a generous donation, Mr Waternoose will be very proud of us!"

Mike was suddenly warming to the idea. "And we'll get lots of press!" he added.

"Sure, why not?" Sulley said with a shrug.

"It's a great idea!" Mike cheered.

"I agree!" Sulley said.

"I'm glad I thought of it!" Mike gave his best friend a huge smile.

"You always have such good ideas," Sulley agreed with a grin.

"It's like I always say," Mike added. "Scaring's important, but it's the brains behind the monster that matter most!"

Pongo Carries a Tune

"I don't know what we're going to do," Roger Radcliffe told his wife, Anita. "We have all these puppies to feed, and I don't have *one* song to sell!"

"Don't worry," Anita told him. "I'm sure you'll be inspired soon."

"I'm glad *you're* sure!" said Roger. "Because all I've got is a bunch of used paper." He pointed to the overflowing wastebasket.

"Don't give up," said Anita. "I know that you can do it."

After Anita left, Pongo watched his pet pace in front of his piano.

"Pongo, old boy, I must have written 10 songs in 10 days. But they're all terrible," said Roger, pointing to the wastebasket. "What am I going to do?"

Pongo wanted to help his pet, but he didn't know how.

That night, Pongo talked to Perdy about Roger's dilemma. They sat in the middle of the living room, surrounded by puppies.

"Roger has already written 10 songs," explained Pongo. "He just doesn't think they're good enough to sell. But I know they are – I've heard him play them, and you don't have a songwriter for a pet without developing a good ear for hit songs. The songs are right upstairs, stuffed inside his wastebasket."

Perdy saw what he was thinking.

"Do you know the way to the music publisher?" she asked.

Pongo nodded. "I've taken Roger for walks there dozens of times."

"I think you should try it," said Perdy.

After Roger and Anita had gone to sleep, Pongo padded into the music room and gathered up the sheet music from the wastebasket. Then he sneaked out of the house, carrying the music to the publisher's office. Pongo pushed all the pages under the door, then trotted back home.

The next day, the phone rang. Roger answered.

"You what?" Roger said into the receiver. "You did …? But how did you …? Oh, I see … well, thank you. Thank you!"

Anita rushed over. "Who was that?"

"My music publisher," said Roger. "He's buying 10 of my songs."

"Ten songs!" cried Anita. "I thought you didn't even have *one* to sell."

Roger scratched his head in confusion. "I didn't think I did."

"So, what happened?" asked Anita.

Perdy looked at Pongo and barked. Her husband could carry a tune too – all the way across town to Roger's publisher!

Stranded

A new toy called Buzz Lightyear had just arrived in Andy's room. He claimed he could fly, then he tried to prove it, by bouncing off a ball and shouting, "To infinity and beyond!"

The other toys were impressed, but Woody rolled his eyes.

"That's just falling with style," he complained.

Poor Woody. Now that Buzz had arrived in Andy's room, nothing was the same.

The cowboy posters on the wall were replaced with space posters. Andy stopped wearing his cowboy hat, and started running through the house in a space costume. Buzz was a hit with the other toys, too. Everyone wanted to spend time with him.

But the biggest shock was at bedtime. When Andy climbed under the covers, he took Buzz with him. Woody was left in the toy chest, awkward, alone and forgotten.

One evening, Andy's mum suggested a trip to Pizza Planet. Andy could take only one toy along, and Woody wanted to make sure he was chosen. Woody's plan was to knock Buzz behind the desk, where Andy couldn't find him. But instead, Buzz fell out the window!

"It was an accident!" Woody tried to explain to the other toys.

"Didn't want to face the fact that Buzz just might be Andy's new favourite toy, so you got rid of him!" Mr. Potato Head said.

Before the toys could gang up on Woody, however, Andy ran into the room. He searched high and low for Buzz, but couldn't find the space ranger anywhere.

Finally, he grabbed Woody, ran downstairs and hopped into the car with Molly and his mum, heading for Pizza Planet. As the car started up, a small figure leaped onto the car's bumper. It was Buzz!

When Andy's mum stopped at a petrol station, Buzz jumped into the back seat with Woody.

"Buzz! You're alive!" Woody exclaimed in relief.

But Buzz wasn't so pleased to see Woody. "Even though you tried to terminate me, revenge is not an idea we promote on my planet," Buzz said. Then his eyes narrowed. "But we're not on my planet, are we?"

Buzz leaped onto Woody, and the two began pummelling each other. As they wrestled angrily, they tumbled out of the car and onto the pavement.

Suddenly, Andy's mum drove off – without them!

Woody and Buzz were stranded at the petrol station. How were they ever going to get home?

January
17

Ready for the Big Race

Finally it was time for the Wings Around The Globe Rally, the race Dusty had been dreaming about his whole life. It started at New York's JFK International Airport.

"Wow!" Dusty cried as he cruised past the city. He'd never seen anything like it before. He landed at the airport. There were so many types of planes from so many countries that Dusty started to wonder if he was out of his league. He was so busy looking around at everything that he was almost run over by a huge jet!

Dusty rolled around looking at all the racing stars arriving for the rally. The first plane he met was a racer from England named Bulldog. Dusty was excited to talk to him about the race but the famous flyer wasn't very friendly.

"This is a competition," Bulldog told Dusty. "Every plane for himself."

Dusty recognized a lot of racing champions on pit row. He wanted to meet all of them, but he was a bit starstruck and he found himself speechless when he bumped into a beautiful racer from India called Ishani.

Suddenly, a masked plane dramatically announced his own arrival as he roared into pit row with a flourish. No one but Dusty knew that this colourful plane was El Chupacabra!

"He's the indoor racing champion of all of Mexico!" the crop duster exclaimed. El Chu was also a singer, a TV star and an author! He was pleased that Dusty was such a big fan and he and Dusty instantly became friends.

Meanwhile, television coverage of the race had begun. The sports reporters were buzzing around Ripslinger because they all thought he would come in first. After all, he had won the race three times before! Clearly Ripslinger believed he would be the winner, too.

Dusty was feeling overwhelmed by all of the excitement around him. It was almost too much for the small-town crop duster.

"Stay focused," El Chu reminded him. "Don't let anything distract—"

El Chu suddenly saw Rochelle, the Canadian rally champ, and seemed to lose all of his own focus! He couldn't take his eyes off her. It was love!

"She is like an angel sent from heaven," said El Chu, dreamily.

But he would have to meet her another time. The race was about to begin. The planes all made their way to the starting line. Dusty took one last glance at the famous planes by his side and then he heard Skipper's voice in his head. This was it – the moment Dusty had been training for all this time.

Bot Challenge!

Evening had settled on San Fransokyo. A dimly lit cable car rattled along the dark street, ringing a bell before rolling down one of the city's steep hills. Neon signs flickered to life and colourful adverts flashed across screens at the top of towering skyscrapers. All around, people's homes whirred with the hum of technology.

Meanwhile, in a dark alley, a crowd began to chant. "Yama! Yama!"

A robot fight was about to begin and the crowd was looking for a challenger.

Fourteen-year-old Hiro Hamada decided he was ready. "I have a robot; I built it myself," he said to the crowd. He placed his robot, Megabot, in the ring.

Hiro bravely met the eyes of his opponent. Yama was an enormous, brutish man – and the undisputed botfighting champion.

Yama laughed when he saw Hiro's simple-looking machine. But he accepted the challenge anyway.

"Two bots enter. One bot leaves. Fighters ready? FIGHT!" the referee shouted.

Hiro took a breath and flicked his robot's remote. Within moments, Megabot had smashed Yama's robot to pieces!

Everyone was stunned ... especially Yama. He called Hiro a cheat and sent his team of thugs after the boy.

Just as the goons were about to close in, Hiro's brother, Tadashi, zoomed to the rescue. He swept in on his moped and whisked Hiro away.

As the brothers zipped out of the alley, Tadashi turned to Hiro. "What were you thinking, you knucklehead?" he said.

Sirens blared in the distance. The police were on their way to break up the bot fight.

Tadashi told Hiro to stop wasting his time on bot fights. A genius like Hiro, who had graduated from high school at the age of 13, had the potential to change the world with his technology. Tadashi wanted Hiro to use his amazing brain and attend San Fransokyo Institute of Technology (SFIT) with him. But Hiro wasn't so sure. He liked bot fights – a lot! School could wait.

Suddenly, the sirens sounded louder. The police had caught up with them! Before they knew it, both brothers were behind bars. There was only one person who could help them now.

The boys had lived with their Aunt Cass for as long as they could remember. She owned a café called the Lucky Cat, and the three of them lived together above it. Usually, Aunt Cass was energetic and cheerful, but Hiro knew she'd be really unhappy when she found out what had happened.

Bambi

The Race

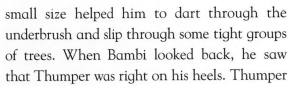

"Good morning, young Prince," Thumper greeted Bambi one bright winter day.

"Good morning, Thumper," Bambi said.

"I have a great idea, Bambi. Let's have a race," Thumper said. "We'll start from here." He drew a line in the dirt. "And whoever makes it to that big pine tree over there first, wins the race."

"But it would be silly for us to race," Bambi told his friend.

"Why's that?" Thumper asked, confused.

"Because I'll win," Bambi said.

"What makes you so sure?" Thumper challenged, puffing up his chest.

"Because I'm bigger and faster than you," Bambi explained.

"If you're so sure you'll win," Thumper said, "why are you afraid to race me?"

Bambi paused to think about this. He didn't want to hurt the little rabbit's feelings. "Fine," he said at last. "Let's race!"

"Great!" Thumper exclaimed. "Ready?"

"Ready!" Bambi said.

"Okay," Thumper said, crouching down. Bambi crouched down too. "On your mark. Get set. Go!" cried Thumper.

They both took off as fast as they could. Bambi, with his long legs and big, wide stride, immediately took the lead. But Thumper's

small size helped him to dart through the underbrush and slip through some tight groups of trees. When Bambi looked back, he saw that Thumper was right on his heels. Thumper took the opportunity to hop past Bambi. Bambi paused to jump over a tree that had been knocked down, blocking the path. Thumper was able to wriggle under it. He popped up in front of Bambi and took the lead.

Bambi took longer and longer strides, running faster and faster. Soon he had passed Thumper. But, in his hurry to go as fast as he could, he got tangled up in a bush. As Bambi struggled to free himself, Thumper hopped past him again.

They were quickly approaching the big pine tree. Bambi was running as fast as he could, jumping over logs and bushes. Thumper hopped as quickly as his bunny legs would carry him, ducking and weaving through whatever obstacles were in his way. As they crossed the finish line, they were in a neck-and-neck tie.

"See!" Thumper said, panting. "Little guys can keep up!"

"You are absolutely right!" Bambi said, also panting.

And the two friends, both winners, sat down together to catch their breath.

The Rally Begins

The official dropped his flag for the start of the Wings Around The Globe Rally. Dusty was lined up beside the most famous planes in the world and was about to take part in the race of his dreams.

The big group of racing planes shot into the sky for the first leg of the rally. It was going to take them from New York all the way across the sea to Iceland!

Dusty wasn't used to racing in among so many planes. When he trained with his coach Skipper back in Propwash Junction, it was just Dusty and the sky! He had raced in the shadow of a passenger plane many times, but it didn't feel anything like this. Dusty panicked as he got bounced around in the wake of the larger racers. They quickly climbed higher into the sky and left him behind. He was still too scared of heights to climb after them!

The racers headed across the North Atlantic into a storm of hail and snow. The other planes kept climbing and flew above it, avoiding being bashed and battered as they raced. But Dusty was too frightened and he stayed low, just like he did at home. But this wasn't Propwash Junction, and flying through the middle of the storm was as tricky a flight as Dusty had ever flown. Dusty's teeth chattered in the freezing temperatures and the wild winds.

Dusty struggled to see through the storm – and nearly hit an iceberg!

After what seemed like an eternity, Dusty finally made it! The shivering crop duster arrived in Iceland hours after everyone else. He was so disappointed that he started to wonder why he was doing this. Plus, to make things even worse, by placing last for the first leg of the rally, it meant he would be the last plane to take off the next day.

So far, things were proving more difficult than Dusty could have imagined.

Dusty was upset when he talked to his friends back home. He felt like he was letting everybody down.

"We believe in you, Dusty," said Chug, trying to reassure his friend.

"We know you can do it," Dottie added.

Despite his friends' well-wishes, Dusty knew he had to do better, but he didn't know how to.

"You've got to fly higher," Skipper told him.

Dusty knew Skipper was right, but he was just too scared. He wasn't looking forward to the next leg of the rally. His big dream was coming crashing down around him and he had only just begun.

That night, Dusty went to sleep and dreamed of storms and freezing winds. He had no idea what tomorrow might bring.

Stuck in Radiator Springs

Lightning McQueen had just raced in the last race of the Piston Cup championship, and it had been a three-way tie. He could have won if he had listened to his team. But instead, he decided to go it alone and ended up sacking them.

Eager to get to California for the tie-breaker, Lightning had forced Mack to drive all night. As Mack struggled to stay awake, some flashy cars had shoved him. Startled, Mack had swerved, and Lightning rolled out of the trailer!

Lightning, feeling terrified, searched for Mack – but he couldn't find him! Lightning was completely lost. Suddenly he heard a siren blaring and saw red lights flashing. A sheriff cruiser was after him!

Panicked, Lightning crashed through a fence, got tangled in fencing wire and roared through a sleepy little town, destroying its main street. He ended up dangling from a telephone pole! "You're in a heap of trouble," Sheriff said just before Lightning passed out.

When Lightning woke up, he was inside an impound lot and saw a rusty old tow truck named Tow-Mater grinning at him.

"Where am I?" Lightning asked.

"Radiator Springs," Mater answered.

Later in court, Doc Hudson, the judge of the sleepy little town, rolled slowly into the room. Doc didn't like racecars.

"Throw him out of here!" Doc ordered. "I want him out of our town!"

That's when the town attorney, a sleek blue sports car named Sally, arrived. She didn't want Doc to let Lightning go. "Make him fix the road," she insisted.

So Doc told Mater to hook Lightning up to Bessie, the road-paving machine. Lightning was furious. But if he wanted to leave, he had to do the job.

While Lightning worked, a couple came down the broken road through town. "Customers!" Sally cried. The townsfolk rushed up to them. But the couple just wanted directions to the Interstate.

"I'm Lightning McQueen," Lightning told the couple, hoping they would help him. But they looked at Lightning as if he were crazy and sped off. There went his last hope of rescue! Lightning hauled Bessie down the road as fast as he could.

"The road looks awful," Sally said.

"Now it matches the rest of the town," Lightning replied grumpily. He was still only thinking of himself, and didn't care about Radiator Springs and the cars that lived there. If he carried on this way, he'd never be allowed to leave for California!

Palindrome-mania!

"Hey, Atta," Flik said. "Did you know that your name is a palindrome?"

Atta gave him a strange look. "What's a palindrome?" she asked.

"It's a word that reads the same forwards and backwards," Flik replied. "Spelled forwards, your name is A-T-T-A. Spelled backwards, your name is also A-T-T-A. See?"

"Oh," Atta said. "That's neat. I've never heard of palindromes before."

"Really?" said Flik. "I love them. There are other names that are palindromes, like *Bob*."

"Or *Lil*?" tried Atta.

"Right!" said Flik. "And *Otto*."

"And *Nan*!" added Atta. "This is fun!"

"What's fun?" said Dot, who had just run over to them.

"Thinking of palindromes," Atta replied.

"Huh?" said Dot.

"Exactly!" said Flik. "*Huh* is a palindrome!" Together, Flik and Atta explained to Dot what a palindrome was.

"Oh!" said Dot. "Wait! Let me see if I can think of another one." Dot looked around, hoping that something she saw would spark an idea. She spotted her mother, the Queen, off in the distance, lounging in the shade.

"*Mum!*" cried Dot. "That's one, isn't it?"

"Not bad," said Atta with a wink, "for a

tot like you!" Atta giggled, pleased that she had got another palindrome into her sentence.

"Oh, yeah?" replied Dot with a mischievous grin. "Well, you ain't seen nothin' yet, *sis*!"

Taking turns, Dot and Atta challenged one another to think of more and more palindromes. Dot came up with *eye*, *pop* and *toot*. Atta countered with *gag*, *noon*, *did* and *redder*.

"Yes," Flik interjected, "*redder* is a nice, long one! It's harder to think of palindromes that have more than four letters. Believe me, I've spent hours on that. But there's always *Aidemedia* – that's a type of bird, you know. And *Allenella*, of course, which is a category of mollusc...." Flik went on to list a longer palindrome for just about every letter of the alphabet – most of them sciencey words that Atta and Dot had never heard before. As he droned on and on and on, Dot and Atta looked at each other and rolled their eyes. Now they were both thinking of the same word, and it wasn't a palindrome: B-O-R-I-N-G.

When Flik had finally finished with his list, he looked up at Dot and Atta with a self-satisfied smile. Each of them had a palindrome ready.

"*Wow*," said Atta flatly, sounding more bored than impressed.

"*Zzz*," snored Dot, who had drifted off somewhere between *V* and *W*.

Captured by Sid

Oh dear! Woody and Andy's brand-new toy, Buzz Lightyear, were stranded at a petrol station. They had been in Andy's mum's car, on the way to Pizza Planet, but because they'd been fighting with each other, they'd fallen out onto the ground! Andy's mum had driven away without them!

Luckily, Woody spotted a Pizza Planet delivery truck. The truck could take him to Andy! But Woody knew he couldn't face the other toys without Buzz.

Woody had knocked Buzz out of Andy's window, and the other toys thought he'd done it on purpose. So, Woody tricked Buzz, telling him the truck was a shuttle that could return him to his home planet – you see, Buzz didn't realize he was just a toy.

At Pizza Planet, Woody quickly spotted Andy. With a little luck, he figured, they could jump into Molly's pushchair.

"Okay, Buzz, get ready and…. Buzz?" Woody turned around to see Buzz striding towards the Rocket Ship Crane Game. The space ranger thought it was a real spaceship!

Buzz climbed into the Rocket Ship Crane Game. Woody followed, still hoping he could make Buzz return to Andy.

Suddenly, the machine started whirring. Then the claw dropped – right on Buzz.

Woody grabbed Buzz and tried to drag him back down. But it was no use. Both toys were pulled into the air and dropped into the prize slot.

"All right! Double prizes!" shouted the kid, seeing the two toys.

To Woody's horror, he saw that the boy was Sid, Andy's nasty neighbour!

All the toys in Andy's room knew Sid. He lived next door and was the cruellest kid on the block. Many times, Andy's toys had watched Sid in his backyard as he tortured toys. Sometimes he even blew them up, just for fun!

Now Sid looked at Buzz and Woody with evil glee. "Let's go home and … play!" he said with a wicked laugh. Woody knew they were doomed.

Sid carried Woody and Buzz home and up to his bedroom. The room was dark and eerie, and Sid had lots of scary tools that he used for toy 'operations'.

Then, Woody and Buzz heard strange rustling sounds – distorted toys were creeping out of the darkness. Sid had modified his once-normal toys, turning them into terrifying mutants!

Woody and Buzz clung on to each other in fear – how would they escape…?

Mango Hunting

Once upon a time, long before Mowgli came to the jungle, Bagheera the panther met Baloo the bear for the first time.

This is how it happened.

Bagheera was younger then, but no less grave. He took himself very seriously indeed. When Bagheera hunted, he moved silently, with grace and speed. He never tripped, and he certainly never fell. When he slept, he kept one eye open. When he spoke, he chose his words carefully. And he never, ever laughed.

One day, Bagheera was edging along the branch of a mango tree leaning out over a river. There was one perfectly ripe mango right at the end of the branch, and Bagheera loved mangoes. The only problem was, the branch was slender, and, when Bagheera moved towards the end of it, it began to creak and bend alarmingly. The last thing Bagheera wanted was to break the branch and go for an unplanned swim in the river. His dignity would never allow such a thing.

So Bagheera, crouched on the middle of the branch, was just coming up with a clever plan, when he heard a "harrumph." He looked down and saw a great big grey bear. "It looks like you could use a hand," said the bear.

"No, thank you," said Bagheera politely. "I prefer to work on my own." But the bear paid him no heed, and began climbing up the tree.

"I'll tell you what," huffed the bear. "I'll just sit at the base of that branch and grab your tail. You can climb out and grab the mango, and I'll keep a hold of you in case the end of the branch breaks off. Then we can share the mango!"

"No, I don't think that's a very good idea," said Bagheera impatiently. "I doubt this branch can hold both of us any – "

Snap!

The bear had, of course, ignored Bagheera and climbed out onto the branch. And the branch had, of course, snapped under their combined weight. And now a very wet, very unhappy panther sat in the river next to a very wet, very amused bear.

"Oh, ha-ha-ha-ha!" hooted Baloo (for it was Baloo, of course). "Oh me, oh my, that was an adventure! Oh, come now," he said, seeing how angry Bagheera was, "it's not a total loss, you know." And Baloo held up the broken branch, with that perfect mango still hanging from the end of it.

"I'll tell you what," said the bear, "let's go climb onto that rock and dry off in the sun while we eat this mango. I'm Baloo. What's your name?"

"Bagheera," said the panther, as they climbed up onto the warm, flat rock. And then, almost despite himself, he smiled. And then, very much despite himself, he laughed.

And Baloo laughed right along with him.

DISNEP·PIXAR

MONSTERS, INC.

A Monstrous Mix-up

One morning at work, Mike Wazowski opened the door to his locker to find a note taped inside. It said:

Mike,
Roses are red.
Violets are blue.
I have got my eye on you!
Sealed with a kiss from …
Your Secret Admirer.

Mike's mouth fell open. He showed the note to his best friend, Sulley.

"Who do you think it could be?" Sulley asked.

"I have no idea!" Mike replied. "Hey, you don't think it could be that six-armed cutie down in Purchasing, do you? Or that sassy, one-eyed receptionist, Celia, with the pretty hair?"

"I guess it could be anyone," Sulley said. "But, hey, it's time to get to work."

On the way to the Scare Floor, Mike's mind was racing. Who could his admirer be? Then Mike heard his least favourite voice.

"Wazowski!"

It was Roz, the humourless and strict Dispatch Manager, sliding up behind them. "You owe me some paperwork!" she said.

"Oh … right," said Mike. "I'll get that to you ASAP, Roz. See ya." He and Sulley turned on their heels and hurried on down the hallway.

"All right, Wazowski," Roz called out to Mike, shaking her finger. "But remember: I've got my eye on you. I'm always watching…."

Mike and Sulley froze in their tracks and stared at each other.

"Did she just say…?" Sulley began.

"'My *eye* on you?'" Mike said, recalling the wording in the note from his secret admirer.

Sulley gulped. "Your secret admirer is *Roz*?"

"NOOOOOOOOO!" Mike's scream filled the hallway just as Celia came sauntering around the corner.

"Hey, Mike," she said batting her eye at him. "Rough morning?"

"Oh. Hey, Celia," Mike replied sullenly, still traumatized by the idea that Roz liked him.

"Gee," said Celia, "I thought my note would make your day."

Mike stared at her. "*Your* note?" he said, stunned. "Celia, you're my secret admirer?"

She sighed. "Wasn't it obvious? 'I have got my eye on you'? As in, I have one eye, just like you?"

A wave of relief swept across Mike's face.

"I was going to ask you if you wanted to go out sometime," Celia continued. "But if you don't want to …"

Without a word, Mike leaped into Celia's arms and clung to her. "Thank you, thank you, THANK YOU!" he exclaimed.

Celia giggled. "So … I guess that's a yes?"

Wherever You Go, There You Are!

"Oh, dear! Oh, dear!" said Amelia Gabble. The goose and her twin sister, Abigail, had been waddling along the road to Paris, when Amelia suddenly stopped.

"What's wrong?" asked Abigail, bumping into her.

"Just look and you'll see," said Amelia. Stretching out one big white wing, she pointed to the road ahead. Abigail looked, and then the two geese put their heads together and began to argue in low voices.

Behind the geese, Thomas O'Malley, Duchess and her three kittens gathered together.

"I wonder what's wrong," said Duchess.

"Guess I'd better find out," said O'Malley.

He sauntered forward. "Ladies, ladies, what's going on?" he asked the twin geese.

"We know this is the road to Paris," Amelia explained. "But up ahead, the road divides."

Sure enough, the single road split in two.

"I think we should go right," said Amelia.

"And I think we should go left," said Abigail.

The three kittens began to worry.

"Mr O'Malley, are we lost?" asked Marie in a small, frightened voice.

O'Malley smiled down at the little white kitten. "Lost? What's lost? I don't know the meaning of the word."

"I do," said Berlioz. "If you're lost, then you don't know where you are."

"But you know exactly where you are," said O'Malley. "You're right here – with your mother and me and the Gabbles. So how could you be lost?"

Duchess shook her head and said, "Mr O'Malley, if we want to get to Paris and we don't know the way, then I do believe that we are lost."

"But Paris is just a place," said O'Malley. "And places are easy to find."

"Look, Mama, look!" Toulouse shouted. "I see something over that hill. It's the top of the Eiffel Tower!"

"Toulouse, you're right!" said Duchess.

"Nice going, little tiger," said O'Malley. Then he turned to the Gabble sisters. "Well, ladies, looks like Paris is thataway!"

Soon they arrived in Paris, where the Gabble sisters met up with their Uncle Waldo. The geese waved goodbye.

Marie sighed with relief. "I'm glad we're not lost any more."

"Aw, honey," said O'Malley, "someday you'll understand. Places may come and places may go but, when you're a free spirit, you can never be lost."

"Never?" asked Marie.

"Never," said O'Malley. " 'Cause wherever you go, there you are!"

Marie nodded. She liked the sound of that!

Disney
Pinocchio

Geppetto's Gift

One day, Geppetto was in his workshop painting a clock, when he had an idea. "I know what I will do with that pine log I just found," he told his little cat, Figaro. "I will make a splendid puppet!"

He put down the clock and got to work. When he had finished making the puppet, he got out his jars of paint and some fabric. "Now," he said to Figaro, "should my puppet's eyes be blue or green? Should her hair be yellow or brown or black? Should her dress be red or purple?"

Suddenly, Geppetto heard a noise outside. He went to the window and looked out. He saw groups of children on their way home from school. Geppetto watched them skip past, laughing and shouting and swinging their schoolbooks. He sighed sadly. "How I wish I had a child of my own," he said.

Just then, he noticed a little girl walking quietly with her mother. Like the other girls, she carried a schoolbook under her arm. When a group of girls skipped by her, she looked at them shyly.

"That little girl must be new in town. She looks like she could use a friend," Geppetto said. Suddenly, he had an idea.

"Excuse me, young miss," he called from the window. "I wonder if you could lend me a hand?"

The girl hurried over, tugging her mother after her. Why, an invitation to Geppetto's workshop – how grand!

"As you can see, my friend here needs some eyes," Geppetto said, pointing to the puppet. "But I don't know what colour her eyes should be."

The girl thought hard. "Green," she decided.

Geppetto picked up his pot of green paint and painted two big green eyes.

"Now, what colour do you suppose her hair should be?" Geppetto asked.

"Brown," the girl said.

Carefully, Geppetto painted brown curls on the puppet's head. "She'll need a dress," he said next. "What do you think? Red? Green?"

"Blue," the girl told Geppetto.

So Geppetto made a little blue dress for the little puppet. Then he added a smiling red mouth to the puppet's face.

"Now there's just one last thing," Geppetto said. "I'm busy in my shop all day long, and I'm afraid this little lady might be lonely. Could you take care of her for me?"

The girl's face lit up with delight. "Thank you!" she cried. Hugging the puppet in her arms, she carried her out of the workshop.

"Thank you," the girl's mother said. "You know, you'd be a wonderful father."

Geppetto smiled. *If only!* he thought.

THE INCREDIBLES

Super Annoying!

Dashiell Robert Parr was bored. It was Saturday afternoon and he had nothing to do. He had already taken a twenty-mile run, but that had only taken about two minutes thanks to his Super speed.

"You know, you could do your maths homework," his mother Helen said.

Homework, now? Dash thought. I'll do that tomorrow. Right now I want to do something fun.

Brrrng! The telephone rang and Dash's sister, Violet, raced out of her bedroom to answer it. Dash had spotted his target. He grinned slyly and hurried into Violet's room.

Five minutes later, Violet returned. Things were not as she had left them. Her whole room was rearranged! Only one person could have done it.

"Mum!" Violet yelled. "Dash messed up my room!"

As Helen walked down the hall, a breeze whipped through Violet's room. Helen looked inside. "It looks fine to me, honey. Now I've got to get dinner ready," she said. Violet looked at her room again and saw that everything was back in place. Then her eyes fell on the closet door, which was slightly ajar.

"Dash!" Violet exclaimed. "Get out of here, you little insect!"

Dash zoomed around Violet's bedroom – up onto the bed, down to the floor – all at such Super speed that Violet couldn't tell where he was. Dash only came to a halt when he spotted Violet's diary, which had fallen open on her bed.

"Ooooh," Dash said, picking up the diary. "What have we here?"

That was it. Violet had had enough of Dash. "Give that back!" she yelled.

Dash tried to race out of the room, but Violet threw a force field in front of the door. Dash ran into it head-on and was knocked to the floor. Violet grabbed her diary, but before she knew it Dash had taken it again. Violet turned invisible and lunged at her brother.

Dash and Violet continued to chase each other around Violet's room in a blur of Super powers, until they heard their mum calling.

"Time for dinner!" she cried.

Dash froze. Then, in the blink of an eye, he zipped out through the bedroom door and down the hall to the kitchen table.

"Dash," Helen asked, "did you finish your homework?"

Then Violet appeared at the table. Her hair was all messed up.

"Nah," Dash replied with a smile. "I found something much better to do."

Disney · PIXAR
RATATOUILLE
(rat·a·too·ee)

Discovering Paris

Deep in the French countryside, a colony of rats was busy sifting through a compost pile for food. It was one rat's job to make sure the scraps of food were safe to eat. That rat's name was Remy. Remy had a highly developed sense of taste and smell and was the 'poison checker' for the rest of the rat colony.

Emile, his younger (but bigger) brother, ate anything in sight. He was always impressed by Remy's gift. Secretly, Remy had much bigger dreams. He wanted to be a great chef, like his idol, the great chef Auguste Gusteau. In fact, Remy had even learned to read Gusteau's cookbook: 'Anyone Can Cook!'

The cookbook and the compost pile belonged to an old woman named Mabel. Her attic was home to the entire rat colony, though she didn't know it. One day, Remy and Emile sneaked into her kitchen together. Remy always enjoyed looking for spices in her cupboards. The nervous Emile did not. Their father, Django, always said humans were dangerous.

Suddenly, Remy raced from the kitchen to the TV. He saw his idol Gusteau on the news! Remy learned that Gusteau had died from a broken heart when his restaurant lost its five-star status. Remy was so shocked by the news about Gusteau that he didn't notice Mabel waking up! He and Emile had to scramble to escape as Mabel chased them! In the chaos, the ceiling cracked and the entire rat colony fell to the floor!

"Evacuate!" Django shouted to the rats.

As the others headed out of the door, Remy went back into the kitchen for the cookbook. He couldn't leave it behind. But it was Remy who got left behind, as all the other rats made it to the evacuation boats.

Separated from his family, Remy used his cookbook as a raft. He got swept down the sewer currents. Remy finally found a landing place and started drying out the pages of his cookbook.

Suddenly, Gusteau seemed to come to life on one of the pages! "If you are hungry, go up and look around," said Gusteau. "If you focus on what you've left behind, you will never be able to see what lies ahead."

So Remy climbed up and up until he saw … Paris! "All this time I've been underneath Paris? Wow! It's beautiful!" he said.

Remy looked to his left. His jaw dropped. There was the sign for Gusteau's restaurant! To Remy, this was a dream come true, and he knew his adventures were only just beginning.

DISNEY·PIXAR
MONSTERS, INC.

Mike's Worst Nightmare

"AAAAAAIEEEE-AHHHH!" Sulley sat bolt upright in bed. The anguished yell was coming from his friend Mike's bedroom. Sulley raced out of his bedroom and threw open Mike's door.

"Hi," said Mike in a shaky voice. "I guess I must have had a bad dream." He swallowed hard, then sat up in bed and gave Sulley a sheepish grin. "I haven't had one since I was little."

Sulley nodded. "Okay, well, good night, Mike."

"Uh, Sulley, don't you want to hear about it?" Mike asked with a hopeful grin.

Sulley came over and sat down on the edge of his friend's bed. "Okay," he said.

"I dreamed …" Mike began. "This is going to sound really, really crazy, I know, but … I dreamed that there was a kid, a human kid, in my closet over there!" He pointed across the room and laughed nervously.

"Now, now," said Sulley good-naturedly. "Maybe it was the movie you watched tonight."

"*Kidzilla*?" Mike scoffed. "Nah. I've seen it a dozen times and it's never bothered me before."

"Well, why don't you try to go back to sleep?" said Sulley, suppressing a yawn.

Mike cleared his throat shyly. "I remember when I was little, my mum would bring me a sludgesicle when I had a bad dream," he said.

Sulley sighed patiently, then went to get Mike a sludgesicle from the kitchen.

"She would sing me a little lullaby too," said Mike.

In his low, scratchy voice, Sulley began to sing:

> Rock-a-bye, Mikey, Googley-Bear,
> With sharp little fangs and shiny green hair!
> Morning will come when the sun starts to rise,
> You'll wake up and open those googley eyes!

"Googley *eye*," Mike corrected his friend, snuggling under his blanket. "Uh, my mum also always checked the closet."

With another patient sigh, Sulley opened Mike's wardrobe door and stepped inside. "Nope. Nothing in here!" he called. Suddenly, there was a loud clatter and a landslide of junk spilled out of the wardrobe door. A yellow mop fell out. It looked just like blond hair!

"AHHHH!" shrieked Mike, leaping out from under the covers. Then he relaxed. "Oh, sorry, pal. In this dim light, I thought that mop was, you know, a human child!" He shuddered and gave Sulley another sheepish smile.

Sulley chuckled at the idea. "Don't be silly, Mike," he said. "A kid will never get loose in Monstropolis – what a disaster that would be!"

"No, you have a point," Mike agreed sleepily. "Good night, Sulley."

"Good night, Mike."

Disney · PIXAR

BRAVE
Legends are Lessons

Long ago, there was a kingdom called DunBroch in the Scottish Highlands. Though the kingdom was young, the land was ancient – a place full of magic … and danger.

King Fergus and Queen Elinor had brought peace to the clans of the kingdom. They were also raising their own clan: triplets (Harris, Hubert and Hamish) and one teenaged, adventurous princess called Merida.

Queen Elinor had high hopes for Merida. She thought a princess should be well rounded …

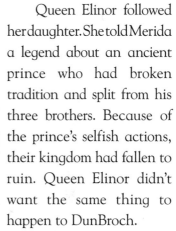

knowledgeable about her kingdom … and above all, perfect in every way. In Queen Elinor's eyes, Merida had much to learn.

But Merida lived for her rare days of freedom, when she could grab her bow, climb onto her horse, Angus, and spend the day in the forest. Merida was a skilled archer and rarely missed a shot.

One day, Merida returned to the castle to find her family eating dinner. King Fergus was telling his favourite story: how he had fought a bear called Mor'du and lost his leg! Mor'du hadn't been seen since. They'd all heard the story a hundred times.

Just then, some letters arrived from the lords of three neighbouring clans. At the Queen's invitation, they would each present a son to compete for Merida's hand in marriage!

Merida was horrified. She didn't want to marry!

"I won't go through with it!" she shouted, and ran from the room.

Queen Elinor followed her daughter. She told Merida a legend about an ancient prince who had broken tradition and split from his three brothers. Because of the prince's selfish actions, their kingdom had fallen to ruin. Queen Elinor didn't want the same thing to happen to DunBroch.

"Legends are lessons," Elinor told Merida. "They ring with truths."

Merida was not convinced. She saw marriage as something that would take away her freedom. She had so many more adventures planned!

"I don't know what to do," Queen Elinor said to King Fergus later. "If only she could try to see that I do this out of love!"

Meanwhile, Merida was complaining to Angus….

"I don't want my life to be over. I want my freedom! I swear, Angus, this isn't going to happen," she vowed.

Merida was determined to follow her own path in life. The last thing she wanted was to be like her mother.

Would Merida ever learn to understand Queen Elinor's point of view?

101 DALMATIANS

Rolly's Midnight Snack

"Time for bed!" called Pongo.

"Aw, Dad," complained Patch, "we're not tired!"

"No arguments," said Pongo. "Little puppies need their rest."

With a sigh, Patch joined the line of puppies climbing the staircase.

"I'm hungry," Rolly complained as the puppies settled down for the night.

"You're always hungry," said Patch.

"And you always want to stay awake and have adventures," said Rolly.

Patch sighed. "Too bad we never get what we want."

Hours later, Rolly felt a tap on his shoulder. "Is it morning?" he asked with a yawn.

"No," said Patch. "It's midnight. Wanna explore? I'll get you a snack."

"A snack!" cried Rolly excitedly.

"Shhhhh!" said Patch. "Come on."

Rolly followed Patch to the kitchen.

Patch nodded towards the table. "After dinner, I saw Nanny put some juicy bones up there. She's saving them for tomorrow's soup."

"Soup!" cried Rolly. "What a waste! Bones are for chewing on!"

So, Patch and Rolly came up with a plan.

First, Patch climbed onto Rolly's shoulders to reach the table.

Everything went fine until Patch threw down the first bone and it landed in the dustbin. Rolly took off after it and leaped inside!

Rolly was stuck. Patch tried hard not to panic. He thought and thought until he came up with another plan – a Rescue Rolly Plan!

Patch went upstairs and woke Lucky and Pepper. The two puppies followed Patch into the kitchen. Then Patch found his father's long lead and tossed one end into the dustbin.

"Take hold of the lead!" Patch told Rolly.

"Okay," said Rolly.

Patch turned to the other puppies and said, "Now, let's all pull on this end of the lead, on the count of three."

The three puppies pulled. The dustbin fell over and Rolly tumbled out onto the kitchen floor.

"Thanks!" said Rolly.

The puppies licked their brother, and they all returned to bed.

Before Rolly drifted off to sleep, he whispered to Patch, "Guess you finally got your adventure."

"Yeah," said Patch. "But I'm sorry you didn't get your snack."

"Sure, I did," said Rolly. "While I was waiting for you to rescue me, what do you think I was doing? I was eating that juicy bone. And, boy, was it good!"

Disney·PIXAR
FROM THE MOVIE **INSIDE OUT**

Emotional Rollercoaster

Hi, there! I'm Joy. Do you like my blue hair? I'm in charge of being ... joyful! And let me tell you, there are a lot of things to be happy about. Like dinosaurs! And sprinkles on cupcakes. And monkeys – it's fun watching them swing. Ooh and bouncy balls! Making goofy faces is great, too. And twirling – you've just got to twirl sometimes. Sunshine is my absolute favourite. Ooh, but rain is my favourite, too! And new adventures are just the best! But most of all, I've found that happiness is being with your friends and family!

Sigh. Hi, I'm Sadness. I usually feel pretty blue. I just don't understand the world sometimes. Like why does ice cream fall off the cone? Or why do pencils break? I do like some things. I like rain – it makes you shivery and droopy. Puppies can be cute ... but then they chew on your new jumper. I always seem to lose something. Or, sometimes, I'm the one who's lost. I like crying. It helps me slow down and obsess over the weight of life's problems. Then I feel better. But then I feel sad again.

Hey! What are you looking at? Fine! I'll introduce myself. I'm Anger. Are you really saying you can't tell which one I am? Let me give you a clue – I'm RED! I like to honk my way through the traffic jams of life. But if there's one thing that burns me up – more than sunsets and scented candles – it's putting vegetables where they don't belong! Broccoli on pizza – did you really think I wouldn't notice?!

I'm Disgust. I'm the fashionable one in green. There are a lot of gross things out there. Like feet – who decided people should walk around on smelly blobs with toes sticking out the end? Oh! And socks and shoes? Peee-ewwww! While we're at it – crabs. What are they doing crawling sideways like that? Creepy-crawly things are so gross. Like spiders, I mean, ew!

H-hello! I'm Fear. I-I'm the shaky one. The world is full of terrifying things – I have a list! – so I consider every day we don't die a success. There's the stairs down to the basement – it's dark down there. And Grandma's vacuum cleaner sounds like a monster. And, dare I say it, clowns. But let me tell you what I do like. Safety. I love to relax in the evenings, sip a cup of tea and watch a peaceful nature show. Until they show the animals. They're so scary.

Disney PLANES

A New Beginning

The second leg of the Wings Around The Globe Rally was about to begin. Dusty had rested well after a disastrous first leg. He had been so excited about taking part in the race, but so far it had been really tough. The planes had flown across the Atlantic in freezing storms, and because Dusty was too afraid to fly up high above the clouds, he had been battered all over the place by wind, rain and hail.

This next leg of the rally was a night flight to Germany. Dusty hoped that the weather would be clear – that would be his best chance. Starting out, things were looking good and Dusty felt encouraged.

During the journey Bulldog, the English racer, began to leak oil. Dusty had met Bulldog before the rally started and tried to talk to him, but Bulldog had been quite mean to Dusty. Dusty saw the oil pouring out, fast,and covering Bulldog's windshield so completely that he couldn't see where he was going! Poor Bulldog was lost and in danger of crashing.

Dusty was determined not to let that happen. He pulled up beside the English racer and talked him through what was happening. He told Bulldog what to do, where to turn and guided him through the skies, eventually helping him to land safely. Bulldog was so

relieved and grateful. He felt bad that he hadn't been nice to Dusty in the first place.

Dusty had done a wonderful thing for Bulldog, but his good deed had slowed his own race and kept him in last place. It was another bad day for him in the rally.

Later on, the racers gathered at the local oil hall. As Dusty talked to his friend, El Chu, a timid German car named Franz rolled up. Franz told Dusty that he was a big fan and thanked him for representing all of the little planes. Then suddenly, Franz transformed from a car into a plane! Now he was no longer the meek little car, Franz – he was the arrogant flyer Von Fliegenhosen!

Von Flieghenhosen the plane turned back into Franz the car and suggested that Dusty make a transformation himself.

"Would you not be much faster without the pipes and tank and whatnot weighing you down?" he asked. Dusty had lots of bits and pieces attached to him that he needed for crop dusting. But he was a racer now, his crop-dusting days were behind him … at least until after the rally. So, Dusty got rid of the extra equipment that was weighing him down.

Once he was transformed, Dusty went for a quick test flight to try out his new, lightweight bodywork. He felt like a new plane!

A Race Against Doc

Lightning McQueen was lost in a sleepy town called Radiator Springs. All he wanted to do was get to California for a tie-breaker race – the last race in the Piston Cup championship had ended in a three-way tie – but Lightning couldn't leave because he'd ruined the town's main road. The judge, Doc, had ordered him to resurface the road, but selfish Lightning had done a bad job.

"Scrape the road and start again," Doc ordered.

"I'm not a bulldozer – I'm a racecar," Lightning argued.

So Doc challenged him to a race. "If you win, you go. If I win, you do the road my way."

Lightning agreed. He was sure he could beat the old car.

When the race flag dropped, Lightning roared off. But on a sharp left turn, Lightning lost control. He skidded off the road and plunged into a cactus patch.

That night, muttering angrily, Lightning scraped the road. When the rest of the cars awoke, they saw Mater – the town's tow-truck – driving on a perfectly smooth road. Even Doc was impressed. But where was Lightning? Doc thought he knew.

Sure enough, the stubborn racecar was out on the dirt track, trying again and again to make that tricky sharp left turn – and spinning out of control every time.

"You've got to turn right to go left," Doc told Lightning. As usual, Lightning scoffed. What did Doc know about racing?

Later, Lightning finished repaving the road. It looked great! Luigi, who ran the town's tyre shop, even offered Lightning a great deal on new tyres. Everyone in town was happy, except Lightning. He was hot, tired and grumpy!

Suddenly, Red the fire engine blasted Lightning with water. "Do you want to stay at the Cozy Cone?" Sally asked. "If you do, you have to be clean." She was beginning to like Lightning, and he realized he liked her, too.

That night, Mater took Lightning tractor-tipping. Mater sneaked up on a sleeping tractor and beeped. The startled tractor woke up and fell over! Then Lightning revved his engine so loudly, all the tractors keeled over at once. Mater and Lightning could not stop laughing.

As they returned to the Cozy Cone Motel, Mater showed off his amazing backwards-driving tricks. Lightning was impressed.

"Maybe I'll use it in my big race," Lightning said thoughtfully. He was starting to enjoy himself in Radiator Springs, but had he learned to appreciate the help of others?

DUMBO
Hide-and-seek

For quite a while, Dumbo was the newest baby in the circus. But then, one day, the stork arrived with a brand-new delivery – a baby girl giraffe.

"You know, Dumbo," said his friend, Timothy Q. Mouse, "I think we should ask that new baby to play with us."

Dumbo nodded. He loved making new friends!

So together, Timothy and Dumbo made their way to the giraffes' pen.

"Hello, Mrs Giraffe," Timothy said. "Can your lovely new baby come out and play?"

Dumbo gave Mrs Giraffe a big, hopeful smile. "Well … I suppose so," she said.

She gave her baby a kiss, and sent her off in the care of Timothy Mouse – and Dumbo.

"Okay, kids," said Timothy, standing before the two, "what do you feel like playing?"

Dumbo and the baby giraffe stared back at him blankly.

"Hmm … I see," said Timothy. "You don't know that many games. May I suggest hide-and-seek?"

Dumbo and the giraffe nodded happily, as Timothy closed his eyes and counted.

"Ready or not," he said finally, opening his eyes, "here I – hang on! Don't you guys know you're supposed to hide?"

No, actually, they did not.

"Okay," Timothy sighed. "Let's take it from the top. When I close my eyes, you guys hide. You find a place where you can't see me and I can't see you. Like this …" Timothy ducked behind a popcorn tub. "Get it?"

Dumbo and the giraffe slowly nodded.

"Okay then, let's try this again. One, two, three …" Timothy counted to 20, then opened his eyes. "No, no!" he groaned. "You can't hide behind the popcorn. You're too big. Let's try this one more time."

Again, he closed his eyes and counted. Then, very slowly, he opened them and looked around. "Much better!" he said, surprised. Of course, it didn't take him long to find Dumbo's wide body behind a narrow tent pole, or the giraffe's tall neck sticking up from behind the clowns' trunk. But they were getting closer!

"This time, guys, try to find a place for your whole body to hide," Timothy said.

So, Dumbo and the giraffe waited for Timothy to close his eyes once more, then they quietly sneaked behind the pole and trunk again. This time, the tall, skinny giraffe hid behind the tall, skinny pole. And short, wide Dumbo hid behind the short, wide trunk. And do you know what? They were hidden so well, Timothy Q. Mouse may still be looking for them to this very day!

The Induction

Nemo still had a satisfied smile on his face from the previous night's induction ceremony. I'm part of the club! he thought.

"So, Shark Bait, what did you think of the ceremony?" Gill asked.

"It was the best!" Nemo exclaimed.

"If only we could get Flo to be part of the ceremony," Deb mused. "But she never seems to want to come out at night."

"So, kid, what was your favourite part?" Jacques wanted to know.

"I think my favourite part was swimming to the top of Mount Wanna … wannaha … ha …" Nemo tried unsuccessfully to pronounce it.

"Wannahockaloogie," Bloat said.

"Yeah," Peach reminisced. "I have a soft spot for my first climb too."

"I wonder," Nemo said. "Who came up with that name?"

Bubbles pointed at Gurgle, who pointed at Bloat, who pointed at Peach, who pointed at Deb, who pointed at Flo.

Deb shrugged. "I guess we came up with it together," she said.

"Why do they call it the Ring of Fire if there's no fire?" Nemo asked.

"Well, you see, it's like this – I don't know," Peach had to admit.

"But who made it up, then?" Nemo asked.

"I think Bubbles came up with the Ring of Fire," Gurgle offered.

"Aren't they beautiful?" Bubbles mused.

"I find it very unsanitary to swim through others' bubbles," Gurgle complained. "Which is why I came up with the chanting part of the ceremony. It's very cleansing both for the body and the mind, and circulates carbon dioxide through the gills."

"That makes sense," Nemo agreed, although it really didn't.

"Don't forget about the kelp fronds," Peach piped up.

"Oh, there's no big secret there," Deb confided. "I just like giving a good whack with the old kelp fronds every now and then." And she demonstrated by whacking Bloat, who immediately began to swell up.

"Was that really necessary?" Bloat asked as he floated away.

"What can I do in the next ceremony?" Nemo asked eagerly.

"Hopefully, we won't have another one. Not if we break out of here first, Shark Bait," Gill answered.

"Well, you never know," Deb said forlornly. "Maybe Flo will come around."

Everyone rolled their eyes, including Nemo.

Disney · PIXAR

Just a Toy

After losing Andy and his mum at Pizza Planet, Woody and Buzz had found themselves in nasty neighbour Sid's house! Sid had modified his once-normal toys, turning them into terrifying mutants. Trying to escape, Buzz and Woody ran into the hall – and straight into Scud, Sid's vicious dog!

Buzz ducked through an open door. Inside, he heard, "Calling Buzz Lightyear! This is Star Command!" Then the voice continued: "The world's greatest superhero, now the world's greatest toy!" It was a TV advert for Buzz Lightyear toys! At the end of the ad, a voice added: "Not a flying toy."

Buzz was stunned. Was the ad true? He walked to the stairs and saw blue sky through the hall window. He knew he could fly … couldn't he? Wasn't he a space ranger? Gathering courage, he climbed to the top of the stair railing – and leaped. "To infinity and beyond!" he cried.

For a moment, Buzz seemed to hang in the air. Then, he fell *CRASH!* onto the stair landing, and his left arm broke off.

Buzz Lightyear finally understood the truth: he was a toy.

Upstairs, Woody searched for Buzz. He peeked into a room and saw Sid's little sister,

Hannah, playing with her dolls. Woody stared as he realized: one of the dolls was Buzz!

Hannah had found the space ranger and added him to her tea party. Woody waited until Hannah left, then ran to help Buzz. But Buzz didn't want to move. He was upset because he wasn't a real space ranger. "Look at me," he moaned. "I can't even fly out the window."

The window? With wide eyes, Woody turned around towards Sid's bedroom. Sid's window was directly opposite Andy's bedroom window! Woody picked up a Christmas decoration from the floor and ran into Sid's room, pushing Buzz in front of him. He climbed up onto the desk, where he could look out of the window. On the other side of the garden he saw Andy's window! On top of the desk inside Andy's room, Hamm and Mr. Potato Head were playing battleships and, as usual, Hamm was winning. Woody opened Sid's bedroom window.

"Hey there, guys! It's me!" Woody called out to them, full of hope. The two toys turned to look, amazed.

"Woody's in nasty Sid's bedroom!" exclaimed Hamm. "Hey, guys, come and look, it's Woody!"

All of Andy's toys rushed to the window. Surely now Woody and Buzz were saved?

Tag!

Early one morning, Simba woke up ready to find Nala and continue their game of Tag. The night before, when their mothers had made them stop ("Time for bed, Simba!" "Time for bed, Nala!"), Simba had been It – which is a terrible way to go to bed! – and he was eager to tag Nala and make *her* It as soon as possible. But, when he arrived at the pride's meeting place, everyone, it seemed, was there except for Nala.

"Where's Nala?" he asked his mother.

"Oh, I heard her mother say she wasn't feeling well," she replied. "So they're staying in the cave and resting until she's better."

"But she has to come out," protested Simba. "I'm It and I have to tag somebody!"

His mother smiled. "I'm afraid you'll just have to wait, little Simba," she said.

"But that's so boring!" Simba groaned.

"You can play by yourself, Simba," she reminded him.

"Aw, all right." Simba sighed. First, he tried hunting grasshoppers. But they jumped so high and so far – and so fast! – he soon grew tired and frustrated.

Then he tried climbing trees. But the birds didn't much like a lion cub messing around among their branches and shooed him away.

Finally, he tried just lying down and finding pictures in the clouds. But that was Nala's favourite game, and it made him miss her.

He rolled over and swatted a bright wildflower with his paw. "Tag, you're It," he said half-heartedly. Then, suddenly, an idea popped into his head. What if he picked some wildflowers and took them to his sick friend? It might even make her feel better!

With newfound energy, Simba picked as many flowers as he could carry in his mouth and made his way back to the pride's cave.

"Dees ah fur Nana," he said, dropping the flowers at Nala's mother's feet. "These are for Nala," he repeated. "I hope she feels better really soon."

"Oh, thank you, Simba," the lioness said. "But why don't you give them to her yourself? She seems to be feeling much better. Nala!" she called. And out came Simba's friend, smiling and looking very glad to see him.

She sniffed at the pretty flowers. "Are these for me? Gee, thanks, Simba." Then she turned to her mother. "Can I go out and play with Simba now, Mama?"

"I don't see why not," said her mother.

"Grrreat!" said Nala.

"Yeah, grrreat!" said Simba. Then he reached out and gently tapped her with his paw. "Tag! You're It!"

DISNEY·PIXAR
MONSTERS, INC.

Win Some, Lose Some

Sulley and his assistant, Mike, were in a race to become the Top Scare Team. But Randall and Fungus were right behind them. So it was lucky that Sulley and Mike were racking up the scares!

"We'll beat Randall easily," said Mike, giving Sulley a high five.

"Just keep that paperwork in order," Sulley warned. "You know how Roz hates when it's late!"

Suddenly, the Scare Floor exploded in panic. George Sanderson had returned from his cupboard

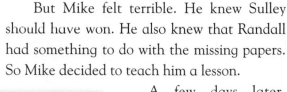

with a ball stuck to his foot with chewing gum. Now, special teams from the CDA, the Child Detection Agency, swarmed into the factory to decontaminate George.

During the excitement, Randall creeped over to Sulley's workstation. He stole Mike's paperwork and tossed it into a shredder.

After George had been cleaned – and shaved! – the Scare Teams got back to work.

"My paperwork is gone!" Mike cried, his eye blinking in confusion.

"Oh, no!" cried Sulley. "Without that paperwork, none of today's work will count."

"Too bad," said Randall, chuckling. "That makes me today's Top Scarer."

Mike was sad, but Sulley wasn't upset in the least. "Cheer up," said Sulley. "You win some, you lose some. Tomorrow is another day."

But Mike felt terrible. He knew Sulley should have won. He also knew that Randall had something to do with the missing papers. So Mike decided to teach him a lesson.

A few days later, Randall was ahead of everyone else in scares.

"This is my best day ever!" Randall crowed to the other Scarers. "Pretty soon I'll be Scarer of the Month!"

But, just then, the alarm went off. George had come back with a lollipop stuck to his ear.

As the teams rushed to decontaminate George, Mike sprang into action. When no one was looking, he hurried over to Randall's and Fungus's workstations and grabbed all their paperwork.

"This is contaminated, too!" Mike cried as he tossed the papers to the floor.

"Burn it!" commanded the CDA decontamination team leader.

With a *whoosh*, a flamethrower burned all of the papers to ashes.

"Where's the paperwork?" Randall cried when he returned to the scare floor.

"Yikes!" Fungus yelped. "Where did it go? It was right here!"

"Well, this is just great," Randall said. "Now my points don't count."

"Looks like you're cooked. Just like your paperwork," Mike said with a chuckle.

Carl and Ellie's House

After their first meeting, Carl and Ellie became best friends. Every day they would meet at Ellie's clubhouse to play and dream together about exploring the world.

One sunny morning, they decided there was no two ways about it – one day, they would go to South America and live next to Paradise Falls.

The years passed and Ellie grew up to be a cheerful and rather talkative young woman. Carl grew into a dependable and quiet young man.

Their friendship grew into love, and they got married when they were both aged 19. They bought the little empty house they had played in as children and set up home there.

Of course, the old house needed doing up! Ellie busied herself filling in the holes in the roof and Carl fixed a new weather vane.

They also patched up the walls, the windows and the floors. Finally, they painted the whole house in bright colours, exactly as it looked in Ellie's adventure book.

One morning, the only thing left was the letterbox. Ellie decided to paint it, but she had hardly given the metal its first lick of colour when Carl leant carelessly against it!

Ellie burst out laughing at the big mark left by his hand. She then pressed her own hand to the side of the box. When she lifted it off, the two prints seemed to be joining as if to hold hands....

To earn enough money for their journey to South America, the couple found jobs at the town zoo. Ellie looked after the animals and Carl sold balloons to the children.

When they returned home in the evening, they were pleased to get back to their pretty house.

Ellie painted a superb picture of Paradise Falls, which she stuck above the fireplace. In front of it she placed a piece of pottery and a small statue of a tropical bird.

Carl added a pair of binoculars and his *Spirit of Adventure* model. Then he put a jar on a table in which, every month, they put aside some money for their trip.

Unfortunately, whatever they managed to save steadily disappeared! They had to buy new tyres for the car, pay for a plaster cast for Carl and then replace the roof of the house.

But over the years they continued to dream, enjoy themselves and, in the evenings, dance together in their lounge.

Neither of them was worried. They knew that one day they'd leave and live out their big adventure.

THE
LION KING

Simba's Secret

Simba and Nala were best friends. They liked to tell each other secrets.

"I'm scared of mice," Nala told Simba one day. "Don't tell anybody."

"Don't worry, I won't," Simba said.

One day, Simba and his father, Mufasa, were out for a walk. "Look at that mouse stuffing her cheeks with seeds," said Mufasa.

"That's so funny!" said Simba. "I don't know why Nala's scared of mice."

Nala had heard Simba talking with his dad, and she got really mad with Simba.

A few weeks later, Nala said, "I'm going to tell you a secret but it's a really big one. If you tell this time, I'll be so mad at you."

"I promise I won't say anything!" said Simba.

"Okay," said Nala. "Here's the secret: I found a huge cave yesterday, down in the red cliffs. I'm going back to explore it today."

Simba played all day without Nala. Before dinner he began to wonder when she was coming back. Nala's mother was worried. "Simba," she asked, "do you know where Nala is?"

"No," he answered. He'd made a promise to Nala, and he didn't want to break it. The sun went down and the moon shone in the sky.

Sarabi, Simba's mother, went to her son. "Do you know where Nala is?" she asked.

"I can't tell," said Simba. "It's a secret. I can't tell, no matter what!"

"Simba," said his mother, "you're a good friend to try not to tell Nala's secret. But there are some secrets that are good to keep and others that are important to tell."

Simba thought about what his mother had said. He decided that he had to tell everyone where Nala was.

The whole pride hurried to the red cliffs. At last, they heard a small voice. "M-mother?" It was Nala!

The lions rushed to the entrance of a cave, but it was almost completely blocked. A rock slide had trapped the little cub! The lions dug and dug, and finally they had cleared the rocks away. Nala rushed out of the cave and ran to her mother.

A few minutes later, Simba walked over and hung his head. "I'm sorry I told your secret, Nala," he said.

"If you hadn't said anything, I'd still be here. It was a stupid secret!" said Nala.

When they got home, it was time for bed. Nala and Simba snuggled together. "I'm happy you're home," said Simba. "And that's not a secret!"

A Lady's Touch

Late one night, Lady's ears perked up and her eyes flew open with a start. The baby was crying! Lady had grown to love the new baby in the house, and she was very protective of him. If he was crying, she was going to find out why. She climbed out of her basket, pushed open the swinging door with her nose and tiptoed up the front stairs.

Meanwhile, Jim Dear and Darling were trying to calm the baby. "Oh, Jim, I just don't know what's the matter with him!" said Darling. She was holding the baby in her arms, trying to rock him and soothe him, but his little face was a deep red and covered with tears. Jim Dear sat groggily at the edge of the bed and looked at his wife helplessly.

"Well, we know he isn't hungry," said Jim Dear, "since we've just given him a bottle." He massaged his temples as though they hurt. Then he noticed Lady, who had walked tentatively into the bedroom. "Hello, Lady," he said to her.

Lady took a few steps closer to the cradle, where Darling was laying the baby down. His little fists were closed tight, and his shrieks had turned to loud sobs.

"We just don't know what's the matter with the little guy," Jim Dear said wearily to Lady. "We've fed him and changed him, and I've sung him every lullaby I know. Maybe you can figure out what's bothering him!"

That was all the invitation Lady needed. She jumped up onto the bed and peered into the cradle. The baby's eyes were squeezed shut and his cheeks were wet with tears. His little legs were kicking the covers. Lady reached in and tugged at the covers to smooth them out. The baby opened his eyes and looked at Lady. His cries dropped to a whimper, and he reached out to touch her. His tiny hand grabbed hold of her ear and tugged. Lady winced but held still.

With her chin, she began to rock the cradle and, with her furry tail, she beat a rhythmic *thump, thump, thump* on the bedcover.

"Ga!" said the baby as he broke into a gummy smile, his big blue eyes looking like wet forget-me-nots. Still holding Lady's ear, the baby giggled.

"Oh, look, Jim Dear!" cried Darling delightedly. "Lady has got him to stop crying!"

"I just don't know what we'd do without you, Lady!" Jim Dear said gratefully.

Rock, rock, rock went the cradle. *Thump, thump, thump* went Lady's tail. Soon the baby's eyelids grew heavy, and then his eyes closed. Tears still streaking his little round cheeks, he relaxed his grip on Lady's ear, smiled and fell asleep.

Mowgli Finds a Friend

Bagheera the panther found Mowgli in the jungle when he was just a baby, and decided to take the boy to a wolf family that lived nearby.

The mother wolf agreed to take care of him, and for 10 years she raised him as one of her own. Mowgli was a very happy Man-cub.

One day, bad news arrived in the jungle. Shere Khan the tiger had returned after a long absence. The tiger was mean and hated everything. More than anything though, Shere Khan hated Man. This meant that it was no longer safe for Mowgli to live in the jungle. The wolves decided that he should go to a Man-village at once.

Bagheera had kept watch over Mowgli through the years and volunteered to take him. Later that night, the boy rode on the panther's back as they made their way through the jungle.

But Mowgli did not want to leave the jungle. It was his home. "I don't want to go to the Man-village!" he shouted. Then he added, "I can take care of myself."

Although Bagheera cared a lot for Mowgli, he eventually became tired of the Man-Cub's fighting, and he walked off into the jungle, leaving Mowgli alone.

Mowgli began to worry that maybe he couldn't take care of himself.

Before long, a bear named Baloo walked out of the jungle and spotted Mowgli. The bear tried to be friendly, but Mowgli told Baloo to go away and leave him alone. But Baloo did not listen. He decided the little Man-cub needed to have some fun.

"Hey, kid, Baloo's gonna learn you to fight like a bear," he said, jumping around. The bear's silly behaviour made Mowgli laugh and soon he was dancing and boxing just like Baloo. When they finished, Mowgli jumped up on his new friend's stomach and tickled him. "You're all right, kid," Baloo said gently.

Just then, Bagheera walked over to them. He had returned to make sure Mowgli was okay. The panther told Baloo that he thought Mowgli should go to the Man-village so he'd be safe from Shere Khan.

Baloo didn't want his little buddy to go to a Man-village. "They'll ruin him. They'll make a man out of him," the bear said.

Bagheera sighed. He knew it would be hard to persuade Mowgli to leave now that he had made friends with Baloo.

The panther watched as the pair jumped into the river and floated lazily away.

HERCULES

A True Hero

"Hercules! Slow down!" Amphitryon yelled to his son, who was pulling their cart to the market. His son was headed straight for a marble archway that was under construction. Because Hercules didn't understand how strong he really was, his attempts to be helpful often turned into disaster.

Later, Amphitryon and his wife, Alcmene, decided to tell Hercules the truth: they weren't his real parents. They'd discovered him when he was a baby and raised him as their own.

Amphitryon handed Hercules a medallion. "This was around your neck when we found you," he said. It had a thunderbolt on it – the symbol of the gods.

Hercules wanted to know more, so the next morning, he left for Zeus. Once he arrived, he stood before the giant statue of Zeus. Suddenly, a great stone hand reached down. "My boy. My little Hercules," Zeus said.

Hercules' eyes widened. Zeus, the most powerful of all gods, was his father! Zeus explained that as a baby Hercules had been stolen and turned into a human. Hercules' super-strength was the only god-like quality he still had.

"If you can prove yourself a true hero on Earth, your godhood will be restored," Zeus told him. "Seek out Philoctetes, the trainer of heroes." With that, Zeus whistled and a winged horse, Pegasus, flew into the temple.

That night, Hercules and Pegasus flew to Philoctetes' home. Phil, as Hercules called him, started training him. Hercules succeeded with all of his hero lessons and grew into a strong man.

Finally, Hercules felt he was ready to test his strength in the real world. Phil took him to Thebes, where Hercules heard that two boys were trapped in a rockslide! He and Pegasus flew to the boys. Hercules lifted a giant boulder and freed the trapped children.

There was no time to celebrate, though. A terrible monster called the Hydra was emerging from a nearby cave … and it was hungry. With a massive head and sharp claws, it went after Hercules. Hercules slashed at the monster with his sword. But when he cut off its head, more grew back. The more heads he chopped off, the more appeared!

Then the Hydra trapped Hercules in one of its claws. Hercules slammed his arms against a cliff wall with all his might. Within seconds, the wall broke apart. Huge boulders tumbled down, killing the monster. Hercules was overjoyed. He was well on his way to becoming a true hero.

The Importance of Being a Toy

Woody and Buzz were trapped at Andy's nasty neighbour Sid's house, and Buzz had just discovered he wasn't a real space ranger. He was feeling hopeless, but Woody had an idea. He ran to Sid's bedroom window and waved out towards Andy's house. "Hey, guys!"

Looking outside from their own window, Andy's toys were surprised to see Woody. The cowboy threw them a string of Christmas lights – an escape line from Sid's bedroom. But the toys still didn't trust Woody, because he'd pushed Buzz out of Andy's window. He'd only meant to push him behind the desk, so Andy would pay attention to Woody again, but the plan had gone wrong.

Buzz refused to come to the window to prove he was okay. So, using Buzz's broken arm, Woody tried to show everything was fine – but the trick made it look like he'd hurt Buzz!

Andy's toys dropped the lights and walked away from the window. Woody felt terrible. And when he turned back into Sid's room, things seemed to be getting even worse – Sid's mutant toys had surrounded Buzz!

Woody tried to fight them off but they grabbed Buzz's arm and pushed Woody away. Then, after a moment, the mutants stepped away. Buzz sat up in surprise, flexing his left arm, which was now attached and working perfectly. Sid's mutant toys had fixed his arm! Although they looked scary, it turned out Sid's toys were friendly.

Suddenly, the toys heard Sid racing up the stairs. Everyone scattered – except for Buzz, who wouldn't move. He was still sad because he was just a toy. When Sid burst into the room, he strapped a rocket onto Buzz's back! Blast-off was the next morning!

All night, Woody pleaded with Buzz to escape. "Over in that house is a kid who thinks you are the greatest. And it's not because you're a space ranger. It's because you're a toy. You are his toy," Woody said.

Woody nearly lost hope, but Buzz finally realized Woody was right. Being a toy was important! Buzz ran over to Woody, to help the cowboy break free, too. But suddenly, the alarm clock started ringing and Sid jumped out of bed. "Time for lift off!" he yelled, grabbing Buzz and running outside.

Woody knew he had to do something fast. As soon as Sid left, Woody gathered the mutant toys and laid out a rescue plan. Buzz was a good toy, he explained, and they couldn't let him get blown up. "We'll have to break a few rules," he told the mutants. "But if it works, it'll help everyone."

Disney·PIXAR
MONSTERS, INC.

The Late Shift

The shift on the Scare Floor at Monsters, Inc., had just ended when Sulley pulled Mike aside.

"Mike, our paperwork is always late," he said. "I'm worried about us getting a bad reputation."

"You're right, Sulley," Mike said earnestly. "From now on, I'm a new monster. In fact, I'm going to start getting caught up tonight. I'm going to stay at work late, just you see. Why, Celia will be so proud of me – uh-oh …"

"What is it, Mike?" Sulley asked.

"Oh, nothing!" Mike grinned. "Sulley, I'll see you later. I've got lots of catching up to do. Paperwork, here I come!"

Sulley gave Mike a suspicious look but allowed himself to be pushed out the door.

But, as soon as Sulley was gone, Mike's smile faded. "What do I do?" he cried. "I have a date with Celia, and I'm already late!" Finally, Mike came to a decision. "I'll catch up tomorrow," he said to himself. "That paperwork is so late that one more day won't make a difference."

With that, Mike headed for the locker room, whistling a jaunty tune. He had just entered the quiet, empty room when he heard a noise.

"Daaaa," said a tiny voice. Mike jumped straight up in the air and gave a yelp.

"Who's there?" he asked nervously.

"Gagoooo," said the voice. That was definitely a child! Mike turned to run – but he tripped over a can of odorant someone had left on the floor and went flying across the room.

Footsteps sounded behind him. Mike looked up, expecting to see a human child. But he saw Sulley instead! "What gives?" he asked Sulley grouchily. Sulley was laughing so hard he couldn't even talk. Finally, the big blue monster calmed down enough to explain.

"I just couldn't resist!" Sulley said, helping Mike up. "After you shooed me out I ran into Celia, who told me about your date. I knew you would rather skip the paperwork than disappoint Celia."

Mike nodded, embarrassed.

"But I told her that you were really behind on your work," Sulley continued, "and I asked if it would be okay for you two to have your date tomorrow night instead."

Mike looked up, surprised. That hadn't even occurred to him. "Did she say yes?" he asked.

"She sure did," Sulley said. "And she also said that since I'm your partner and all, I should really stay here to help you catch up. So, here I am! Now, let's grab some sludgesicles and get to work."

"Okay, Sulley," said Mike. And the two monsters went off to show that paperwork what they were made of.

More to Life

Lightning was in a sleepy town called Radiator Springs. He'd crashed there on his way to California, and had ruined the main street. The judge, Doc, had ordered him to fix the road – and he wasn't allowed to leave until he'd done it.

Doc even challenged Lightning to a race – and won! Lightning couldn't understand how the old car had beaten him.

Lightning eventually did a good job fixing the road, and the residents of the town were grateful. Sally offered him a place to stay and Mater took him tractor-tipping.

Lightning told Mater that winning the Dinoco 400 tie-breaker race in California meant getting a new sponsor with private helicopters. Mater asked if he could ride in a helicopter some day! Lightning said yes.

"I knew I made a good choice for my best friend," Mater said.

Sally overheard their conversation. "Did you mean it?" she asked. Sally was worried that Lightning didn't understand the importance of keeping his promise to Mater.

The next morning, Lightning wandered into Doc's shop and noticed something on a shelf. A Piston Cup! Then he saw two more. Lightning was amazed. Doc Hudson was the "Hudson Hornet" – a racing legend!

Doc was furious when he found Lightning in his shop. "All I see is a bunch of empty cups." He pushed Lightning out.

Lightning rushed over to Flo's Café to tell everyone that Doc was a famous racecar. But no one believed him. While the other cars were laughing, Sally filled Lightning's tank. Sheriff worried that Lightning would escape, but Sally surprised everyone – including Lightning.

"I trust him," she said.

"Let's go for a drive," Sally suggested.

As the two cars zoomed up a winding mountain road, Lightning realized he was actually racing just for fun for the very first time.

Sally told Lightning how she'd found Radiator Springs. "I was an attorney in L.A., living life in the fast lane – but I never felt happy. So I left California, just drove and drove and finally broke down right here."

"I fell in love – with this," Sally continued, leading Lightning to view point. Far below lay a gorgeous valley surrounded by mountains. In the distance, Lightning saw cars speeding past on the Interstate.

"They don't even know what they're missing," he murmured. Lightning was finally beginning to understand that there was more to life than winning.

Bambi

Growing Up

One day, Bambi and Thumper were playing in the meadow.

"Look, Bambi!" exclaimed Thumper.

A herd of stags was thundering towards them.

"I wish I could be a stag!" Bambi exclaimed.

"Well, you know what my father always says," said Thumper.

"I know," said Bambi. "'Eating greens is a special treat. It makes long ears and great big feet.'"

"No, not that!" said Thumper. "I mean, he does say that, but he also says, 'If you want to hop well, but your hop is all wrong, then you have to practise all day long!'"

"I have to hop all day long?" asked Bambi.

"No!" cried Thumper. "If you want to become a stag, you have to practise!"

Bambi glanced back at two big deer. They suddenly ran towards each other, locking horns to test their strength. They looked so powerful and majestic. Bambi wanted to be just like them!

"Okay," Bambi told Thumper.

"Okay," said Thumper. "Follow me."

Thumper hopped to the edge of the meadow. He stopped by a big oak tree. "Lower your head," he told Bambi.

Bambi lowered his head. "Now what?" he asked, staring at the ground.

"Run straight ahead," said Thumper.

Bambi ran straight ahead – towards the trunk of the old oak tree! But, before he got there, a voice cried, "Stop!" Bambi did, skidding to a halt only a few inches from the tree trunk.

Thumper and Bambi looked up. Friend Owl looked down at them with big curious eyes. "Bambi, why were you going to butt my tree trunk with your head?" asked Friend Owl.

"I'm practising to become a big stag," said Bambi. "Stags butt heads to show their strength."

Friend Owl laughed and said, "Bambi, the stags have antlers to protect their heads! And becoming a stag is not something you can practise. It's something that will happen to you with the passing of time."

"It will?" said Bambi.

"Of course!" Friend Owl assured him. "Next summer, you'll see. You'll be bigger and stronger. You'll also have antlers – and, I hope, enough sense not to butt heads with an oak tree!"

"Yes, sir," said Bambi.

"Now go on, you two," said Friend Owl. "And don't be in too much of a hurry to grow up. You'll get there soon enough, I promise you!"

"Okay," said Bambi and Thumper. Then the two friends returned to the snowy meadow to play.

Disney • PIXAR

WALL•E
A New Friend

If you lived back in the 29th Century, you would live off in space with all the other people from Earth.

Long ago, Earth had been evacuated because it was too polluted. No one could live there until someone cleaned up the planet. And there was someone left behind to do that work.

WALL•E was a Waste Allocation Load Lifter, Earth-Class. He didn't mind his lonely job of compacting rubbish. He looked at it as a sort of treasure hunt. He never knew what he would find each day in the trash.

But WALL•E wanted more in life. He didn't ask for much, he just wanted to hold hands with someone – someone he loved. He had seen this watching his favourite movie over and over. It was his dream.

One day, WALL•E was out compacting and cubing trash when he found something special. It was a plant. His pet cockroach chirped, knowing that his friend would be really interested in this green thing. Neither one of them had ever seen anything like it before. WALL•E took it home to keep with his other treasures.

Soon afterwards, another robot landed on Earth. WALL•E was very excited to have some company! WALL•E fell in love with the sleek new robot at first sight. Her name was EVE, and WALL•E watched her in awe.

Over time, WALL•E figured out that EVE was looking for something. But she wouldn't tell him what it was.

WALL•E took her to his home and showed her all the treasures he had collected from the trash. He was very proud of the things he had found.

But when WALL•E showed EVE the plant, she immediately grabbed it from him and stored it in a secret compartment in her chest! Then she shut down. She slept and slept, no matter how hard WALL•E tried to wake her up.

Before long, EVE's ship returned to take her away.

No! WALL•E loved her. He didn't want her to leave.

As the ship prepared to fly away with EVE inside, WALL•E decided he couldn't let her go. He latched onto the outside of the ship.

WALL•E had finally found someone he wanted to hold hands with, and he was not going to let her leave without him.

And so, WALL•E followed EVE into space....

Anyone Can Cook

Remy the rat was in Paris – he had just discovered he had been living underneath the city his whole life! He made his way to a skylight in the roof of his favourite chef's restaurant. He peered down and saw an awkward young man. The man's name was Linguini and he was hoping to get a job at the restaurant.

Linguini's mother, like Gusteau, had recently died. She had been a good friend of Gusteau's. The ill-tempered chef named Skinner had no choice but to hire the ungainly Linguini. He would work in the kitchen as a garbage boy. Linguini went right to work, but he was very clumsy. Remy watched in horror from the skylight as Linguini accidentally spilled a pot of soup and began trying to fix it. "Oh no!" Remy shouted. "He's ruining the soup!"

Then, suddenly, the skylight fell open, and Remy tumbled downwards, landing in the kitchen! Quickly, he scrambled across the kitchen floor. Then he smelled Linguini's horrible soup – and stopped short. This was Remy's chance. He could fix the soup! He jumped to the stovetop and started carefully choosing ingredients to put into the pot.

Suddenly, Linguini was staring right at Remy, and Skinner was right behind them! Linguini quickly hid Remy under a colander.

"How dare you cook in my kitchen!" shouted Skinner, and fired Linguini on the spot. But worse things were happening. While Skinner was yelling the waiter whisked a bowl of the soup off to the dining room to an important food critic!

Word came back from the waiter. The soup was delicious! The critic loved it! Colette, one of the cooks, looked at Linguini. "You can't fire him!" she said to Skinner. "Wasn't Gusteau's motto that anyone can cook? Linguini should be given a chance to cook in the kitchen."

Angrily, Skinner gave in. Remy made a move for the window, but Skinner spotted him. He made Linguini catch the rat in a jar. But poor Linguini didn't have the heart to throw Remy out. He started talking to him instead. When Remy nodded, Linguini realized Remy understood what he was saying!

"Wait. You can cook, right?" asked Linguini, and he made a deal with Remy. Linguini would let Remy out if he promised to help him cook. But when the jar was open, Remy ran away!

Then, Remy stopped and turned back. This could be his big chance to cook in a real gourmet kitchen! The little rat decided to trust Linguini and give the partnership a try.

Disney · PIXAR

BRAVE

I Choose Archery!

Merida was a young and adventurous princess who lived in the ancient Scottish Highlands, in a kingdom called DunBroch. Merida's mother, Queen Elinor, wanted Merida to marry a son from a neighbouring clan. This would help to keep peace between the lands.

Merida, however, didn't feel ready to marry. She wanted to go on great adventures and follow her own path in life. Elinor and Merida couldn't see eye to eye.

Soon, the clans' ships sailed into DunBroch. Queen Elinor dressed Merida in a formal gown, ready to greet them.

"I can't move," Merida complained. "It's too tight."

"It's perfect," her mother said, smiling. But Merida wasn't happy at all.

The royal family welcomed the lords and their clans in the castle's Great Hall. Lord MacGuffin, Lord Macintosh and Lord Dingwall, the heads of each clan, stepped forward to present their sons.

Merida was unimpressed by all three of the young lords. She desperately tried to think of a way out of the marriage.

Alas, the peace among the clans proved fragile. A few insults were all it took to set them brawling. Luckily, Queen Elinor soon restored order.

The queen clarified the rules. Only the first-born of each of the leaders would compete for the hand of the princess. The princess herself would determine the challenge.

First born? Merida's eyes lit up as an idea formed in her head. She leaped to her feet, crying, "I choose archery!"

The competition began at high noon. Young MacGuffin took the first shot – and nearly missed the target completely. Young Macintosh's shot was slightly better. His attitude, however, was not. He stomped angrily on his bow. Wee Dingwall was the clumsiest of them all. But to everyone's amazement, he hit the bull's-eye!

Just then, Merida strode onto the field. "I am the first-born descendant of Clan DunBroch!" she declared before the stunned crowd. "And I'll be shooting for my own hand!"

"Merida! I forbid it!" the queen cried. Merida ignored her and raised her bow.

One by one, Merida fired her arrows at the targets. She hit all three bull's-eyes. Queen Elinor was furious! Merida might have just ruined the peace between the clans.

DISNEY·PIXAR
MONSTERS, INC.

A Child in Monstropolis

Late at night, a little boy awoke to see … a monster! He screamed! Then, the monster screamed, too! With a sigh, the teacher turned off the mechanical boy. Then she repeated the rules: "Never scream. And NEVER leave a child's closet door open. Why?"

"It could let in a child!" bellowed Mr Waternoose, the CEO of Monsters, Incorporated.

The Scarers-in-Training gasped. They knew that Monstropolis was powered by children's screams. But letting a child into the world of monsters would be deadly!

Meanwhile, across town, James P. Sullivan was exercising. His assistant (and best friend), Mike Wazowski, was coaching him. Sulley was a professional Scarer.

At Monsters, Inc., Sulley was famous for collecting more screams than anyone else. That was important because the city was having an energy shortage. Human kids were getting harder to scare, and Monstropolis needed all the screams it could get.

It was time for the workday to begin. As other workers watched in awe, Sulley led all the Scarers of Monsters, Inc. onto the Scare Floor. Together, these were the best scream collectors in the business.

One of them was Randall – a creepy and mean monster who was very jealous of Sulley.

As the Scarers prepared for work, a conveyor belt dropped a door at each station. When the red signal flashed, each Scarer would walk through his door – and into the room of a sleeping child. Hopefully, the child would let out a good scream!

Suddenly, an alarm rang out. A Scarer named George had returned from the human world with a child's sock on his back! A squad from the CDA (Child Detection Agency) arrived to decontaminate him. Poor George!

When work was finished, Mike rushed to meet his girlfriend Celia. They had planned a special date. But the company's cranky file clerk blocked Mike's way.

"I'm sure you filed your paperwork," Roz rasped. Mike had forgotten! Luckily, Sulley offered to help.

Back at the Scare Floor, Sulley noticed that someone had left a door behind, its red light still on. Puzzled, Sulley peeked through the door but saw no one. So he closed the door. Then he saw … A CHILD!

"AAAAH!" he screamed.

Human children were the scariest things in the world to the monsters in Monstropolis. What was Sulley going to do now…?

Lightning's New Friends

Rookie racecar Lightning McQueen was beginning to understand that there was more to life than winning. He had been stranded in a sleepy town called Radiator Springs after getting lost on his way to a tie-breaker race in California. Sally, the town's attorney, was explaining to Lightning why Radiator Springs wasn't the busy place it once was.

"Forty years ago that Interstate didn't exist," Sally explained, looking at the busy highway. "Folks here never had to travel because the world came to them."

"What happened?" asked Lightning.

"The town got bypassed just to save 10 minutes of driving," Sally replied.

Later that day, as Lightning worked on the town's main street – which he had ruined when he arrived – a herd of escaped tractors stampeded through town! When Lightning followed a stray into the desert, he saw Doc roaring around the dirt racetrack.

"You're amazing!" Lightning told the old pro. But Doc raced off. Lightning had just found out that Doc, the town's judge, had once been a famous racecar.

Lightning followed Doc to his office. "How could you quit at the top of your game?" he asked.

Doc showed Lightning a newspaper article about a wreck he had been in. After he was repaired, Doc wanted to return to racing. But he had been replaced – by a rookie. That was why Doc didn't like Lightning when he first arrived!

The next morning, the road was finished. But where was Lightning? Had he left for California? Everyone felt sad. But then Lightning rolled up. He hadn't left!

"I knew you wouldn't go without saying goodbye!" Mater exclaimed.

Lightning said before leaving he wanted to say thank you for the way the town's residents had treated him. "I'm not sure these tyres can get me all the way to California," he said. In a flash, Guido and Luigi proudly fitted Lightning with four shiny new tyres!

And that was just the beginning. Before long, Lightning made his way to every shop in town. He filled up on Fillmore's organic fuel, tried out night vision goggles at Sarge's Surplus, picked out a bumper sticker at Lizzie's and got a new paint job at Ramone's body shop. Lightning liked helping the town's small businesses.

It was one of the first times Lightning had put others before himself, and he liked teaming up with his new friends.

THE JUNGLE BOOK

Go Fish!

"**O**kay, small fry," said Baloo the bear. "Today I'm going to teach you to fish like a bear!"

Mowgli was delighted. He loved his new friend Baloo. Unlike Bagheera the panther, who kept insisting that Mowgli should live in the Man-village for his own protection, Baloo made no such demands on Mowgli. Baloo was much more interested in having a good time living in the jungle, and so was Mowgli.

"Now, watch this, kid," said Baloo as they arrived at the riverbank. "All ya gotta do is wait for a fish to swim by and then …"

Whoosh! Quick as a flash, Baloo held a wriggling silver fish in his paw. "Now you try it!" he said to Mowgli.

Mowgli sat very still, waiting for a fish to swim by. Then – *splash!* – he toppled headfirst into the water.

"Hmm," said Baloo after he had fished Mowgli out and set him down, dripping. "Now I'll show you my second technique."

Baloo and Mowgli walked towards another part of the river. This time, the fish could be seen occasionally leaping out of the water as they swam down a little waterfall. Baloo waded a few steps into the water, waited for a fish to jump, then – *whoosh!* – he swiped a fish right out of

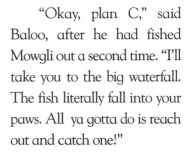

the air. "Now you try, buddy."

Mowgli waded in just as Baloo had done. He waited for the fish to jump and then leaped for it. *Splash!*

"Okay, plan C," said Baloo, after he had fished Mowgli out a second time. "I'll take you to the big waterfall. The fish literally fall into your paws. All ya gotta do is reach out and catch one!"

Mowgli followed Baloo to the big waterfall. Sure enough, silvery fish were jumping all the way down the fall. Catching one would be easy!

In the blink of an eye Baloo held up a fish for Mowgli to admire.

"I'm going to do it this time, you watch me, Baloo!" said Mowgli excitedly. He scrunched up his face with concentration. Then – *flash!* – for an instant, Mowgli actually had a silvery fish in his hands. But, a second later, the fish shot out of his grasp and jumped into the water again. Mowgli looked down at his empty hands with a sigh.

"You know what, kid?" said Baloo, clapping a huge paw on Mowgli's skinny shoulders. "I think you're working too hard. That's not how life in the jungle should be! It should be fun, happy and carefree. So, come on. Let's go shake a banana tree instead!"

And Mowgli cheerfully agreed.

Scaring Sid

Andy's nasty neighbour Sid had taken Buzz Lightyear prisoner, and had strapped a firework to his back! The boy was planning to blast Buzz into space!

Woody knew he had to do something fast. As soon as Sid left, Woody gathered Sid's mutant toys and laid out a rescue plan. Buzz was a good toy, he explained, and they couldn't let him get blown up. "We'll have to break a few rules," he told the mutants. "But if it works, it'll help everyone."

The toys started by sending Legs and Ducky through the air ducts. Arriving above the front door, they unscrewed the socket of the porch light bulb and then Ducky, hanging from the hook of Legs' crane, slipped through the hole, dangled down and managed to swing himself to ring the doorbell.

While Sid's little sister, Hannah, rushed to open the door, the other toys unbolted Sid's bedroom door, allowing Wind-up Frog, the speediest toy in the house, to slip out onto the landing. Sid's dog Scud immediately jumped up and chased Wind-up Frog all the way to the garden, allowing Woody and the others, piled up on Roller Bob's skateboard, to leave the room unnoticed. They hurtled down the stairs and swept into the kitchen, aiming for the cat flap.

Everything went like clockwork and in a matter of minutes they were outside!

In the backyard, Sid was preparing to launch Buzz into outer space.

With a cruel grin, Sid leaned over to light the big rocket's fuse as he began the countdown. "Ten, nine, eight, seven …"

Suddenly, he heard – "Reach for the sky!"

It was Woody, lying nearby. Sid turned and picked Woody up. How did the cowboy doll get outside? And was something wrong with its pull string?

Then, one by one, the mutant toys stood up and staggered out of the sandbox … splashed out of the mud puddle … and crawled from under the dog dish! Together, slowly and steadily, they surrounded the astonished human boy.

But Woody wasn't done with Sid. "From now on, you must take good care of your toys. Because if you don't, we'll find out," Woody warned. And then he leaned in very close and looked Sid right in the eye. "So play nice!"

"AAAHH!" Sid threw up his arms and shrieked in terror. Screaming, he ran into the house and slammed the door.

The toys cheered – their plan had worked! Buzz was saved! And best of all, Sid's days of torturing toys were over.

Bird Trouble

It was the height of the rainy season, and the roof of the ant colony had sprung a leak. "Bucket brigade!" shouted Princess Atta. The ants obediently lined up and began catching the water in cupped leaves, passing them along the length of the line and dumping them into the stream. It was exhausting, but the ants were used to hard work.

"There's got to be an easier way," Flik said. "Tomorrow I'm going to invent a way to fix the roof!"

"What are you doing, Flik?" Dot asked the next morning. The rain had let up for a moment, and the two were outside. Flik had arranged dozens of torn pieces of leaves along one side of the sloping roof.

"I'm fixing the leak," he said cheerfully. "See, these leaves act as rain deflectors. Then the water will run into these hollowed-out flower stems that will act as gutters."

"Wow," said Dot. She was the only ant who thought Flik's inventions were worthwhile.

"The only thing I'm missing is some sort of deflection device for the ant hole itself," he said. "Aha!" he shouted a moment later. He had spotted a buttercup. "That flower should work perfectly. Come on, Dot. Give me a hand. Boy, oh, boy, is this invention ever going to impress the Princess!"

Together, the two ants dragged the buttercup to the top of the anthill.

"What on earth are you two doing?" It was Princess Atta.

"Flik figured out a way to fix the leak!" shouted Dot triumphantly.

Flik shrugged modestly. "It's very simple, really. See, what I did was –"

Suddenly, the ant lookout began shouting, "Bird! Bird! Bird coming!"

Flik, Atta and Dot ran for cover. Sure enough, a hummingbird was hovering just above the anthill.

"It's going for the flower!" shouted an ant. The hummingbird pressed its long beak into the buttercup Flik had dragged over the anthill.

"Avalanche!" shouted the ants. The delicately built anthill began to collapse. Ants scrambled to get out of the way. The bird flew off.

"Nice work, Flik," said Princess Atta. "This is going to take weeks to rebuild."

Flik sighed and hung his head.

"Don't worry, Flik," whispered Dot. "Someday you'll do great things."

"Oh, you're sweet, Dot," Flik said sadly. "If only it hadn't been for that bird. I should have known it would like the flower. Birds are so predictable." Flik looked thoughtful. "Maybe someday I could use that to my advantage."

Flik smiled at Dot. "Imagine that," he said. "An ant using a bird in his plan!"

Pinocchio

Follow Your Star

Jiminy Cricket was a wanderer. He loved the independence, the excitement and the simplicity of his way of life. For many a season, he had roamed the countryside, stopping to rest in towns along the way, and moving on when he grew restless.

But lately, Jiminy Cricket had noticed that there was one thing missing from his vagabond lifestyle: a purpose. Camping one night by the side of the road, he sat on his sleeping bag and gazed into his campfire.

"I wonder what it would feel like to be really helpful to someone," he said.

Jiminy lay on his sleeping bag and tried to get comfortable on the hard ground as he gazed up into the starry night sky. As his eyes scanned the many tiny points of light, one star to the south jumped out at him and seemed to shine brighter than all the rest.

"Say, is that a Wishing Star?" he wondered aloud. Since he couldn't know for certain, he decided it would be best to make a wish on it, just in case. "Wishing Star," he said, "I wish to find a place where I can make a difference and do a bit of good."

Then, his wish made, Jiminy Cricket suddenly felt a strange impulse: an urge to get up, gather his things and follow that star – the Wishing Star. He couldn't quite explain the feeling, but he felt it just the same.

So do you know what Jiminy Cricket did?

He put out the campfire. He gathered his things. And he took to the road. He followed that star all through the night. He walked for miles along highways and byways, across fields and over hills. He walked until the sun came up and he could no longer see the star to follow it. Then he made camp and he slept.

He did the same thing for several more nights and several more days.

Then, one night, he came to a village. Looking up at the Wishing Star, Jiminy Cricket noticed that it seemed to hang directly overhead.

It was very late at night as Jiminy Cricket walked into the village and looked around. Every window of every house was dark – except for one window in a shop at the end of a street. So Jiminy Cricket hopped over to the window. Peering inside, he saw that it was a woodcarver's workshop, dimly lit by the embers of a fire dying in the fireplace. It seemed a warm and pleasant place to stop for the night.

Little did Jiminy Cricket know that it was the home of Geppetto, a kind old woodcarver who had just finished work on a puppet he called Pinocchio.

And little did he know that he had just found a place where he would do more than just a bit of good.

Bad Guys Don't Win Medals

Wreck-It Ralph worked in the *Fix-It Felix, Jr* video game. Every time someone played the game, Ralph would come on-screen and yell, "I'M GONNA WRECK IT!"

Then Fix-It Felix, the Good Guy, would arrive with his magic hammer and fix everything. All the Nicelanders cheered for Felix and gave him pie and a medal. But Ralph? They threw him off the building and into the mud.

The *Fix-It Felix, Jr* game had been in Litwak's Family Fun Centre for 30 years now. It was one of the arcade's original 8-bit games, and kids had been helping Felix fix up the Nicelanders' building for a very long time.

Inside the game, Felix and the Nicelanders were happy. Felix enjoyed his work, and the Nicelanders were glad to reward him … game after game, year after year.

Ralph, however, was getting tired of that mud puddle. It didn't feel fair. He was just doing his job. Why did Felix always get to be the Good Guy, while he ended up covered in mud?

On the game's anniversary, Ralph travelled through the power cord to a support group for video game Bad Guys. He told the group that he wished he could be the Good Guy, just once.

"We can't change who we are," the others said. Then they all recited the Bad Guy Affirmation: "I am Bad. And that's good. I will never be Good. And that's not bad. There's no one I'd rather be than me."

Ralph headed home through Game Central Station, the hub for all the games in the arcade. As usual, Surge Protector stopped him for questioning. Ralph knew it was just because he was a Bad Guy.

Then Ralph dropped off treats for the homeless video game characters living in the station. Their games had been unplugged, so they had nowhere to live.

That evening, the Nicelanders held a big anniversary party in their apartment building. Ralph couldn't believe that he hadn't been invited. "I am going to that party!" Ralph declared.

At the party, Ralph tried to be polite. Then he noticed the cake, with a Felix figurine on top, wearing a medal. Ralph wanted his own figurine to wear a medal, too. But Nicelander Gene said, "Bad Guys don't win medals!"

Ralph was so upset that he accidentally wrecked the cake!

Ralph sighed. Would he ever be able to have his very own medal…?

Disney MICKEY & FRIENDS
Leaping Leap Year

It was a sunny morning, and Mickey and Pluto were outside playing catch. Mickey threw Pluto a ball. Pluto took a deep breath, did a fancy spin and leaped into the air to catch it.

"Nice job," Mickey said, cheering him on. "Great catch! Great leap!"

Great leap? Mickey's words echoed in his head. "Oh, my goodness, do you know what today is?" he asked Pluto.

Pluto leaped into the air again and again. He wanted Mickey to take the ball from him and toss it again.

"I almost forgot. Today is leap year!" Mickey exclaimed.

Pluto dropped the ball at Mickey's feet.

"I mean, today's not actually a year – it's a day," Mickey continued, talking to himself.

Pluto wasn't sure Mickey understood him. He wanted to play! So he leaped into the air again and again.

Leap! Leap! Leap!

Leap! Leap! Leap!

"That's the spirit!" Mickey encouraged him. "Leap year is something to be excited about! After all, it happens only once every four years. Well, almost every four years."

Mickey took a pad and pencil out of his back pocket and started working out figures. "There's a mathematical equation to figure this out if you really want to be exact." He scribbled some notes. "That's zero divided by ... hmm, let me see here ... carry the...." Mickey started blushing. "Maths is not really my thing." He put the pad back in his pocket. "Let's just say once every four years! Imagine if your birthday were on 29 February – 29 February only comes once every four years. So instead of being 12, you'd be three!" He laughed. "Just kidding ... I think!"

Pluto sat down, panting with exhaustion, as Mickey continued explaining it to him. "Every four years, there's an extra day in the calendar – 29 February – and that's today!"

"Do you know why we have leap year?" Mickey asked. "Because we have 365 days in a year, but it actually takes the earth a little longer to orbit the sun. So we have to make up for lost time!"

The excitement in Mickey's voice got Pluto excited again. He was back on his feet, tail wagging, ball in his mouth, leaping up and down.

"That's right," Mickey agreed, and joined Pluto in his leaping.

Leap! Leap! Leap!

Leap! Leap! Leap!

"Hooray!" shouted Mickey. "It's leap year!"

BIG HERO 6

Hi-Tech Dreams

After young Hiro Hamada had used his own bot invention to defeat a champion bot-fighter, he and his brother, Tadashi, had been arrested by the police while leaving the illegal bot fight.

They'd had to call their Aunt Cass to come and bail them out. Hiro took one look at Aunt Cass's face as she entered the police station. Usually, she was a very cheerful woman. Tonight, she was anything but.

Uh-oh, Hiro thought. *I've really done it this time.* But that wasn't going to stop him. As soon as they got home, Hiro was looking for his next bot fight.

"I'll take you," said Tadashi.

Tadashi wasn't pleased about Hiro going to another fight, but he wasn't going to let his little brother go alone. On the way, Tadashi told Hiro he wanted to check on an experiment. But really Tadashi wanted Hiro to see how amazing his school was. If Hiro was going to use his brain, then the San Francisco Institute of Technology (SFIT) was the place to start.

Hiro gasped as he entered the robotics lab. It was filled with the most advanced high-tech equipment – as well as Tadashi's friends! Go Go Tomago was a mechanical engineer of few words. Wasabi No-Ginger was a physicist who loved precision. Honey Lemon worked with chemicals. And Fred, well, he liked comic books and hanging out with clever people.

To demonstrate what he was working on, Tadashi put duct tape on Hiro's arm, then ripped it off.

"Oww!" Hiro shouted, prompting a robot to inflate from inside a suitcase.

"Hello," said the large, white robot. "I am Baymax, your personal health-care companion." Baymax scanned Hiro, diagnosed him and soothed his pain.

Tadashi showed Hiro the green nurse chip that was inside Baymax's access port. "I programmed him with over 10,000 medical procedures. This is what makes Baymax … Baymax."

"I cannot deactivate until you say you are satisfied with your care," Baymax said.

Just then, Tadashi's robotics teacher, Robert Callaghan, walked in. He spotted the bot in Hiro's hand and examined it carefully.

"Have you ever thought of applying here?" he asked.

When Tadashi explained that Hiro's interest lay in bot fighting, Callaghan shrugged and added, "Then my programme wouldn't be for you. My students go on to shape the future."

Hiro thought about what Callaghan had said – especially the bit about shaping the future. Maybe Tadashi was right. Maybe going to university was a good idea after all….

DISNEY·PIXAR

MONSTERS, INC.

Boo!

James P. Sullivan – aka Sulley – was a professional Scarer and worked at Monsters, Incorporated in Monstropolis. His best friend, Mike Wazowski, trained him. The screams of human children powered Monstropolis, so it was important they collected lots of them!

Although their job was to scare children, the monsters were actually very scared of humans! There was a rule that no child's door should ever be left open, because a child could enter Monstropolis. But one night, Sulley found a door that had been left open on the Scare Floor – and a child had come through!

At a restaurant, Mike and his date, Celia, were enjoying dinner. Mike was just telling Celia what a beautiful monster she was … when suddenly, he spotted Sulley waving frantically outside the window. Sulley looked terrified.

Quickly, Sulley explained about the child. Mike was horrified … especially when Sulley showed him the kid! Then it began running around the restaurant! When the CDA arrived, Mike and Sulley hid the kid in a takeaway box and ran. They were in big trouble!

Back in their apartment, Sulley and Mike tried not to touch the child. Then Mike accidentally fell and the little girl started to giggle. Strangely, her laughter made the lights burn brighter – until they burned out!

Finally, Sulley put the child to bed. But she was afraid. Sulley realized she was terrified that a monster was in the wardrobe. So Sulley stayed with her until she fell asleep.

"This might sound crazy," Sulley told Mike. "But I don't think that kid is dangerous. What if we just put her back in her door?"

Mike didn't like the idea, but what else could they do? The next morning, they disguised her and took her to work. In the locker room, Sulley and the child played hide-and-seek. "Boo!" she said playfully. Sulley was starting to really like her. But then they overheard Randall – a mean monster that was jealous of Sulley – tell his assistant that he planned to "take care of the kid". Sulley needed to get the child home quickly! But Mike made a mistake. "This isn't Boo's door," Sulley exclaimed.

"Boo?!?" Mike couldn't believe Sulley had named the child.

Oops – they suddenly realized everyone on the Scare Floor could hear them talking! When they stopped, they saw that Boo had slipped away. Would they ever be able to find her and take her home…?

Good Luck in California

In the sleepy town of Radiator Springs, rookie racecar Lightning McQueen had found some great new friends. He had ended up there by accident, while on his way to the tie-breaker race for the Piston Cup in California. At first, he had just wanted to leave, but now he was beginning to realize what it meant to help others – maybe there was more to life than winning races after all.

Lightning had spent the day helping all the town's small businesses, and now the evening was drawing in.

"Is it getting dark out?" he called loudly when Sally, a shiny blue sports car he had become friends with, drove up.

Suddenly Radiator Springs lit up in glowing neon colours, and music played. It was time to cruise! But as the townsfolk drove in pairs together, a helicopter searchlight swept over them.

"We have found Lightning McQueen!" boomed a voice from a loudspeaker.

News vans swarmed into town. Reporters surrounded Lightning, shouting questions. He couldn't see Sally or reach his friends.

"Where are you?" Lightning's agent, Harve, shouted over the speaker phone in the back of Mack's trailer. Lighting tried to tell Harve how great Radiator Springs was, but the fast-talking agent wasn't interested.

"Get out of 'Radiation Stinks' now, or Dinoco is history!" he yelled. Dinoco was the sponsor Lightning would get if he won the tie-breaker race.

As Mack urged Lightning to get into the trailer, Lightning and Sally gazed at each other. Neither of them knew what to say.

"Good luck in California." Sally said at last. "I hope you find what you're looking for."

Sally was heading back to her hotel when she heard a reporter thank Doc for letting the press know Lightning's location. How could Doc do such a thing?

"It's best for everyone, Sally," Doc said.

"Best for everyone? Or best for you?" Sally replied in shock.

Doc didn't like young racecars. He used to be a famous racecar and, when he got older and was involved in a big crash, a rookie had taken his place.

Slowly, Lightning's friends went to their homes and shops. Soon, the street was empty. Doc idled alone. Behind him the neon lights blinked off until Radiator Springs was dark and quiet once more.

Doc sighed sadly. Had he been wrong about Lightning?

The Den of Doom

"Where are we going, Baloo?" Mowgli asked. He and Baloo had been travelling through the jungle for a while now.

"Have you ever heard of the Den of Doom, Man-cub?" replied Baloo in a hushed voice.

Mowgli gasped. "The Den of Doom? They say that the Den of Doom is a giant cave filled with bears who will eat anything – or anyone! They say that those bears can hear for miles and see in the dark! They say that even Shere Khan is afraid of them!" he exclaimed.

"Mmm-hmm," said Baloo. "They do say that. They *also* say that all of the bears in the Den of Doom are over eight feet tall, that their teeth are green and razor-sharp, and that their battle cry is so loud that the whales in the ocean hear it and shake with fright. They say all that, and much, much more."

"And we're *going* there?" Mowgli squeaked. "We can't! Baloo, those bears aren't like you! They're dangerous!"

"Too late, Man-cub," Baloo said with a grin. "We're already there!" He picked up Mowgli, whose knees were knocking together so hard he could barely stand, and strode right into a thicket. The bear ducked under a huge palm frond and emerged into a large, sunlit clearing in front of an enormous cave. Baloo put Mowgli down. The boy looked around in complete and utter surprise.

Mowgli had expected to see hundreds of fierce, angry bears. Instead, he saw hundreds of relaxed, happy bears having a really good time. Bears were swimming in a small pond, splashing and laughing. Bears were resting in the cool shadows of the cave. Bears were playing tag out in the clearing and chomping on piles of ripe, delicious fruit. It was, in short, a bear party.

"I don't understand," Mowgli said to Baloo. "This is the Den of Doom?"

"Yep," Baloo said happily, grabbing a palm frond and fanning himself with it. "It used to be called the Den of Delights, but we had to change the name. See, everyone in the jungle knew that the Den of Delights was the most fun place around. We bears never turned anyone away from our party. But then it got so crowded that it just wasn't any fun any more. So we spread a few rumours, changed the name, and *presto* – it's the Den of Doom! Now no one bothers us bears any more."

"But what about me?" Mowgli said anxiously. "I'm not a bear."

"You're an honorary bear, Mowgli," Baloo replied with a smile. "You sure have enough fun to be one!"

DUMBO
Float Like a Butterfly

One day, Dumbo's best friend, Timothy Q. Mouse, found Dumbo looking sad. "What's the matter, little guy?" the mouse asked the elephant. "Have people been teasing you about your ears again?"

Dumbo nodded. The little elephant looked totally miserable.

Timothy shook his head. The two were very good friends and did everything together. He didn't mind one bit that Dumbo had large ears. In fact, he thought they were great.

Timothy was trying to think of a way to cheer up his dear friend. And then he saw something. "Look, Dumbo!" he cried, racing over to a nearby fence post. Hanging from the fence was a large cocoon. "It's a butterfly cocoon!" Timothy said excitedly.

Dumbo came over to examine it.

"And look – it's about to hatch into a butterfly," said Timothy. He looked thoughtful for a moment, and then he turned to Dumbo. "You know what? You are a lot like the little caterpillar that made this cocoon."

Dumbo looked at Timothy quizzically.

"Yep, it's true. You see, a caterpillar is something nobody really wants around much. They think it's kind of plain looking, and it can't really do anything very interesting. But then one day, the caterpillar turns into a beautiful butterfly, and everyone loves it. And you know what? I think

you're going to be that way, too. When you get older, everyone is going to admire you rather than tease you!"

Dumbo smiled gratefully at his friend, and wiped away a tear with one of his long ears.

Suddenly, it started to rain. "Oh no!" cried Timothy. "The butterfly is going to get its new wings all wet. It won't be able to fly if it gets rained on. What'll we do? We need an umbrella!"

As Timothy looked this way and that for an umbrella, Dumbo smiled and unfurled his long ears. He draped them over the fence post so that they made a lovely roof for the insect, protecting it from the falling droplets of rain.

"Great idea!" said Timothy admiringly. The two friends stood there during the downpour, which didn't last very long. While they waited, they watched the beautiful new butterfly emerge from its cocoon and unfurl its colourful wings. When the rain stopped, the butterfly spread its wings (which were quite dry, thanks to Dumbo) and flew away.

"You know, my friend," said Timothy as they watched it fly away, "I think someday you're going to be a big success. You'll be like that butterfly – happy, carefree and floating along. Well, not floating for real, that's impossible. Imagine that, a flying elephant!"

Disney · PIXAR
FINDING
NEMO

Homesick

Nemo still couldn't believe everything that had happened to him. First, he'd been snatched up by a scuba diver in the ocean. Then, he'd travelled a long way in a big water cooler. Finally, he'd been dumped in a fish tank in a dentist's office. The other fish in the tank seemed nice, but Nemo missed his dad and his old home. He couldn't think about anything except getting back to the ocean. But would their plan to escape really work? It seemed hopeless....

"Hey, kid," Bloat the blowfish swam over to him. "Are you okay? You look a little down in the gills."

"I'll say," said Nigel the seagull.

Peach the starfish glanced over from her spot on the tank wall. "He's just upset," she said. "It's only natural." She smiled kindly at Nemo. "It's okay, hon. We know how you feel."

"How could you know?" he muttered, feeling sorry for himself. "You weren't grabbed out of the ocean, away from your dad."

"Well, no," a fish named Gurgle admitted. "But we all had families back where we came from. We all miss them."

"Really?" Nemo blinked in surprise. He hadn't thought about that.

"Sure," Peach said. "The lady who sold me over the Internet kept lots of us starfish in her basement." She sighed sadly. "I still wonder where all my brothers and sisters ended up. I'd give two or three of my arms to see them again."

"I hear you," Bloat agreed. "I was hatched in somebody's garage. They sold me and a whole school of my brothers and sisters and cousins to Bob's Fish Mart. Just when we made friends with the other fish there, he came in and bought me." He waved a fin towards the dentist in the office outside the tank. "It could be worse, though," Bloat continued. "You guys are the best friends I've ever had."

A fish named Deb nodded. "I'm lucky he bought me and my sister together. Right, Flo?" She smiled at her own reflection in the glass of the tank. When the reflection didn't answer, Deb shrugged. "I guess Flo is too choked up to talk right now. But I can tell by her smile that she agrees. We don't know what we'd do without each other. But we still miss the rest of our family."

"Wow," Nemo said, looking around at his new tankmates. "I guess you guys *do* know how I feel."

Even though he was sad that the other fish had been taken from their families, it made Nemo feel a little less alone. At least they understood how much he wanted to find his way back to his father. Now, a little braver and more determined than ever, Nemo was ready to escape from the tank – no matter what.

THE ARISTOCATS

Bedtime for Duchess

"Come, my precious ones!" Duchess called to Berlioz, Toulouse and Marie. "It's time to go to sleep."

"Oh, Mother!" Toulouse complained.

"But I'm not tired!" Marie joined in.

"I'm not going to sleep," Berlioz added. "Night-time is just when things start happening for us alley cats." Berlioz crouched down low, hindquarters in the air, and pounced on an imaginary opponent.

"Who does he think he's kidding?" Toulouse whispered to Marie, who rolled her eyes in agreement.

"Now, now, it's been a long day," Duchess told them. "I don't want to hear any more protests."

"Mother!" Berlioz whined.

"We need a bedtime story!" Marie insisted.

"A story? My darlings, it's way past your bedtime, and I'm just too tired tonight," replied Duchess.

"Then why don't we tell *you* a story?" Toulouse offered.

"Yeah!" Berlioz chimed in.

"What a lovely idea," said Duchess.

"Once upon a time –" Marie began.

"There was a big, mean, ferocious alley cat," Berlioz continued.

"Berlioz!" Marie protested. "It's not supposed to be scary. She'll have nightmares!"

"Sorry, Mama," Berlioz said.

"That's quite all right," Duchess told him.

"Now where were we?" Toulouse asked.

"Once upon a time –" Marie began again.

"Yeah, once upon a time there was this amazing kitten," Toulouse said. "And he could paint like no other kitten you've ever seen."

"And that's because the model for his paintings was the most beautiful kitten you've ever laid eyes on," Marie added.

"Give me a break!" Berlioz said, grumbling under his breath. He and Toulouse snickered.

"Very funny." Marie was not amused. "Can we get back to the story?"

"This kitten was a painter by day and a smooth-talking, alley-hanging, danger-seeking hepcat by night," Berlioz continued.

Toulouse tapped Berlioz with his paw. He looked up and saw what both Toulouse and Marie were seeing. Duchess herself had fallen asleep!

Berlioz, Toulouse and Marie each gave their mother a kiss good night.

"Good night, Mama," said Marie.

"Good night, Mama," said Toulouse.

"Good night, Mama," said Berlioz.

Then all three curled up beside Duchess and promptly fell asleep too.

THE
LION KING

Just Like Dad

"Dad, when I grow up, I want to be just like you," Simba said to his father.

Mufasa nuzzled his son's head gently. "All in good time, son," he said.

Just then, Simba's friend Nala bounded up to them. "Come on, Simba!" she called. "Let's go play by the river!"

On their way, Simba stopped abruptly. "Listen to this," he said. He threw back his head and roared as loudly as he could. Then he looked at her expectantly. "Do I sound like my dad?"

Nala tried to suppress a giggle. "Not quite," she said.

Soon they reached the river. The waters were high as a result of the recent rains. Simba found a quiet pool at the side and stared down at his reflection. "Do you think my mane is starting to grow?" he asked Nala.

Nala sighed. "Maybe a little," she replied. "But, Simba, what's the big rush? Let's just have fun being young!"

Simba was eyeing a tree branch that extended over the raging river. "Well, I may not be as big as my dad yet, but at least I'm as brave as he is!" he shouted, and raced up to the tree. Climbing its gnarled trunk, he began walking along the branch over the water.

Nala hurried over. "Simba!" she yelled. "Come back here! The branch is going to break!"

But Simba couldn't hear her over the loud waters. Nala bounded away to get help.

Simba felt the branch begin to sag. "Uh-oh," he said to himself.

Suddenly the whole thing broke off and Simba tumbled into the water. The current was strong, and he struggled to swim towards the shore. He was running out of strength, and he realized he might not make it.

Then he felt himself being lifted out of the water and tossed onto the bank. Dripping and coughing, he looked up – right into the angry eyes of his father.

"Simba!" thundered Mufasa. "There's a big difference between being brave and being foolish! The sooner you learn that, the better chance you will have of growing old!"

Simba hung his head. Out of the corner of his eye, he saw Nala, pretending not to overhear. "I'm … sorry, Dad," he said softly. "I just wanted to be brave like you."

His father's gaze softened. "Well," he said. "As long as we're soaking wet, why don't we go to a quieter part of the river and do some swimming?" He looked over to where Nala was sitting. "Come on, Nala!" he called. "Come with us!"

"Yippee!" cried the cubs, and they all went off together.

Disney MICKEY & FRIENDS
Spring Cleaning

Mickey Mouse hummed as he straightened up his messy house. He swept up some leaves that had blown in through the front door. Then he shook the mud off his doormat.

He was picking up some old magazines when one of them caught his eye.

"'Make a Fresh Start with Spring Cleaning,'" Mickey read aloud. "Hmm. Spring cleaning, eh?"

He looked out of the window. It wasn't spring – it was autumn! What was he doing cleaning his house?

"Whew!" he exclaimed as he dropped his broom and flopped onto the sofa. "Looks like I have a whole day free now. I think I'll see if Minnie wants to come over!"

A short while later, Minnie Mouse rang the doorbell. "Hi, Mickey!" she said cheerfully. "What do you want to do to – "

She gasped. Mickey's house was a mess! There was mud on the floor, dust on the shelves, dirty dishes on the table, laundry piled here and there, books and magazines everywhere....

"What's wrong?" Mickey asked.

"Mickey," Minnie said, "er, when was the last time you cleaned your house?"

Mickey laughed. "Don't be silly, Minnie!" he said. "I don't need to clean this place for months."

"M-m-months?" Minnie gasped. She couldn't believe it. In a few months, Mickey's entire house would be buried in mess!

"Sure!" Mickey shrugged. "Haven't you ever heard of spring-cleaning?"

Minnie wasn't sure what to do. She didn't want to be rude, but she had to convince Mickey to clean his house – and it couldn't wait until spring!

"You know, Mickey," she said casually, "I just read something about a fun new trend."

"Really?" Mickey smiled. "What's that, Minnie? Maybe it's something we could do today, since we have the whole day free!"

"Oh!" Minnie pretended to be surprised at the idea. "Why, I suppose we could! I hadn't thought of that."

"So, what's the trend?" Mickey asked eagerly. "Waterskiing? Rock climbing? Fondue parties?"

"No," Minnie said cheerfully. "Autumn cleaning! It's the newest rage."

"Autumn cleaning?" Mickey said doubtfully. He blinked, then smiled. "You know, that's so crazy, it sounds like fun! Come on, let's try it!"

Minnie smiled and picked up the magazine with the spring-cleaning article in it. "Good," she said. She stuffed the magazine into the dustbin. "I'll start right here!"

Disney·PIXAR
MONSTERS, INC.
Banished!

In Monstropolis there was a company called Monsters, Inc., where monsters collected human children's screams to power the city. Sulley was the top Scarer and Mike Wazowski was his best friend.

Mike and Sulley were in big trouble – they'd discovered a human girl in Monstropolis! Monsters were very scared of human kids. They thought letting a child into the world of monsters would be deadly! But Sulley had grown to rather like the human child, and had named her 'Boo'.

Mike and Sulley had brought Boo to the Scare Floor to send her home – but she had gone missing! Mike and Sulley split up to find her, but a mean, creepy monster called Randall cornered Mike. The nasty monster knew all about Boo. He ordered Mike to bring her to the Scare Floor. He said he'd have her door ready.

After Sulley finally found Boo, Mike told him about Randall's plan. Together, they went to the Scare Floor, but Sulley was still worried. "We can't trust Randall!"

Mike disagreed. To prove the open door was safe, he went right through – and was captured by Randall! Sulley and Boo secretly followed Randall. They learned he had invented a cruel new way to capture screams from kids with a scary machine. And he was about to try it out on Mike!

Sulley rescued Mike and raced to the training room. He needed to warn the boss about Randall. But then Boo saw Sulley looking ferocious, and she was terrified! Sulley felt awful. For the first time, he realized how mean it was to scare a child.

The boss, Mr Waternoose, promised he would fix everything – but he was really working with Randall! He shoved Sulley and Mike through a door into the human world. They were banished to the mountains! Sulley knew Boo was in trouble. He had to get back. Racing to the local village, he found a door that led home. He rushed to Randall's secret lab and destroyed the machine.

As Sulley raced away with Boo, Mike arrived to help. But Celia, Mike's girlfriend, couldn't understand what was going on. Quickly, Mike explained Randall's plan. She knew Mike was telling the truth.

Mike and Sulley climbed onto the machine that carried doors to the Scare Floor. The power wasn't on, so Mike made a funny face. Boo laughed, and the power surged! It seemed that human children's laughs were just as powerful as their screams!

Making it Home

Woody, along with Sid's mutant toys, had just terrified the cruel boy by coming to life! It was all a plan to save Buzz from being blasted into space with a rocket strapped to him.

But Woody and Buzz couldn't hang around – a moving van was in front of Andy's house! If they didn't hurry, Andy would leave without them.

The two toys ran towards Andy's house. But Buzz couldn't fit through the fence because the rocket was still attached to his back. "Just go, I'll catch up," he assured Woody.

But Woody wouldn't leave without his new friend. By the time Woody helped Buzz through the fence, though, it was too late. Andy's van had driven away.

Woody and Buzz raced after the moving van. Buzz grabbed a loose strap, then climbed up onto the rear of the truck. He tried to help Woody up, too. But Sid's mean dog, Scud, raced right after them. He leaped up and dragged Woody off the van.

"Nooooo!" Buzz yelled. He jumped onto Scud's head to save Woody. Now Woody was safe, but Buzz was left behind!

Woody rummaged through the boxes in the back of the van and found RC Car. Using the remote, he sent RC back to pick up Buzz.

But Andy's toys didn't understand, and angrily threw Woody off the van! Luckily, Buzz and RC picked up Woody as they came speeding back. Finally, the other toys tried to help … but RC's batteries ran out!

Woody watched as the moving van chugged further away. Then they realized – Buzz still had the rocket on his back! Once the fuse was lit, Woody whooped.

As the rocket began to burn, RC picked up speed, zooming down the street. Buzz and Woody hung on tight as they got near the moving van. But by now, RC car was whizzing so fast, they began to lift off the ground! As they rose upwards, Woody let go of RC, who landed in the van. Buzz and Woody whooshed into the sky. Just before the rocket exploded, Buzz snapped open his space wings.

"Buzz, you're flying!" Woody exclaimed.

"This isn't flying," Buzz replied. "This is falling with style!"

Buzz and Woody glided down towards Andy's car and dropped unnoticed through the open sunroof, landing safely on the back seat. Hearing a thump, Andy looked over.

"Woody! Buzz!" Andy shouted. He hugged them close, thrilled to have his two favourite toys back.

Disney
Lady and the **TRAMP**

Don't Mock Jock

Aunt Sarah had only just arrived to look after the baby while Jim Dear and Darling were away, but already her Siamese cats, Si and Am, had caused nothing but trouble. When they made a huge mess in the living room, Lady had been blamed for it, and Aunt Sarah had taken Lady to be fitted with a muzzle!

Meanwhile, left alone in the house, Si and Am had discovered the doggy door that led out to the garden.

"What works for doggies, works for kitties, too," hissed Si.

They slunk out to the garden. They dug in the flower beds, scared the birds at the birdbath and chased a squirrel up a tree.

Then they found a small hole in the garden fence. They poked their heads through the hole and spied Jock snoozing by his kennel.

"Time for a wake-up call?" said Am.

Si smiled and nodded. They squirmed through the hole and stole silently across the yard until they were sitting on either side of the sleeping Jock. Then, at the same moment, they let loose a shrill, ear-splitting yowl.

Jock awoke with a start. By the time he had identified the culprits, Si and Am were halfway across the lawn, heading for the fence.

Jock tore after them, barking. But, in a flash, the cats squirmed through the small hole and were out of Jock's reach. The opening was too small for Jock. He had to be content with sticking his head through and barking at the cats as they strolled casually up the back steps of Lady's house and through the doggy door. Then they collapsed in a laughing fit on the kitchen floor.

"Dogs are so dim-witted," Si cackled.

They waited a while, then creeped out through the doggy door again, itching to try their trick once more. Peeking through the hole in the fence, they spied Jock, eyes closed, lying in front of his kennel. They squirmed through the hole and creeped towards him.

But, this time, Jock was ready for them. When the cats got within five feet of him, the feisty Scottie leaped to his feet and growled. The cats gave a start, wheeled around and raced for the fence, only to find the way blocked by Jock's friend, Trusty the bloodhound, who stood, growling, between the cats and the hole.

Jock and Trusty chased Si and Am around Jock's garden until Jock was confident they had learned their lesson. Then they allowed the cats to retreat through the hole in the fence.

This time, they didn't stop running until they were up the back steps, through the doggy door, and safely inside.

And inside is where they stayed.

Disney PLANES

World's Best Coach

Dusty had flown two legs of his dream race, the Wings Around The Globe Rally, and so far things hadn't been going as smoothly as he would have hoped. But after helping a fellow plane in need, Dusty had been given some very helpful advice. The plane from Germany, Von Fliegenhosen, suggested that Dusty remove his crop-dusting gear. All of the extra weight was just making his flights more difficult. Dusty had done as he suggested and felt so much lighter! Things were looking up.

Dusty flew like a new plane. In the third leg, he passed one racer after another in the mountains above India. Flying low and weaving around obstacles was his speciality. He couldn't believe how well he was doing – and neither could many of his fellow racing planes!

Dusty moved from last place all the way up to eighth. It was all the sports reporters could talk about! They were astonished that this little crop duster, who had never raced before, was competing in the world's greatest flying competition. The racing newcomer started to have fans around the globe. Everybody loved the determination of the unknown plane from Propwash Junction!

However, not everybody was happy with Dusty's success. Ripslinger, the three-time champion of the rally, was angry at all the attention Dusty was getting. He was supposed to be the star! Who did Dusty think he was?

Reporters rushed to get interviews with the new fan favourite. They asked Dusty where he learned how to race and how he got the confidence to compete against the star flyers.

"From my coach, Skipper," Dusty answered. "He's the reason I'm here. He's a great instructor. And a great friend. And I'm sure if he could, he'd be right out here with us."

Back in Propwash Junction, the whole gang was crowded around the television to watch Dusty. Skipper was very touched that Dusty had talked about him. Suddenly, he felt inspired. There was something he wanted to try....

It had been years since Skipper had flown. Sparky the tug took him everywhere these days. But this time, Sparky pushed Skipper onto the runway. Then Skipper took a deep breath and started his engine.

Seconds later, he shut himself down. Even after all those kind words from Dusty, he couldn't bring himself to fly. Skipper felt totally defeated.

Inside HQ

One day, a little girl called Riley was born. At that very moment, Riley's first Emotion, Joy, stepped up to a console in Headquarters inside Riley's mind.

Joy saw Riley's parents on a screen as it flickered to life.

"Hi, Riley," Joy heard Mum say.

Joy touched the console and Riley smiled with happiness.

In Headquarters, a golden memory sphere suddenly came rolling across the floor towards Joy, and she picked it up. It replayed the moment of Riley's first smile. The sphere was gold because the memory was happy. Joy turned and stored the sphere on an empty shelf at the back of Headquarters.

She returned to the console, which was covered in buttons and levers that could control Riley's feelings and reactions. Just then, Joy noticed somebody standing next to her.

"I'm Sadness," said the newcomer.

Sadness touched the console and baby Riley began to cry.

"Can I just …?" Joy asked, and she took control again. "I just want to fix that. Thanks."

As Riley grew older, Joy and Sadness were joined by three more Emotions – Fear, Anger and Disgust. Each Emotion helped Riley in their own special way.

Joy was the leader of the group, and all she wanted was for Riley to be happy.

Fear helped keep Riley safe. He worked hard to keep Riley far away from potential hazards.

Disgust protected Riley from things that looked, smelled or tasted gross. Like broccoli – eww!

Anger cared very deeply about things being fair for Riley. Most of Riley's tantrums happened when Anger was at the console.

Finally, there was Sadness. Her job was not as obvious as Riley's other Emotions. In fact, Joy wasn't sure why Sadness was there at all.

Over time, the shelves in Headquarters were gradually filled with coloured memory spheres – blue for Sadness, purple for Fear, red for Anger and green for Disgust. But, mostly, the shelves were full of happy golden memories. As the shelves filled up, the older memory spheres were sucked up through tubes to another area of Riley's mind called Long Term Memory, where they were stored until Riley needed to remember them again.

Together, the Five Emotions made important choices for Riley. But with Joy in charge most of the time, everything was perfect. Riley was a happy, contented little girl. Joy saw no reason why anything should change.

Disney·PIXAR

BRAVE
A Gammy Spell

Deep in the ancient Scottish Highlands, in a kingdom called DunBroch, lived a princess called Merida. Her mother, Queen Elinor, wanted Merida to marry a son from one of the neighbouring clans, in order to keep peace among the kingdoms.

But Merida didn't want to marry. She wanted to keep her freedom and choose her own destiny. So, when the suitors came to compete at archery for her hand, Merida took her bow and beat them all.

"You don't know what you've done," the queen told Merida.

Merida was very angry. She couldn't understand her mother's point of view. "You're a beast!" she shouted. "I'll never be like you!"

Angrily, Merida slashed the family tapestry between the images of her and her mother. Hurt and angry, Merida fled from the castle on her horse, Angus. She was crying too hard to watch where they were going.

Suddenly, Angus stopped, sending Merida flying. When she got to her feet, she saw that she was standing inside a ring of giant stones. She saw strange blue lights flickering. They seemed to beckon Merida forward. The lights formed a chain leading deep into the forest. Merida followed the blue lights. They led her to a small cottage in the woods.

The cottage belonged to an old woman who seemed to be a wood-carver. But it didn't take long for Merida to realize the woman was actually a witch.

Merida explained, "If I could just change my mum, then my life would be better."

The Witch told Merida about a prince who had asked, long ago, for the strength of 10 men. Merida would get a similar spell. The Witch set to work, throwing things into her cauldron. When she was done, the Witch pulled out a cake and handed it to Merida.

Back at the castle, Merida gave the cake to her mother. Elinor took a bite.

"Now, why don't we go upstairs to the lords and put this behind us," Elinor said.

But just then, Elinor stumbled. She was feeling dizzy. Merida helped Elinor upstairs and into bed. The next thing Merida knew, a huge shape rose up from the sheets!

"Mum, you're a bear!" Merida cried. "That scaffy witch gave me a gammy spell."

Hearing this, Elinor-Bear let out an angry roar. Merida had wanted to change her mother's mind, but the spell had changed Queen Elinor completely!

All that Merida cared about now was saving her mother from the witch's spell!

THE JUNGLE BOOK

Bagheera Bears Up

Mowgli danced around, humming happily to himself.

"What are you doing, Mowgli?" Bagheera asked from his perch in a nearby tree.

"Practising being a bear," Mowgli told him. "You should try it."

"Me?" Bagheera said, stunned. "I couldn't possibly do such a thing."

"Why not?" Mowgli wanted to know.

"Well, I'm a panther and I happen to like being one," Bagheera replied. "Why on earth would I want to be a bear?"

"Are you kidding?" Mowgli exclaimed. "Bears have the life! They hang out all day long, and they eat ants!"

"Eat ants?" Bagheera asked. "And that's a good thing?"

"Sure!" Mowgli said. "Well, truthfully, they tickle your throat at first. But you get used to it soon enough."

"Have you?" Bagheera asked.

"Not yet," Mowgli confessed. "But I will!"

"Whatever you say, Mowgli," said Bagheera.

Mowgli thought for a moment. "And if you were a bear, you would eat fruit and drink coconut juice, and you would relax, just like us!"

"If you ask me," Bagheera said. "I don't see anything so bad about being a panther. In fact, I like it very much."

"I think you're scared," Mowgli told him.

"Absolutely not!" Bagheera protested. "What on earth would I have to be scared of?" He stood up, stretched and gracefully jumped out of the tree and onto the ground.

"Exactly," Mowgli said. "So, why not try it?"

"You've got to be kidding me!" Bagheera said.

"You know what your problem is?" Mowgli said.

"I'm afraid to ask," Bagheera said.

"You're like a beehive," Mowgli told him. "You work too hard." He stared at Bagheera. "Come on, dance with me!" he cried, grabbing Bagheera's paw and prancing around the panther. After a bit, Bagheera began to dance too, moving his feet and twitching his tail.

"That's it!" Mowgli cheered.

"You know what?" Bagheera admitted. "This isn't so bad after all."

"Now you're getting it!" Mowgli exclaimed. "Now you see why being a bear is so great!" The Man-cub stopped dancing and threw himself on a soft patch of moss. "It's not so bad, is it?"

"Actually," Bagheera said, scratching his back against a rock, "it's sort of fun!"

"One more time!" Mowgli cheered, and they began dancing again.

Disney
MICKEY & FRIENDS
A Perfect Picnic

Mickey Mouse and his friends were planning a picnic!

"We can all make our favourite foods and then swap baskets!" Mickey suggested.

"That sounds like fun. I can't wait!" said Minnie.

The friends raced home and each began to pack a lunch.

Donald made a sandwich and chose a piece of fruit. But as Donald looked at the food, he began to get hungry.

These are my favourite foods, he thought. *I don't want to share them!*

Over at Minnie's house, things were not going well either. Minnie had packed all her favourite foods. But as she got ready to leave, she started to wonder if she would like what her friends had packed.

Meanwhile, Daisy was excited about sharing her lunch. She hummed to herself as she packed her basket. But when Daisy picked up a banana, she began to frown. Maybe she didn't want to share her lunch after all....

Elsewhere, Goofy was making lemonade. He was soaking wet and covered in lemon juice! Goofy tasted his lemonade.

This is my best lemonade ever, Goofy thought. *I want to drink it all myself!*

As Mickey walked to the park, he grew more excited about the picnic. When he got there, Mickey found his friends waiting for him. They all had baskets of food, but they didn't look very happy.

"What's wrong?" Mickey asked his friends.

Donald explained that everyone wanted to eat their own favourite foods.

"Oh," Mickey said, disappointed. "Well, I guess we don't have to share."

Minnie looked at Mickey. He seemed so sad. She didn't want to be the reason he was upset! "I'll trade lunches with you, Mickey," she said.

"Really? Thanks, Minnie!" Mickey said.

Mickey's friends saw how happy Minnie had made Mickey and swapped baskets, too.

Mickey laid out a blanket, sat down, opened his picnic basket and started to laugh!

"What's so funny, Mickey?" Minnie asked. Then she looked in her basket and laughed, too.

Everyone had packed peanut butter sandwiches and lemonade!

The only difference in the baskets was the fruit. There was an orange, a banana, an apple, some grapes and a pineapple!

Then Mickey had an idea. He cut up the fruit, put it all in a bowl and mixed it together, making a big fruit salad.

As Mickey's friends ate their dessert, they realized that Mickey had been right. Sharing was fun, after all!

Disney · PIXAR

FROM THE MOVIE **INSIDE OUT**

The Mind World

Riley's Five Emotions – Joy, Sadness, Fear, Anger and Disgust – loved working in Headquarters inside Riley's mind. The Emotions helped Riley through every day of her life. They protected her, cared for her and always tried to keep her happy!

Over the years, the shelves in HQ became filled up with coloured memory spheres, which eventually got moved into Riley's Long Term Memory. But when something really important happened to Riley, a special extra-bright memory sphere was created.

These spheres were core memories, and they were stored in the core-memory holder inside Headquarters.

Each core memory powered one of Riley's Islands of Personality. Riley had five Islands – Goofball, Friendship, Hockey, Honesty and Family. Each Island was connected to HQ by bridges called lightlines. The Islands were like mini theme parks inside Riley's head, and as long as the core memories stayed in their holder in Headquarters, the Islands of Personality would shine brightly.

Riley loved to mess around and be silly – that's what kept Goofball Island running. Friendship Island was brighter when Riley spent time with her best friend, Meg. Hockey Island was created when Riley scored her first goal playing ice hockey. Riley's parents taught her never to lie and Honesty Island helped her remember this. But Family Island was probably the most important one – there was nothing Riley cared about more than her family. These Islands of Personality made Riley … Riley!

One night, just after Riley had turned 11 years old, the Emotions in Riley's head gazed at the screen as her parents tucked her into bed.

As Riley fell asleep, the screen went dark.

"Woo-hoo! Another perfect day!" Joy called happily.

"All right, we did not die today," said Fear. "I call that an unqualified success."

Joy looked at the wall of brand-new, happy, golden memories. "Nice job everybody! Now, let's get those memories down to Long Term," she said. Joy pulled a lever and a tube dropped down from the ceiling of Headquarters. The new memories were sucked up the tube, and Joy watched from the window as the colourful spheres were taken out across Riley's Mind World, to be stored in her Long Term Memory.

"We love our girl," Joy continued. "She's got great friends, a great house; things couldn't be better. After all, Riley's 11 now. What could possibly happen?"

Carl's Promise

Carl and Ellie had been best friends since they first met as children. They grew up, got married and dreamed of becoming explorers.

But Carl and Ellie didn't become explorers. They both worked at the zoo. However, they still dreamed of travelling to Paradise Falls in South America. They saved all their spare money in a jar to pay for the trip. But they could never quite collect enough.

The years went by, and Carl and Ellie grew older. After Ellie passed away, Carl kept all her things just as they had been. But it wasn't the same. He missed Ellie. To make matters worse, the neighbourhood around their beloved home was being torn down to make room for tall, modern buildings.

One day, Carl heard a knock at his door. A boy in a uniform was standing on his porch.

"Good afternoon," said the boy. "My name is Russell, and I am a Junior Wilderness Explorer. Are you in need of assistance today, sir?"

"No," replied Carl. He didn't want help. He just wanted to be left alone.

But Russell wouldn't leave. He wanted to help Carl so that he could earn his Assisting the Elderly badge.

"If I get it, I will become a Senior Wilderness Explorer," Russell explained.

To get rid of Russell, Carl gave him a task. He asked him to find a bird called a Snipe. "I think its burrow is two blocks down," Carl said.

Russell eagerly set off to find the bird, not knowing that it didn't really exist. Carl had made the whole thing up!

Not long after that, Carl received some bad news. He was being forced out of his house and sent to live in a retirement home. Carl didn't want to leave his house. All his memories of Ellie were there.

That night, Carl sat in his living room, looking through Ellie's adventure book. He remembered Ellie's dream of going to South America. He had promised her he'd take her there in an airship.

The next morning, two nurses arrived to drive Carl to the retirement home. "I'll meet you at the van," he told them. "I want to say one last goodbye to the old place."

As the nurses walked back to their van, a huge shadow fell over them. They turned to see thousands of balloons tied to Carl's house! A moment later, the whole house rose into the air!

"So long, boys!" Carl yelled out of the window. He was going to South America!

Bambi
Spring Has Sprung!

Spring had come at last to the forest. *Sniff, sniff* – Bambi could smell the change in the air. The days were growing longer. The nights were getting shorter. The ice and snow were quickly melting away. Crocuses and daffodils were pushing new green shoots out of the ground.

And the forest didn't feel quite as lonely as it had during the cold weather. In just the last few days, Bambi had noticed that there were more animals peeking their heads out of their holes and burrows and dens.

As he took a walk through the forest very early one morning on the first day of spring, Bambi came upon Mrs Possum and her children hanging upside down by their tails from a tree branch. She and Bambi had not seen one another in a long while. But Mrs Possum recognized him just the same.

"Well, hello, Bambi," said Mrs Possum.

"Hello, Mrs Possum," Bambi replied. "I haven't seen you since autumn. Where have you and your family been all winter long?"

"Oh, we like to spend most of our winter indoors," Mrs Possum replied. "But now that spring is here, it's so nice to be out in the fresh air again." Then Mrs Possum and the rest of her family closed their eyes and dozed off, because they liked to spend most of their days sleeping, you know.

Walking on through the forest, Bambi stopped by a tree filled with twittering birds.

"Hello, Bambi," said one of the birds.

"Hello," Bambi replied. "And where have you birds been all winter long?"

"Oh, we fly south for the winter, to warmer places where we can find more food," the bird explained. "But we are so happy it is spring once more. It is lovely to be back in the forest."

Then the bird joined her voice with her friends' twittering tunes. After so many months without it, the chirps and tweets were sweet music to Bambi's ears.

Bambi walked further, meeting old friends at every turn. He came upon mice moving from their winter quarters back into their spring and summer homes. He noticed the squirrels and chipmunks snacking leisurely on nuts, no longer storing them away in their winter stockpiles. He heard a woodpecker rapping at a pine tree. And he spotted the ducks out for a swim on the pond.

Yes, thought Bambi, it had been a long, cold, difficult winter. But somehow the arrival of spring made him feel that everything would be all right. Everywhere he looked there was life, there were new beginnings … and, most importantly, there was hope.

The Hero of the Race

In a packed stadium in California, the tie-breaker race for the Piston Cup had started. But Lightning couldn't concentrate. He kept remembering the new friends he'd met in Radiator Springs. Somehow, winning was no longer that important.

Lightning had ruined the town's road when he crashed there, and been forced to stay and fix it. He'd learned how good it felt to help others. But the town's judge, Doc, had let the press know where Lightning was. Doc used to be a racing champion and didn't like young racecars like Lightning, because one had replaced him. But Doc had started to change his mind about the young racing star.

Just then, as Lightning was feeling like giving up, Doc's voice came over the radio: "I didn't come all this way to see you quit."

Lightning saw his Radiator Springs friends in his pit – with Doc as his crew chief!

"If you can drive as good as you can fix a road, then you can win this race with your eyes shut," Doc said.

Inspired by his friends, Lightning tore around the track, closing the gap. Chick Hicks tried his usual dirty tricks, but Lightning remembered what his friends had taught him. He drove backwards like Mater had taught him; he took Doc's advice and turned right to go left. And when he blew a tyre, Guido performed a super-fast tyre change!

Lightning was winning! Chick and The King – a veteran racecar racing his final race – were fighting for second place.

Then, Chick rammed into The King! The veteran hit a wall. When Lightning saw The King's crumpled body, he remembered Doc's final crash which had ended his career. Lightning screeched to a stop inches from the finish line. Chick won the race.

"What are you doing, kid?" Doc asked.

"I think The King should finish his last race," Lightning answered. As he pushed The King over the finish line, the crowd erupted in cheers. Chick may have won the Piston Cup, but Lightning was the hero of the race!

Lightning was offered a great new sponsorship deal, but he politely refused, deciding to stay loyal to his original sponsor. He did ask for one favour, however....

Later, Lightning found Sally in Radiator Springs. They heard someone wildly yelling, "Wooo-hoo!" Lightning had promised his new best friend, Mater, that he'd arrange for him to fly in a helicopter, and he had done just that. Sally smiled. It looked as if the rookie racecar had found a new home.

Show Time!

After seeing all the cool inventions Tadashi and his friends made at school, Hiro had decided he was ready to go to uni. Tadashi was thrilled! He told Hiro to enter the school's Tech Showcase. If Hiro invented something that impressed the judges, he would get into the university.

Hiro started working like crazy. He sat at his desk, filling his notebook with doodles. But each time he had an idea, he threw it away, thinking it wasn't good enough.

Luckily, Tadashi was there to encourage him every step of the way. "Hey, I'm not giving up on you," Tadashi told Hiro. "Look for a new angle!"

Inspired by his brother's words, Hiro finally came up with what he thought was possibly the best invention of his life.

The night of the showcase arrived. The hall was filled with technology experts, inventors and eager spectators. Aunt Cass and Tadashi's friends waited anxiously in the audience while, backstage, Hiro was feeling nervous.

Tadashi found his little brother and held him firmly by the shoulders.

"Hey!" he said. "You've got this!"

Hiro gave Tadashi a fist bump, then strode into the presentation area.

Hiro began by introducing his microbots. As he explained how they worked, he started to feel more confident. He showed how he was able to control the tiny robots with his thoughts, using a neural transmitter in his headband. The microbots swarmed together to make whatever he imagined: bridges, skyscrapers – they could do anything!

At the end of Hiro's presentation, the applause was thunderous. Tadashi's teacher, Professor Callaghan was clearly impressed, and Hiro couldn't help feeling pleased with himself.

After the show, a man called Alistair Krei offered to buy Hiro's microbots. He was the founder of Krei Tech – a large and powerful tech company.

But Callaghan warned Hiro. "Mr Krei has cut corners and ignored sound science to get where he is."

Out of respect for Callaghan, Hiro decided he had to refuse Krei's offer.

Krei walked away, still holding one of the microbots. When Tadashi reminded him he still had it, Krei laughed and handed it back.

When the showcase ended, Hiro gave a whoop of joy. He had won a place at SFIT!

Outside, Tadashi put his arm around his brother. "I knew you were in," he said proudly. "Your tech – it's a game changer."

"Thanks for not giving up on me," Hiro said, gratefully.

A Dangerous Shortcut

Dusty had enjoyed a fantastic third leg of the Wings Around The Globe Rally. After removing his crop-dusting gear, he felt as light as a feather. He had passed one racer after another and moved up from last place to eighth! He was starting to believe he really might have a chance in this race!

The following day, Dusty radioed his friends in Propwash Junction. He talked through his plans for the next leg of the race. It would take him over the Himalayas, some of the highest mountains in the world. Dusty was still afraid of heights so he wanted to go through the mountains, not over them.

"Bad idea," said Skipper, when Dusty told him this part of the plan. "It's time to lug nut up. You can fly a whole lot higher than you think."

After the call, Dusty bumped into his racing friend, El Chu. The Mexican flyer had a crush on another plane, Rochelle, the Canadian rally champ. But he told Dusty he was having no luck getting her to like him back! Just then, Ishani, the beautiful racer from India, rolled up. El Chu could tell Dusty had a crush on her. He winked and left the pair alone.

Dusty was thrilled when Ishani invited him to fly over the Taj Mahal. While they enjoyed the view, Ishani talked about the race. She knew Dusty liked to fly low and gave him a tip. He didn't have to fly above the mountains on their next leg. Instead, he could follow the train tracks through a valley.

The next day, the leg to Nepal began. The other racers headed over the mountains. Dusty flew low above the train tracks – but they disappeared into a tunnel! There was no way he could go through it. He would have to fly higher, he had no choice!

Dusty tried, but his fear of heights sent him straight back down into the valley. What was he going to do? He gathered his courage, tipped sideways – and flew inside the tunnel.

Suddenly, Dusty saw the light of a train approaching! He powered forwards with everything he had. He escaped the tunnel just seconds before the train chugged into it!

Dusty flew on to Nepal, where he landed in a quiet valley. "Have the others left already?" Dusty asked an official when he saw no other planes around.

"No one else is here yet," the official replied. "You're in first place!"

Yard Sale

"Hey, Woody! Ready to go to Cowboy Camp?" Andy shouted, bursting into the bedroom.

Woody the cowboy doll was very excited about cowboy camp, though he couldn't show his feelings to Andy. Toys were supposed to stay very still whenever people could see them.

Andy had a few spare minutes before he had to leave for camp, so he grabbed Woody and Buzz, his two favourite toys, for a quick adventure.

"Never tangle with the unstoppable duo of Woody and Buzz Lightyear!" he proclaimed, linking the toys' arms together.

Suddenly, there was a loud *RIIIPPPP!*

Woody's shoulder had ripped open!

Andy's mum suggested fixing Woody on the way to camp, but Andy shook his head and sighed. "No, just leave him."

"I'm sorry," his mum replied. "But you know toys don't last forever."

Woody sat on the shelf and watched sadly as Andy left for cowboy camp without him. He couldn't believe it.

Woody didn't feel any better when he found Wheezy, an old toy penguin who'd been sitting broken and forgotten on the shelf for months.

Was that Woody's future, too?

Suddenly, the toys spotted something truly terrifying – Andy's mum was putting up a sign outside: YARD SALE!

Andy's mum came into Andy's bedroom looking for some items to sell. And she chose Wheezy as one of the sale items!

Thinking quickly, Woody waited until Andy's mum was out of sight, then whistled loudly for Buster, Andy's friendly – and helpful – puppy.

Together, Woody and Buster sneaked outside, grabbed Wheezy, and headed back to safety. But because his arm was injured, Woody lost his grip and tumbled to the ground!

Just then, a strange man noticed Woody, picked him up … and stole him! From their upstairs window, the other toys watched in horror as the man threw Woody into the boot of his car.

Buzz couldn't let Woody be taken away so easily, so he jumped out of the window and slid down the drainpipe, racing to rescue his friend – but he was too late. All Buzz saw was the car's licence plate, LZTYBRN, and a few feathers floating in the air.

Buzz was horrified. He decided there and then, he would do everything he could to rescue his friend and bring him back home.

Disney·PIXAR

FROM THE MOVIE **INSIDE OUT**

On the Move

All was well inside Riley's Mind World. Joy, Sadness, Fear, Anger and Disgust – Riley's Five Emotions – worked hard to keep their girl happy. Riley had great friends, a great house – things couldn't have been better.

But one day, just after Riley had turned 11 years old, her parents told her that the whole family was moving from their home in Minnesota, across the country to San Francisco over 1,900 miles away!

"Wha…." Joy said, shocked by the news.

"Aiiiiighh!" screamed Sadness, Disgust, Anger and Fear.

"Okay, not what I had in mind…." said Joy, as she tried to find the positives.

During the long car journey, Riley's family drove past fields and city suburbs, on mountain roads and seemingly never-ending highways. While the other Emotions were panicking, Joy tried to cheer everyone up.

"Hey, look!" she said, as they arrived in San Francisco. "The Golden Gate Bridge! Isn't that great? It's not made out of solid gold like we thought, which is kind of a disappointment, but still!"

Riley tried to imagine her new house, but, when the car finally arrived there, her new home was not at all how she'd hoped it would be. Riley's Emotions were speechless. The house looked dark and dreary.

Riley decided that checking out her new room might make her feel better. It didn't. Her room was small and dark with a sloped ceiling. Joy tried to help by picturing where all of Riley's stuff would go. All she needed was her bed, her desk and a few other things, and the place would soon feel like home. Riley's butterfly curtains would certainly brighten it up!

Minutes later, Riley's parents told her some bad news. The removal van carrying the family's belongings was lost. Riley would have to sleep in a sleeping bag until her bed arrived!

Through all of this, Joy desperately tried to keep Riley happy. She stepped up to the console in Riley's head and helped her look on the bright side.

Riley picked up a broom and started to play goofball hockey with her dad. Before long, even Mum joined in. The family collapsed into a hug, and soon after, yet another happy memory rolled into Headquarters.

Mum smiled at Riley. "Thank you," she said, "Through all of this confusion you've stayed our happy girl."

Perhaps things wouldn't be so bad in San Francisco, after all.

Secret Agents and the World Grand Prix

A British secret agent called Finn McMissile had received a distress call from a fellow agent. Finn travelled to the agent's location in the middle of the Pacific Ocean, to an oil derrick. Using his grappling hooks and magnetic wheel armour, Finn drove up the side of the oil derrick. He hid inside and saw a wanted criminal named Professor Z. Beside the Professor and his crew was a special TV camera. Then Finn saw his fellow agent – he had been crushed into scrap metal!

Suddenly, Professor Z spotted Finn and sent his gang after him. When they cornered Finn, he leaped off the derrick, turned into a submarine and escaped!

Meanwhile, in the town of Radiator Springs, Mater had called all his friends together to welcome home his best friend, Lightning McQueen. The racecar had just won the Hudson Hornet Memorial Piston Cup!

Lightning finally arrived home and the friends were overjoyed to see each other. Mater wanted to hang out with his best buddy, but Lightning was exhausted. He went off to spend a quiet evening with his girlfriend, Sally. Mater was disappointed.

Later that night at the Wheel Well restaurant, Mater called in to a TV show. He defended Lightning against an Italian race car, Francesco Bernoulli, who swore he was faster than Lightning. Soon, Lightning was on the phone too. He agreed to race in the World Grand Prix – a three-event race hosted by former oil tycoon, Sir Miles Axlerod.

Mater, Luigi, Guido, Fillmore and Sarge all offered to be Lightning's pit crew. Soon "Team Lightning McQueen" was on a plane heading off to the first race in Japan!

Lightning and his friends had a fantastic time sightseeing in Tokyo. There were skyscrapers and high-tech gadgets everywhere! They all went to a fancy welcome party. Finn McMissile and another British agent, Holley Shiftwell, were also there. They were looking for an American agent who had some top-secret information.

Mater embarrassed Lightning at the party by leaking oil on the floor right in front of Miles Axlerod! Lightning sent Mater to the bathroom to clean up. Outside Mater's cubicle, Professor Z's goons, Grem and Acer, had cornered the American agent, Rod "Torque" Redline. When Mater came out, the agent secretly stuck the top-secret information on Mater.

Holley thought Mater was the American agent she was supposed to meet! Little did Mater know, but this was just the beginning of his secret agent adventures.

DISNEY·PIXAR
MONSTERS, INC.
The Chase

At Monsters, Inc., things had become a bit scarier than usual! Best friends Sulley and Mike had discovered a human child in their world. Monsters were scared of human children because they were told they were deadly to monsters – but Sulley had realized they weren't so bad after all.

Sulley was the top Scarer at Monsters, Inc. He was the best of the best at collecting children's screams to power the city. But, thanks to Boo – the child they'd found – he'd discovered that laughs were just as powerful as screams.

Unfortunately, the boss of Monsters, Inc., Mr Waternoose, was working with a mean monster called Randall. They had invented a machine to suck screams out of human kids!

Sulley had torn the machine apart and raced away with Boo, but Randall was chasing them. They made it to the Scare Floor. But to send Boo home, they still needed to find her door. They jumped in and out of closets, until Randall grabbed Boo! But Boo fought back.

"She's not scared of you anymore," Sulley told Randall. Working together, they beat Randall once and for all.

But Sulley, Mike and Boo weren't safe yet. Now Waternoose and the CDA (Child Detection Agency) were controlling the doors. While Mike distracted the CDA, Sulley escaped with Boo. Unfortunately, Waternoose saw everything. "Give me the child!" he yelled, running after Sulley.

But luckily, Mike recorded Waternoose yelling, "I'll kidnap a thousand children before I let this company die!"

Now everyone knew that Waternoose planned to take children, and he was arrested!

It was time for Boo to go home. Sulley followed her into her room. Gently, he tucked her into bed. Sadly, Sulley returned to Monstropolis. The CDA shredded Boo's door – it couldn't be used for scaring anymore.

After that, Sulley became president of Monsters, Inc., and the Scare Floor became a Laugh Floor! It was all because Sulley had discovered that laughter produced more power than screams. Sulley still missed Boo, though. He had one tiny sliver of her door, but the rest had been destroyed by the CDA.

But before long, Mike surprised his pal. He'd put Boo's door back together! It was missing just one little piece. Sulley inserted the piece, opened the door, and saw....

"Boo?" Sulley whispered.

"Kitty!" an excited voice replied.

The two friends were reunited at last.

THE JUNGLE Book

Dance, Daddy-o!

Deep in the jungle at the temple ruins, the monkeys and their ruler, King Louie, were always looking to have a swingin' time.

"Let's have a dance-off!" King Louie suggested to the monkeys one evening.

"Hooray!" the monkeys cheered.

"What's a dance-off?" one monkey asked.

"You know, a contest," said King Louie. "An opportunity for everyone to get down, strut their stuff, cut a rug! And whoever lays down the smoothest moves is the winner!"

"Hooray!" cheered the monkeys.

King Louie rubbed his chin. "The first thing we need is some music," he said, pointing at the monkey musicians. "Hit it, fellas!"

The musicians blasted out a jazzy tune, blowing through their hands like horns, knocking out a beat on some coconuts and drumming on a hollow log. Soon, all the monkeys were gathered around the musicians, tapping their toes and shaking their tails.

"Now," said King Louie, "who will dance?"

All the monkeys raised their hands. King Louie looked around. "Let's see," he said scratching his head, "I choose … me!"

"Hooray!" the monkeys cheered. They were disappointed not to be chosen. But, after all, King Louie *was* their King.

So King Louie moved his hips from side to side. He waved his arms in the air. He closed his eyes so he could really feel the beat.

"Dance, Daddy-o!" one monkey cried.

King Louie boogied and bopped like he had never boogied and bopped before. Then, when the song was over, King Louie stopped dancing and scrambled onto his throne. "Now it's time to choose the winner!" he said.

"But King Louie …" one monkey began to object. All the other monkeys were thinking the same thing: didn't you need more than one dancer to have a dance-off?

"Oh, silly me," said King Louie with a chuckle. The monkeys looked at each other and smiled, expecting that the King had realized his mistake. But, King Louie said, "Of course, we need a judge! Who will judge?"

Everyone raised their hands. King Louie looked around, then said, "I choose … me!"

"Hooray!" the monkeys cheered.

"And as the judge, I will now choose the winner of the dance-off," King Louie continued. He looked around at all the monkeys. "Now, let's see. I choose … me! Let's hear it for the winner!"

"Hooray!" the monkeys cheered, because, after all, King Louie was their King – and a pretty swingin' dancer, too!

Hero's Duty

Wreck-It Ralph worked in the *Fix-It Felix, Jr* video game, and he was sick and tired of always being the Bad Guy. At the end of every game, he got thrown in the mud by the other characters, and he was fed-up with it. He wanted a medal to prove that he could be a Good Guy, just like Fix-It Felix.

So, Ralph decided to do something that no character had done before – he decided to leave his game. He was searching for a medal in another game when a dazed-looking soldier staggered in.

The poor fellow was so confused, he couldn't stop walking into the wall. The soldier's name was Markowski, and he muttered that he'd just come from a new game called *Hero's Duty*, where he'd been battling swarms of cy-bugs. The goal of the game, the soldier explained, was to climb a tower and find the Medal of Heroes.

Suddenly a tiny beetle scuttled across the table, and Markowski fainted. That gave Ralph an idea. Maybe HE could take the soldier's place in the game – and win that medal! Finally he could prove to everyone that he could be a good guy for a change!

Ralph borrowed Markowski's armour and sneaked into Hero's Duty.

As Ralph waited with the other soldiers and the first-person shooter – the robot that handled the game player's actions – it looked as though Ralph's plan might work!

But once the game started, huge, hungry cy-bugs attacked! They gobbled up characters, vehicles and weapons. Then they turned into freakish versions of whatever they ate! Ralph was TERRIFIED!

Ralph grabbed the first-person shooter game player and begged for help. But before the girl could wonder why a game character was talking so strangely, a cy-bug chomped her avatar. A loud voice boomed: "GAME OVER!"

Inside Hero's Duty the game began to reset. Characters went back to their places and a beacon appeared on top of the huge tower in the centre of the game. The cy-bugs flew into the light, which zapped them all.

The soldier's leader, Sergeant Calhoun, was furious! "Never interfere with the first-person shooter!" she yelled at Ralph.

But he wasn't listening. He wanted the Medal of Heroes, up in that tower. This was his chance to prove he could be a Good Guy!

Ralph headed towards the tower. He was determined to get his medal and prove himself, no matter what he had to do.

Disney Pinocchio

A Helping Hand

"Oh, Pinocchio!" cried Geppetto. "I can hardly believe that my little puppet is alive!" It was the morning after the Blue Fairy had visited Geppetto's house and brought Pinocchio to life. "You must get ready for school, my boy," said Geppetto.

Pinocchio was full of curiosity. "Why must I go to school, Father?" he asked.

"Why, so that you can learn!" Geppetto replied. "Now be a good boy and go make the bed while I clear away these dishes."

Ever eager to help, Pinocchio ran over to Geppetto's workbench. He found a hammer, a nail and a piece of wood, and began to pound loudly with the hammer.

"Pinocchio! Whatever are you doing?" cried Geppetto.

"Well, you asked me to make the bed," said Pinocchio. "So I was starting to make one."

With a little smile, Geppetto patted him on the head and said, "Perhaps it would be better for you to put the cat out."

As Geppetto turned back to the breakfast table, Pinocchio jumped up and grabbed a pitcher of water. Hurrying over to Figaro, Pinocchio threw the water onto the cat.

"*YEEEEOOWWWW*!" shrieked Figaro.

"Pinocchio!" shouted Geppetto. "Why did you do that?"

"You … you told me to put the cat out. I thought he had caught fire," said Pinocchio in a small voice.

"Oh, my dear boy, you have much to learn!" Geppetto sighed as he dried off Figaro. "Okay, you can be a helpful boy by helping me to pick up the house a bit before you leave for school."

"All right, Father!" said Pinocchio, and he raced out the front door.

"Where in the world is he going?" Geppetto wondered aloud, as he followed Pinocchio outside.

Pinocchio was crouching at the base of the house, trying with all his might to lift it.

"What are you doing, son?" asked Geppetto with a twinkle in his eye.

"Trying to pick up the house, Father," said Pinocchio, his voice straining with effort.

Geppetto chuckled and gently guided Pinocchio back inside. "My boy, the sooner you go to school and learn about the world, the better for us both," he said. He collected Pinocchio's hat, his schoolbook and an apple for the teacher, and sent him on his way.

As Geppetto watched his new son walk off to school, he shook his head worriedly. "I hope he manages to stay out of trouble today," he said to himself. "My little boy has much to learn about the world."

RATATOUILLE
(rat·a·too·ee)

Discovering the Truth

In the kitchen of Gusteau's restaurant in Paris, Remy the rat was hiding in a human chef's shirt. Remy was trying to help Linguini with his cooking. Remy tried to guide Linguini by biting and tickling him, but it wasn't working.

Suddenly, a mean chef called Skinner burst in and caught a glimpse of Remy. "The rat! I saw it!" shouted the nasty man. Linguini quickly hid Remy in his chef's hat and ducked out – almost colliding with a waiter! But Remy tugged Linguini's hair at the last minute and Linguini jerked backwards like a puppet. Could this be their new system? They went home to practise cooking. Remy guided Linguini by tugging his hair and before long, Linguini could even cook blindfolded!

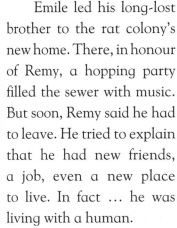

In the meantime, Skinner was reading a letter that Linguini's mother had left for him when she passed away. The letter said that the late great chef, Auguste Gusteau, was Linguini's father! That meant the restaurant rightfully belonged to Linguini. Skinner was horrified. He had always thought the restaurant would be his! He had to do something to make sure Linguini never found out.

The following night, Remy the rat was relaxing in the alley behind the restaurant, enjoying his cooking success, when his brother, Emile, appeared. They hadn't seen each other since the family escaped the human house they used to live in.

Emile led his long-lost brother to the rat colony's new home. There, in honour of Remy, a hopping party filled the sewer with music. But soon, Remy said he had to leave. He tried to explain that he had new friends, a job, even a new place to live. In fact … he was living with a human.

Remy's father scowled and tried to convince his son that humans were dangerous. But Remy was sure Linguini was different. Against his father's wishes, Remy headed back to the restaurant.

On his return, Remy found the letter in Skinner's office saying that Linguini was the rightful owner of the restaurant! Remy grabbed the papers and ran. Skinner chased him. Skinner did not want those papers to get into the wrong hands!

Remy escaped, and by the time the soaking-wet Skinner got back to Gusteau's, Linguini was in his office. Linguini had discovered the truth – that the restaurant was rightfully his! Linguini fired Skinner on the spot. Remy smiled. He was excited, and happy he had chosen to stick with his new friend, Linguini.

Disney·PIXAR

FROM THE MOVIE **INSIDE OUT**

A New School

When Riley and her parents moved to San Francisco, things didn't go smoothly. The removal van filled with their stuff got lost, and the new house wasn't as nice as their one back in Minnesota. But despite this, Joy tried to keep all Riley's Emotions feeling positive – as long as Riley was happy, everything would be fine.

Soon it was time for Riley to start at her new school. In Headquarters, Joy gave each of the Emotions an important job to do. She carefully drew a chalk circle round Sadness's feet.

"This is the Circle of Sadness," Joy explained. "Your job is to make sure all the sadness stays inside it."

At school, the teacher asked Riley to tell the class something about herself. Smiling shyly, Riley shared a happy memory of playing hockey with her family. Then, suddenly, her smile faded.

In Headquarters inside Riley's mind, Joy realized that Sadness had touched the hockey memory sphere – and it had changed from a happy, golden memory to a sad, blue memory!

"Sadness, what are you doing?" Joy cried.

"Oh no, I'm sorry," Sadness said, confused. Riley began to cry in front of her new class.

While the other Emotions tried to stop the sad memory playing in Riley's mind, Sadness was alone at the console. As Riley cried, her first-ever blue core memory was created.

In a panic, Joy grabbed it as it rolled across the floor. She pulled a lever and a tube came down from the ceiling, ready to vacuum up the memory.

"Joy, no!" cried Sadness. She tried to grab the blue core memory back from Joy. As they struggled, they knocked the core-memory holder. The five golden core memories, which powered Riley's Islands of Personality, fell out! The Islands – everything that made Riley who she was – went dark.

"Ahh!" Joy scrambled to collect up the core memories.

In the chaos, Joy, Sadness and all six core memories got sucked up the vacuum tube! They all travelled through Riley's mind and were dumped out in Long Term Memory. Joy knew they had to get back to Headquarters to get the Islands of Personality working again, before Riley forgot about everything she loved.

But the closest route back was across the narrow lightline bridge that connected Goofball Island to Headquarters..

"If we fall we'll be forgotten forever!" said Sadness.

"We have to do this. For Riley," Joy answered. "Just follow my footsteps."

Disney MICKEY & FRIENDS
Goofy at Bat

One sunny day, Goofy was walking past the sports stadium when he heard a baseball recruiter calling to passers-by. "Come one and all, put your skills to the test. Try out today! Our new team needs the best!"

Goofy decided to sign up. He knew his friends would teach him to play!

After signing his name, Goofy gathered Mickey, Minnie, Donald, Daisy and Pluto. They went to the park to practise, but Donald wasn't happy about having to spend the day teaching Goofy to bat.

"Donald, please help," Goofy said. "You're the best player I know!"

Donald agreed and walked Goofy to the centre of the field. First, Donald demonstrated how to hold the bat. "Grip it like that and hold it really tight."

After a few practice swings, Mickey threw the ball. It curved in the air, swinging and swooping. Goofy tried to follow the ball's path, but ended up in a big Goofy-knot!

After his friends untangled him, Goofy was ready to try again.

"Goofy, try to hit this one far," Donald said. But it took Mickey so long to get ready to pitch that Goofy fell fast asleep and the ball ended up hitting Donald on the head!

"Gawrsh, sorry, Donald," Goofy said sheepishly.

Next, Mickey threw a fastball. Goofy stood still, determined not to let the ball pass him. The ball got closer and closer. Goofy swung hard and the ball rebounded fast and low.

Coach Donald called, "Hurry up, run, go!"

Goofy was so excited that he ran straight to the last base by mistake!

"No! Run to third base!" Donald cried out.

Goofy felt confused – his feet went one way, while his body tried to head in the opposite direction, and he fell flat on his face.

"Okay, let's give catching a go," Donald suggested.

Minnie stepped up to bat. Goofy picked up his mitt and waited for the pitch. Mickey threw the ball and Minnie struck it straight towards Goofy. He ran backwards, fast, hoping he'd be better at catching than he was at batting.

The ball started to fall. Goofy raised his gloved hand … and caught the ball right in the middle of his mitt! All his friends cheered.

"That was great, Goofy!" said Donald. "Now, try it again."

Mickey threw, Minnie hit and Goofy caught the ball again! And again. And again!

"Goofy, you're going to go far. This is clearly your game." Donald said.

"I couldn't have done it without your help," Goofy told him. "Thanks, buddy."

The Good Thing About Rain

"**R**ise and shine!" cried Pongo. One by one, he nudged each of his 15 Dalmatian puppies with his nose.

The puppies yawned and stretched.

But Rolly just rolled over and slept on.

"Aw, come on, Rolly," Pongo whispered in the pup's ear. "It's morning! Don't you want to go out?"

At the mention of the word 'out,' Rolly was instantly wide awake!

Rolly was not alone. As if by magic, the sleepy group had become a pack of jumping, barking puppies. They raced together through the kitchen to the back door, where they jumped up and down, waiting for Nanny to let them out into the garden.

"Okay, here I come," said Nanny, as she made her way across the kitchen. Then she flung the door open wide and stepped out of the way to let the puppies race past.

But they didn't move. It was raining!

"Oh, go on," said Perdita, trying to nudge the pups out the door. "It's only a little water."

But they wouldn't budge.

The next morning, Patch awoke with a start. With a few sharp barks, he helped Pongo wake the other puppies. Within seconds, all 15 were crowding around the back door.

Nanny rushed to open the door again.

And once again, the puppies were very disappointed to see raindrops falling.

"Well," said Pongo with a sigh, "April showers bring May flowers!"

The next morning, the puppies weren't in any hurry to go outside. After all, it was probably still raining. They thought that all they had to look forward to was another whole day spent inside.

So, when Nanny opened the door on a sunny morning, the puppies were so surprised that they didn't know what to do.

Then, springing into action, they tumbled over one another in their rush to get out the door. They raced off in different directions, ready to sniff, dig, roll and explore.

But then, almost at once, all 15 puppies froze in their tracks. They looked around at each other, then down at themselves. What was this stuff getting all over their spotted white coats? It was brown. It was wet. It was squishy. It was mud! And it was FUN!

From the doorway, Pongo and Perdita looked out at their muddy puppies and laughed.

"You know what this means, don't you?" Pongo asked Perdita.

Perdy nodded. "Baths."

Pongo smiled, watching the frolicking puppies. "Let's not tell them – just yet," he said.

Abracadabra!

Manny was not at his best. Gypsy could tell. Already that day, he had lost two magic wands and stepped on his turban.

And with the matinee show at P.T. Flea's World's Greatest Circus about to begin, Gypsy knew she had to be on her toes. Manny was going to debut his new trick: the Levitating, Flaming and Disappearing Water Torture Chamber of Death.

"Ladies and gentlemen," Manny announced, "prepare to be stunned and amazed by the Levitating, Flaming and Disappearing Water Torture Chamber of Death. You will watch as my lovely and talented assistant, Gypsy, climbs inside this chamber" – Manny motioned towards the empty sardine can at his side – "where I will bind her hands and feet. Then I will fill the chamber with water, seal it, levitate it five inches off the ground and set it ablaze. And, finally, you will watch in awe as the chamber disappears before your very eyes!"

Manny and Gypsy had rehearsed the act thoroughly. Everything was planned down to the last detail. But, if one little thing went wrong with the trick, Gypsy could be in big trouble.

As it turned out, one little thing didn't go wrong – three big things went wrong!

Manny made his first mistake when he tied Gypsy's hands and feet together. He was supposed to leave the strings loose so that Gypsy could wriggle out of them once she was inside. But Manny accidentally tied them too tight!

Then Manny filled the chamber too high with water. In rehearsals, he had left a bit of space at the top so that Gypsy had some air inside. But, this time, he forgot!

Manny's third mistake was locking the trapdoor. Together, he and Gypsy had rigged an escape hatch in the back side of the sardine can. Once Manny sealed her inside, Gypsy wriggled out of her bonds, opened the trapdoor, and, unseen by the audience, escaped from the chamber before Manny levitated it, set it on fire and made it disappear. But, this time, Manny accidentally nudged the latch that secured the trapdoor from the outside. Gypsy was locked inside.

Luckily, Gypsy hadn't left anything to chance: she had stowed a sharp shard of glass inside the sardine can. She had learned to hold her breath for 10 minutes. And she had put a release latch on the inside of the trapdoor.

She was safely out of the chamber in one minute flat.

At the end of the trick, Manny called Gypsy in front of the audience. "How did you do it, my dear?" he asked dramatically.

"It was magic!" she replied, with a smile and a sigh of relief.

Secret Agent Mater!

British secret agents Finn McMissile and Holley Shiftwell were on the trail of a wanted criminal named Professor Z. They were in Tokyo, where Lightning McQueen was racing in the first World Grand Prix event. Holley had just mistaken Mater for an American spy!

Professor Z then questioned the real American spy, and guessed he had passed a secret device to Mater. The Professor sent his goons, Grem and Acer, to find Mater and get the device.

On the day of the race, Finn and Holley watched all the cars fill up with a new alternative fuel called Allinol. Miles Axlerod, the inventor of Allinol, was hosting the World Grand Prix to introduce the fuel.

Grem and Acer aimed Professor Z's special TV camera at one of the race cars. The camera emitted a beam of radiation that made the Allinol in the car boil and explode! Then Acer headed down to the pits to grab Mater. Holley spoke to Mater through his headset and guided him to safety. Mater happily followed Holley's instructions. He thought he was going to meet her for a date!

Suddenly, Grem and Acer started to close in on Mater – but Finn jumped in to save him.

Mater thought the fight was the best karate demonstration he had ever seen!

Back at the race, Lightning lost to Francesco Bernoulli. Lightning was upset – he had listened to Mater watching the 'karate demonstration' and followed his instructions. Lightning thought Mater had given him bad racing tips.

Reporters surrounded Miles Axlerod and asked him if Allinol was to blame for the engine blowouts during the race. He insisted his fuel was absolutely safe.

Meanwhile, Mater had returned to the pit garage and was trying to explain to Lightning what had just happened.

But Lightning didn't believe him. He was angry with Mater for making him lose the race. Mater felt terrible. He left a goodbye note for Lightning and went to the airport to fly home. But Finn, who was disguised as an airport security guard, was there waiting for him. Finn still thought Mater was a secret agent!

Soon Grem and Acer showed up and tried to capture Mater again. Holley saved Mater and Finn from the attack by whisking them off on a spy plane named Siddeley.

At the hotel, Lightning read Mater's note. Lightning hadn't wanted him to leave, but at least now he wouldn't have to worry about Mater getting into trouble – or would he?

DUMBO

You're Gonna Be Huge!

Dumbo sat in the corner with a big frown on his face.

"What's the matter, kid?" Timothy asked.

Dumbo just shook his head.

"You've got nothing to be sad about," Timothy continued. Dumbo didn't say anything.

"Well, if you're not going to tell me what's bugging ya, I guess I'll just have to figure it out for myself," Timothy said. "I know!" he exclaimed. "You're hungry?"

Dumbo shook his head.

"Thirsty?" Timothy asked.

Dumbo shook his head again.

"Concerned about the June-bug population in Saskatchewan?" Timothy suggested.

Dumbo shook his head doubly hard.

"Well, then," Timothy concluded. "It can only be one thing. It pains me to say it, but I think you have a case of 'feeling sorry for myself-itis'."

Dumbo's large ears pricked up.

"Yes," Timothy continued. "It's a dangerous disease that has affected many of us. Even the strongest cannot avoid it."

Dumbo looked to his left and to his right, then pointed to himself.

"Yes, that's right – you!" Timothy said. "I bet I know what's got you down – your above-average ear size."

Dumbo nodded.

"And the fact that people make fun of you," Timothy continued.

Dumbo nodded even more.

"And, on top of all that," Timothy said, "you've been separated from your mother."

A tear started to form in Dumbo's eye.

"Don't feel sorry for yourself!" Timothy ordered. Dumbo looked up, surprised.

"You know why?" Timothy asked. "Because one day you're gonna be huge!"

Dumbo blinked in disbelief.

"We're talking autographs, your name in lights. They're gonna eat their hats for the way they treated you," Timothy predicted.

Dumbo looked nervous.

"I don't mean eat their hats for real," Timothy explained. "It's just a figure of speech. Not that some of them wouldn't deserve having to eat their hats. But that's not what we're talking about. They're gonna be really sorry they treated you so bad, understand?"

Dumbo nodded his head.

"All right then," Timothy said. "Feeling better?"

And Dumbo nodded doubly hard as visions of success, happiness – and being with his mother again – filled his head.

HERCULES
Destructo-boy

"Hercules!" Amphitryon called. "This hay pile is about to fall over. Could you hold it up while I go to get the cart?"

"Sure, Pop!" Hercules told his father.

Hercules was the strongest boy in his village. He could easily hold up the enormous stack of hay bales with one hand.

Soon, another farmer approached, struggling to hold onto a team of six disobedient mules.

"Need any help?" Hercules asked.

"Hercules!" the farmer gasped. "If you'll hold these mules, I can go get my sons to help me get them home."

"Be glad to!" Hercules took the mules' leads with his free hand.

Just then, a woman came by dragging a cart filled with pottery. She was panting.

"Good day, ma'am," Hercules said politely. "Could I give you a hand with that?"

"Why, thank you," the woman replied. "But it looks like you have your hands full!"

"Oh, I'll be finished here in a second," Hercules said. "Then I can …"

His voice trailed off. He'd just noticed some children his own age running down the road, laughing and shouting as they tossed a discus.

Hercules gazed at them longingly. For some reason, he'd never seemed to fit in with the other village children. Perhaps it was because they didn't understand him. Or perhaps it was because Hercules had once challenged them to a 50-yard dash – and beaten them all by 49 yards.

"Hey, guys!" he called as the discus sailed towards him. "I've got it!"

He lunged towards the discus. The mules' leads went flying. The haystack teetered.

"Uh-oh," Hercules said.

He tried to grab the hay and the mules at the same time, but he accidentally tripped one of the mules, which crashed into the haystack, which fell right onto the woman's cart, and all over the boys.

Hercules winced at the sounds of breaking pottery and shouting boys. The mules were already running off towards the horizon.

"My pottery!" the woman wailed.

"What's the big idea?" one of the other children demanded, standing and brushing himself off.

"Yeah." Another boy grabbed the discus from Hercules. "Stay out of our way from now on … Destructo-boy!"

Hercules' shoulders slumped. Why did this sort of thing always happen to him? Whenever he tried to help, he only made things worse. But he knew that, one day, his strength would help him be a hero. He just hoped that day would come soon. There was only so much unbroken pottery left in Greece!

FINDING NEMO

A Change of Scenery

Dr Sherman had left for the day when Gill called everyone together for a Tank Gang meeting.

"We need to make some changes around here," Gill began. "We've all been living in this glass box for how long now? And every day we stare at the same scenery – the same volcano, the same sunken ship, the same treasure chest and tiki hut. Well, seeing as how we can't change what's in our tank, I propose we rearrange things a little. Who's with me?"

"Great idea!" cried Peach the starfish.

"I'm with you," said Deb. "And Flo is too," she added, pointing at her reflection.

Everyone agreed. "We can completely transform the place," said Bloat.

"All right!" said Gill. "Then how about we start with the tiki hut? Bloat, you hoist it up. Gurgle and I will help you move it. The rest of you guys tell us where you think it should go."

Gill, Bloat and Gurgle swam over to the tiki hut. Bloat wriggled his body underneath it and blew himself up, hoisting the hut a few inches off the gravel. Meanwhile, Gill and Gurgle stationed themselves on either side of the hut and prepared to push.

"Let's try it over there," said Peach, pointing to a far corner of the tank.

With blown-up Bloat acting as a cart underneath the hut, Gill and Gurgle pushed the tiki hut into the corner.

"Oh, no," said Deb, "that's all wrong. Can we see what it looks like over there?" She pointed to the opposite corner of the tank.

So Gill, Gurgle and Bloat worked together to move the tiki hut again.

"That's a disaster!" exclaimed Jacques.

"Yeah, he's right," said Nemo.

Gill, Gurgle and Bloat were getting worn out by all the moving. "Can we all just agree on where it should go?" said Gill. "And quickly?"

"Ooh! I know!" said Deb. "Bring it over this way." She led Gill, Gurgle and Bloat over to a shady spot next to some plastic plants. "Put it down here," she said. So they did.

"I like it!" exclaimed Peach.

"The perfect spot," said Jacques.

"Mmm-hmm," said Bubbles.

Gill stepped back and looked around. "Guys, this is where it was in the first place!"

"Is it?" asked Peach.

Deb giggled. "Well, no wonder it just seems to fit here!"

The other fish nodded – except for Gill, who sighed in frustration. And that was the end of the tank redecoration for the evening.

THE LION KING

Pictures in the Stars

Ever since Mufasa had died and Simba had left the Pride Lands, Timon and Pumbaa had been Simba's only friends – but what fun the three of them had together. One of their favourite things to do after their evening meal was to lie on their backs in the tall grass and gaze up at the night sky, looking for shapes in the stars.

"Okay, okay, I got one," said Pumbaa, lifting a foreleg to point to one area of the sky. "See, over there, that long, thin, curving outline? It's a big, juicy, delicious slug!" Pumbaa licked and smacked his lips, imagining the taste of a slug snack. "Mmm-mmm!"

Simba chuckled. "Pumbaa, how can you still be hungry? We just ate!"

Pumbaa shrugged. "It's a gift," he said.

Timon cleared his throat. "I hate to disagree with you, Pumbaa my friend, but that's no slug you see up there. That's an elephant's trunk. If you follow that curving line of stars, you see it connects with the elephant's head at one end. And there are the ears," Timon said, tracing it all out with his finger, "and there are the tusks."

Simba chuckled again. "Somebody still has his mind on that elephant stampede we almost got flattened by this afternoon," he said.

"Hey …" Timon said defensively, "what's that supposed to mean?"

"Oh, no offence, Timon," Simba replied.

"I just think it's funny that the things you and Pumbaa see in the stars just happen to be the same things that are on your mind at the time."

"Ooh! Ooh! I've got another one!" Pumbaa interrupted. "A big bunch of tasty berries right over there," he said, pointing at a grouping of stars. "Don't they look good?"

"See what I mean?" Simba said to Timon, gesturing at Pumbaa.

"All right, all right, Mr Smarty-Pants," Timon replied. "So what do you see in the stars?"

"Well, now, let's see," said Simba, gazing intently at the tons of tiny points of light twinkling down at them. There were so many that you could see practically any shape in them that you wanted to. It all depended on how you looked at them. But just to get Timon's goat, Simba wanted to find something really bright – something really clear. Something Timon couldn't deny that he saw too.

Just at that moment, a shooting star streaked the entire length of the night sky.

"I see a bright streak of light rocketing across the sky!" exclaimed Simba.

"Ooh! Me, too!" said Pumbaa. "Timon, do you see it?"

Timon had to admit that he did. "Yeah, yeah, I see it," he muttered grudgingly. "Ha-ha. Very funny, Simba."

The Rookie Star

It had been a rather testing fourth leg for Dusty in the Wings Around The Globe Rally. In an attempt to avoid flying high over the Himalayas, Dusty had taken the advice of Ishani, the pretty plane from India. She had told him he could follow the train tracks through a valley in the mountains all the way to the finish line. Dusty had been delighted … until he came to an unexpected train tunnel that he had to fly through!

After surviving that scary incident, another surprise awaited Dusty. But this time, a good one! Dusty's shortcut through the tunnel had got him to the end of the leg in record time and he had beaten all of the other planes. He was now in first place!

When Ishani landed, Dusty noticed she had a new propeller. It was the kind Ripslinger's team used. Ripslinger was a three-time champion of the rally and he wasn't pleased that a new plane like Dusty was doing so well. Dusty realized that Ishani had tricked him. She was helping Ripslinger to try to knock Dusty out of the race! He was so disappointed that she would lie to him and put him in danger.

"I really thought that you'd just turn around," Ishani tried to explain to Dusty.

Meanwhile, Dusty had become the star of the race. Reporters were all over him everywhere he went. Millions of working vehicles all over the world were following his progress! They loved to see the determined little plane taking on the might of Ripslinger. They cheered him on as he flew the next leg of the race to Shanghai, China. The rookie was now Ripslinger's main competition. Dusty was the biggest story in sports news!

While he was in China, Dusty talked to his friends back home about the next stage. He needed their advice and encouragement. This leg would take him across the Pacific to Hawaii for a fuel stop and then on to Mexico. He was worried about crossing a big ocean again. Last time, it had almost ended in disaster!

"Serious monsoons," warned Skipper. "Could tear your wings right off. Be careful."

Dusty believed him. He could remember what those fierce winds felt like. But how was he going to be able to avoid them? Dusty was worried.

But his best buddy Chug had a surprise for Dusty. Something that would definitely cheer him up….

The gang was going to come and meet up with Dusty in Mexico!

Woody's Roundup Gang

Woody had tried to save Wheezy from being sold at Andy's mum's yard sale, but had ended up being stolen by a stranger!

The man brought Woody to a high-rise flat, and posed him inside a glass case. Then, to Woody's surprise, the toy-napper put on a chicken suit! He spoke to someone on the phone, then glanced at Woody and chuckled. "You, my little cowboy friend, are gonna make me big buck-buck-bucks!" he laughed.

Once he was alone, Woody ran to the door to escape. But it was no use. He was trapped.

POP! A cardboard box suddenly burst open, and Woody was knocked off his feet by a galloping toy horse.

"Yee-haw! It's really you!" shouted a cowgirl, squeezing Woody in a big hug. The cowgirl said her name was Jessie, and the horse was Bullseye. Then she introduced the Prospector, a mint condition toy who had never been out of his box.

"We've waited countless years for this day," said the Prospector.

Woody couldn't understand how the other toys recognized him. "How do you know my name?" he asked.

Bullseye dimmed the lights to reveal that the room was filled with items showing Woody's picture: posters, magazines and toys. Woody couldn't believe it! Then Jessie showed him an old TV show, *Woody's Roundup* – Woody was the star!

Woody laughed as he, Jessie and Bullseye looked at all the *Woody's Roundup* things.

"Now it's on to the museum!" the Prospector exclaimed.

"What museum?" Woody was confused.

The Prospector explained that the *Roundup* toys had become valuable. Al planned to sell them, as a set, to a Japanese museum for a lot of money.

Woody told Jessie he couldn't go to the museum because he had to get back to Andy.

Jessie sadly explained that she had had an owner once, too – a little girl named Emily, who used to play with her all the time. But as Emily grew up, she played with Jessie less and less. Finally, she abandoned Jessie.

"You never forget kids like Emily or Andy," said Jessie. "But they forget you."

Woody began to worry that Andy would forget about him one day, too. Should he take his chance? Should he let Al take him to the museum? Perhaps he should....

Albatross Taxi Service

Orville the albatross was feeling low. His maintenance job at the Central Park Zoo (hours: 9–3; duties: eating all the popcorn, pretzels and half-finished hot dogs that the little children dropped) had just ended for the season. What would he do next?

Orville sighed and leaned against a lamp post at the busy junction of 45th and Broadway. He liked to watch the cars zoom back and forth. Just then there was a tap on his wing. He looked down to see an elderly mouse couple. "Excuse me, sonny," said the grandfather mouse. "Would it be possible for you to help us cross this busy street?"

Orville looked confused. "You want me to go in the middle of the street and stop traffic?"

"Perhaps you could give us a lift … *over* the traffic," the grandmother mouse suggested. "We'll buy you a hot dog as payment."

Mmmmm! Orville couldn't say no to the promise of a tasty hot dog with mustard and sauerkraut, so he readily agreed. Besides, it was the right thing to do, lending another animal a helping wing. "It's a deal!" he said.

Just then, the grandmother mouse whistled to a group of mice standing nearby. "Harvey, Mildred, Polly, Carl – let's go. We have a ride!"

"Wait!" Orville said. "I can't give *all* of you a ride. Just how strong do you think I am?"

"Think about it this way," said the grandfather mouse. "More mice, more hot dogs."

Well that was certainly true. With that in mind, Orville agreed to help all the mice across the road. It took three trips. The mice held on just a bit too tightly to his feathers, and Orville's landings left something to be desired, that was certain, but soon everyone was across the road, safe and sound.

"Here are your hot dogs!" the mice said. Orville was disappointed to see that they were offering him hot dogs from the mouse hot dog stand, which were considerably smaller than the humankind. Still, a deal was a deal, and Orville was not one to look a gift horse – or mouse – in the mouth.

Orville then found a discarded sardine tin, which he used for seats, and thus began the Albatross Taxi Service for Mice. Word spread, and soon Orville couldn't keep up with the demand! He was a very successful businessbird.

Then one day it hit him – he was selling himself short! Forget about Albatross Taxi Service – it was time to think bigger. He'd get himself a scarf and goggles and start Albatross Airlines! He sold his taxi business to an entrepreneurial pigeon and set up shop at the airport.

Now, if he could only learn how to land, everything would be perfect!

BIG HERO 6

A Hero for Hiro

After wowing the audience with his microbot invention at the San Francisco Institute of Technology Tech Showcase, Hiro had won a place at the university!

After the show, Hiro was outside celebrating with his brother, Tadashi, when suddenly, people began to run from the hall. Smoke was trailing through the doors, and there was an orange glow behind the windows. The hall was on fire!

Tadashi looked around and noticed that his teacher, Professor Callaghan, was still inside!

Tadashi knew what he had to do. He rushed back towards the hall doors.

"Tadashi, no!" Hiro shouted.

"Someone has to help!" Tadashi yelled, his baseball cap falling to the ground as he ran.

Minutes later, a tremendous explosion knocked Hiro to his knees.

"Tadashi!" Hiro screamed. Hiro knew there was no way Tadashi or Callaghan could have survived. Hiro realized his brother was gone.

In the days that followed, Aunt Cass tried to comfort Hiro. She told him they would get through it together if only he could talk about how he felt. But no amount of comforting or talking helped. To Hiro, nothing seemed to matter any more.

At the funeral, everyone huddled under big black umbrellas in the rain, and it almost felt like it wasn't real. But it *was* real. Hiro had lost his big brother and his best friend, and there was nothing anybody could do about it.

Days passed, then weeks. Classes started at SFIT, but Hiro sat alone in his room. He and Tadashi were meant to go to SFIT together. Hiro couldn't go without him.

One day, Hiro was playing with Megabot, when the bottom half of it fell off and landed on his toe.

"Ouch!" he yelped.

Suddenly, there was a noise on the other side of the room. *Whoooosh!*

"Hello. I am Baymax, your personal health-care companion," the giant bot said, emerging from his suitcase. "On a scale of one to ten, how would you rate your pain?"

Hiro didn't know whether to laugh or cry. Here, in his room, was a walking, talking reminder of his brother. Tadashi's best-ever invention, in fact. But what use was a robot when Hiro just wanted his brother back?

Hiro refused to be scanned. "I cannot deactivate until you say you are satisfied with your care," Baymax said.

"Fine!" Hiro shouted. But he wasn't satisfied, not really. He didn't want to talk to anyone right now, especially not someone who reminded him so painfully of Tadashi.

Disney·PIXAR
MONSTERS, INC.
Celia's Bad Hair Day

"Some encrusted evening," Mike sang to himself as he danced around the bathroom getting ready for his date. He could not wait to see his girlfriend, Celia. The round green monster was in the mood for love.

Pulling his car into the restaurant car park, Mike hopped out and hurried inside. "Here I come, my little Schmoopsie-Poo," he murmured.

When Mike caught sight of his snake-haired sweetie, his heart skipped a beat. The stunning cyclops was sitting alone at a table for two. Her green scales glowed in the candlelight. She was monstrously beautiful.

But, as Celia turned towards Mike, he noticed something. Rather than rustling happily, her hair-snakes were writhing angrily!

"How's my little Schmoopsie Woopsie?" Mike decided to ignore the grumpy-looking snakes. He leaned in to kiss Celia on the cheek, but the closest snake lashed out at him.

"Yowch," Mike exclaimed, jumping back. "Bad-hair day, snookums?"

"Oh, Googly Bear." Celia sighed, running her hand through her serpentine tresses. "It's just awful. I'm out of conditioner, my shower went cold on me, and I've been in an awful tangle ever since. Are they terrible?"

Choosing a seat far enough away from his sweetie to avoid being bitten, Mike looked closer. Celia's snakes glared at him, their fangs bared. Mike tried not to flinch when they hissed at him. But, he had to admit, they were a little knotted, and they did not have their usual body or lustre.

"They're not so bad," Mike fibbed. He blew Celia a kiss from across the table and tried to smile. This was not the romantic evening he'd been looking forward to.

At the next table a pair of many-armed monsters held hands and hands and hands. They rubbed their warty noses together and whispered sweet nothings into each other's many ears. Mike sighed. They looked so cosy. Then he had an idea.

"Excuse me, my sweet." Mike stood up and approached the couple. When he came back to the table, he was holding a large purple hat. "Amelia, Ophelia, Octelia, Bobelia and Madge," Mike addressed Celia's snakes. "How would you like to cosy up in this until we can get you untangled?" Celia's snakes cooed in delight.

"Oh, Googly Bear!" Celia cried. She wound her hair-snakes and stuffed them into the hat. "You even know how to fix a bad hair day!"

With her hair contained, Celia gave Mike a big hug and a well-deserved smooch.

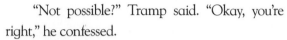

Tony and the Tramp

Tramp licked the last of the tomato sauce from his chin. "So, what do you think, Pidge?" he asked Lady.

"That was the most wonderful meal I've ever had," Lady gushed.

"What did I tell ya?" Tramp boasted. "There's no one in the world who can cook up a meal like Tony!"

"I couldn't agree with you more," Lady said. "Can I ask you a question?"

"Sure thing," Tramp said. "Ask away!"

"I was just wondering," Lady began, "how you and Tony met."

"How I met Tony?" Tramp laughed. "Now that's a story!"

"I bet!" Lady said.

"Well, see, it goes like this," Tramp began. "It was a cold and snowy night. I don't think it had ever been that cold before, and I know it hasn't been since. I had been walking uphill for miles. Icicles were hanging from the tip of my nose."

"Wait a minute!" Lady interrupted. "You were walking for miles – uphill? In this town?"

"That's right!" Tramp said. "You've never seen the likes of it."

"Exactly!" Lady told him. "You know why?"

Tramp shook his head.

"Because it isn't possible! There are no big hills around here!" Lady said.

"Not possible?" Tramp said. "Okay, you're right," he confessed.

"So, then, what's the truth?" Lady asked.

"The truth is," Tramp began, "I wasn't always the slick, handsome devil you see before you."

"Is that right?" Lady was amused.

"And this one afternoon I was being harassed by a group of mangy mutts who outnumbered me ten to one. So, I took off as fast as my paws could carry me. And as they were chasing me, along came this dogcatcher!"

"Oh, no!" Lady cried.

"Exactly!" Tramp continued. "The mutts scattered out of sight, so I didn't have *them* to worry about any more. But now the dogcatcher was closing in! I thought I was a goner!"

"What happened?" Lady asked.

"Then Tony came running out with a bowl of steaming hot pasta," Tramp explained. "He told the dogcatcher I was his dog. The dogcatcher didn't believe him. But, when Tony put the bowl of pasta down in front of me, he had no choice. Let me tell you, I thought I'd died and gone to heaven."

"I can relate to that," Lady said, recalling the meal.

"And the rest," Tramp said, "as they say, is history!"

"And a tasty one at that!" Lady concluded.

Should I Stay or Should I Go?

Wendy sat watching Michael and John play with Peter Pan and the rest of the Lost Boys.

"John and Michael seem so happy," Wendy said to herself. "And why wouldn't they? Never Land is such a beautiful place, and the flying is so much fun!

"Still," she had to admit, "it is also dangerous. Who knows what sort of trouble we could get into, especially with Captain Hook running about?

"And," Wendy said, "I don't think that Tinker Bell likes me very much."

Wendy considered this, then burst out, "What am I talking about? I'm making it sound like it's an awful place, but the truth is, Never Land is the most wonderful place on earth!

"Perhaps that explains it!" Wendy suddenly realized. "Maybe I really want to stay in Never Land, but in my heart of hearts I know I shouldn't. After all, Mother and Father must miss us terribly. And we miss them too! Oh, and what about Nana?" Wendy began to fret. "She must worry about us endlessly!

"That settles it!" Wendy stood up abruptly. "We must leave for home immediately.

"But if I stay – " Wendy stopped herself. "I'll never have to grow up!"

"Then again, I always wanted to be an adult someday," she concluded.

Just then, Peter Pan swooped down beside her. "What are you doing, Wendy?" Peter asked.

"Oh, nothing," Wendy told him.

"Then why don't you come join us?" he suggested.

"I will," Wendy told him. "In a minute."

"All right! But last one there is a rotten – " Peter took off before he could finish his sentence.

"How can I ever leave Peter and the Lost Boys?" Wendy wondered. "They need me so much.

"But so do our parents," she quickly reminded herself. "Should I stay?" she wondered aloud. "Or should I go?"

Wendy's eyes fell upon a daisy. She bent over and pulled it out of the ground. "Should I stay?" she asked as she pulled a petal from the daisy. "Or should I go?" she asked as she pulled a second petal from the daisy.

Wendy did this over and over again until there was only one petal remaining on the daisy.

"Well," she said, "this flower says we should go back home. And I suppose it's right. We'll go back ... but maybe not just this minute."

Wendy stood up. "Hey, Peter, wait up!"

And with that, she flew off after Peter, her mind at ease at last.

Disney · PIXAR
BRAVE
Elinor-Bear

Merida was a princess who lived in the ancient Scottish Highlands, in a kingdom called DunBroch. Her mother, Queen Elinor, wanted Merida to marry a son from a neighbouring kingdom, in order to keep peace in the land. Merida, however, wasn't ready to marry. She wanted to have her own adventures!

Merida and her mother couldn't understand each other's point of view. They argued and Merida angrily slashed the family tapestry. She rode into the woods and met a witch, who gave her

a magic cake. Merida thought the spell would change her mother's mind about the marriage, but instead it turned her into a bear!

Merida and Elinor-Bear were upstairs in the castle. Downstairs, King Fergus – Merida's father – suddenly smelled a bear. Ever since a huge bear called Mor'du had bitten off his leg, the king had hunted down every bear he'd come across. And now it seemed there was a bear in his castle! King Fergus quickly gathered the clans for a hunt.

Merida knew that she and her mother had to get out of the castle and find the Witch. While Merida's three little brothers distracted King Fergus and the clan lords, Merida and Elinor-Bear sneaked out through the kitchen.

"I'll be back soon," Merida told the triplets.

In the forest, Merida and Elinor-Bear found the Witch's cottage – with a message she'd left behind: "Fate be changed, look inside, mend the bond torn by pride."

Suddenly, a cloud surrounded them. When it cleared, the cottage was in ruins. They searched for something to turn Elinor into a human again – but they found nothing.

They spent the night in the ruins of the Witch's cottage. In the morning, they were hungry. Merida caught a fish for breakfast. Acting like a queen, Elinor-Bear refused to eat it until it was cooked.

Before long, though, Elinor-Bear was catching fish on her own. Soon Merida and her mother were playing together in the stream. For the first time in a long while, they enjoyed each other's company. This strange adventure was bringing them closer together.

Then, suddenly, Elinor-Bear's eyes turned cold. She sniffed at Merida as if she didn't recognize her. Merida screamed, but just then, the warmth returned to the bear's eyes.

"You changed," Merida told Elinor-Bear. "Like you were a bear on the inside, too."

Merida and Elinor-Bear were worried. What if Elinor turned into a bear for good? Suddenly, their argument didn't seem to matter as much as it did before.

April 18

A Rescue Mission to Al's Toy Barn

Woody had been stolen! In Andy's room, Buzz and the other toys held an urgent meeting. They were trying to solve the mystery: Who took Woody?

Buzz thought about the clues – the licence plate, the chicken feather – and finally figured out the man must be from Al's Toy Barn, a toy shop they'd seen on TV. He had to be Al, the owner who dressed in a chicken suit!

But now that they knew who the culprit was, what could the toys do?

"Woody once risked his life to save me," Buzz told the others. "I couldn't call myself his friend if I weren't willing to do the same."

Buzz decided to lead a rescue party to the toy store, to see if they could find Woody. Together, with a little help from Slinky, they jumped off the roof. "To Al's Toy Barn and beyond!" Buzz cried.

By early morning, Buzz and his rescue team had almost reached Al's Toy Barn. They just needed to cross one last, very busy, street. Luckily, Buzz noticed a pile of orange traffic cones. He told everyone to grab one and then, slowly, they ventured across the street, hiding under the cones.

Soon, the street was filled with skidding, honking, crashing cars, all trying to avoid the strange, moving traffic cones. But the toys didn't notice. They'd arrived at Al's Toy Barn.

Inside, aisles of shiny new toys seemed to stretch into the distance. Everyone looked up in awe – how would they ever find Woody here?

The only one who didn't seem worried was Rex, who had picked up a strategy book on how to defeat the evil Emperor Zurg in the Buzz Lightyear video game. Rex loved playing the video game, and desperately wanted to beat Zurg. Rex couldn't stop reading, even as the toys spread out to search for Woody.

Buzz discovered an aisle full of brand new, updated Buzz Lightyear toys! He gasped when he saw each figure's fancy new utility belt.

He reached out to touch the belt – suddenly, a hand clamped onto his wrist. It was a new Buzz Lightyear, who believed he'd caught an escaped space ranger! Quickly, he tied Buzz into a box. Then New Buzz ran to join Andy's toys – and not one of them realized they'd left the real Buzz behind.

Buzz struggled free from his box just in time to see his friends head out the front door, inside Al's bag! Racing to catch up, he crashed – *SMACK!* – into the automatic doors as they slid shut. How was he ever going to catch up with his friends?

Out of Order

Inside the *Hero's Duty* computer game, Sergeant Calhoun, the leader of the soldiers, was yelling at Wreck-It Ralph.

"Never interfere with a first-person shooter!" she cried. Ralph belonged in his own game, *Fix-It Felix, Jr*, but he wanted to get the Medal of Heroes from Hero's Duty to prove he could be a Good Guy. He was fed up of always being the Bad Guy in his game.

Meanwhile, a girl who was playing in Litwak's Arcade moved to play on *Fix-It Felix, Jr*. She put in the coins to play, but there was a problem … Ralph wasn't there to wreck anything!

"Mr Litwak!" the girl called out, "This game's busted!"

Mr Litwak taped an 'Out of Order' sign to the screen. The characters in the game were stunned! What if their game was unplugged? Luckily, someone had seen Ralph enter *Hero's Duty*. Felix decided to bring Ralph back. "I can fix this!" he told everyone.

Over in *Hero's Duty*, Ralph had just climbed the tower which contained the Medal of Heroes. By this time, the arcade was closed for the night, so no game players could see him. The tower contained loads of cy-bug eggs. Every time the game started, the eggs hatched, and the soldiers had to battle hundreds of dangerous cy-bugs! Ralph tip-toed past the eggs … and he made it! The Medal of Heroes was his!

But, just then, Ralph knocked over an egg. It cracked open and a baby cy-bug hurled itself onto Ralph's face. Ralph fell backwards into an escape pod. Instantly, the escape pod launched into the sky – with the cy-bug still attached to Ralph's face!

At that same moment, Felix stepped into Hero's Duty. "Have you seen my colleague, Ralph?" he asked Calhoun. Suddenly, the escape pod zoomed past. They could see Ralph – and the cy-bug – inside! The ship whooshed down the tunnel to Game Central Station.

Ralph's escape pod ricocheted through the station and finally landed in a world made entirely of sweets. Ralph was ejected from the ship, and the cy-bug disappeared in a lake of toffee.

Ralph realized he was in a racing game called *Sugar Rush*. His medal had landed in a peppermint tree!

Suddenly, a little girl called Vanellope showed up. She thought the medal was a gold coin. "Race you for it!" she yelled.

Poor Ralph lost the race – and his medal! How would Ralph ever prove he was a Good Guy now?

A Good Day for a Sail

One lovely summer day, Mickey Mouse asked Minnie if she'd like to go for a boat ride.

"I would love to," Minnie said with a smile.

Mickey and Minnie were preparing to set sail when Goofy came running by on the shore.

"Hiya," he said. "What a great day for sailing!"

Distracted, Goofy didn't see a squirrel in front of him and he accidentally stepped on its tail. The squirrel squealed, then leaped up and landed in the boat! Mickey and Minnie were so startled that they jumped, making the boat rock.

Mickey tried to stop the rocking, but the boat tipped over, and Minnie shrieked as she and Mickey fell into the water.

Donald Duck came up in his speedboat and helped Mickey and Minnie into his boat. "Why don't you ride with me?" he suggested.

Relieved, Mickey and Minnie sat back and started to relax. But moments later, the boat's engine suddenly stopped.

"What do we do now?" Minnie asked.

"I have an idea," Donald said. He took off his hat and started to paddle with it. Mickey and Minnie did the same. Huffing and puffing, they made their way back to shore.

"How about some lunch while we dry off?" Mickey said. So they sat in the sun, eating hot dogs.

As they were enjoying their lunch, Pluto came running by. When he saw the delicious hot dogs, he decided he wanted one, too. He jumped into Mickey's lap and tried to grab the food.

"No, boy!" cried Mickey.

But it was too late. Pluto knocked Mickey and Minnie into the water again!

Mickey and Minnie swam to shore and climbed out of the lake. Coughing and spluttering and really fed up, they settled on the grass to dry off yet again.

Not long after, Huey, Dewey and Louie came by in their sailing boat.

"Would you like to borrow our boat?" called Dewey. "There's a good wind today."

"Yes, please!" said Mickey. He and Minnie hopped into the triplets' sailing boat and took off.

"Aah, this is the life," Mickey said.

Just then, the wind stopped blowing.

"Oh, no!" Mickey groaned, "Not again!"

Mickey and Minnie tried to paddle with their hands, but it was no use. The boat just kept going round in circles. As they huffed and puffed, Mickey saw Goofy and Donald coming towards them in rowing boats.

"We thought you might need some help," said Donald.

As Donald and Goofy towed the sailing boat, Mickey and Minnie sat back and relaxed. They had finally got their nice, easy boat ride!

Gas-Guzzling Engine

Lightning, Mater and their friends from Radiator Springs had been in Tokyo, where Lightning had taken part in the first event of the World Grand Prix – hosted by oil tycoon Miles Axlerod. During the race, some cars working for a known criminal, Professor Z, had used a special TV camera to blow up one of the cars! The press had asked Axlerod if his new alternative fuel, Allinol, was to blame – he said it wasn't.

Two British secret agents called Finn and Holley were on the trail of Professor Z. In Tokyo, an American spy had placed a secret device on Mater – then Finn and Holley thought Mater was the American spy! Professor Z had sent his goons, Grem and Acer, to find the tow truck and get back the device. Mater had then accidentally caused Lightning to lose the race, and Lightning was upset. Mater felt bad and decided to fly home, but Finn and Holley met him at the airport!

Mater didn't realize that Finn and Holley thought he was a secret agent – but he helped them anyway. Together they looked at a holographic photo that was on the device that the real American spy had given Mater. Mater said the photo was of a poorly made, gas-guzzling engine with some expensive new parts. But he didn't know who the engine belonged to.

Finn, Holley and Mater flew to Paris. Finn was hoping a parts dealer named Tomber could tell them who the mysterious engine in the photo belonged to.

Mater explained the engine must belong to a Lemon – a car that didn't work right. Gremlins and Pacers were both types of Lemons. Tomber said there was going to be a big meeting of Lemons in Porto Corsa, which was also the location of the next World Grand Prix race!

Lightning and his crew had just arrived in Italy for the next race. Their first stop was Luigi and Guido's hometown!

Lightning told Luigi's Uncle Topolino about his quarrel with Mater. The wise, old car told Lightning that even good friends fight sometimes. But it's important to make up fast. No fight is more important than friendship.

Meanwhile, Holley was disguising Mater as one of the Lemons' tow trucks so that he could sneak into the meeting. She gave Mater lots of cool spy gadgets, too!

Lightning was starting to really miss his best friend, Mater. He didn't realize that Mater was actually nearby – and had been caught up in a secret agent adventure!

Bambi

First Impressions

Bambi was just discovering the wonders of the forest. His mother had brought him to a little clearing in the woods. The sudden sunshine and bright green grass surprised and pleased him, and he bounded around on his still-wobbly legs, feeling the warm sun on his back and the soft grass under his hooves. While his mother grazed nearby, Bambi began to explore.

He found a patch of green grass and clover, and he bent down to eat. This was not an easy feat, as his long legs made it difficult for his little neck to reach the ground. When his nose was just a few inches from the tips of the grass, he suddenly leaped backwards in alarm. A leaf had just sprung up from the patch of grass and had landed a few feet away. A hopping leaf? he wondered. He followed it and, as soon as he drew close, the leaf hopped away from him again!

Bambi looked around at where his mother stood, still grazing. She seemed to think they were in no great danger. So, he followed the leaf all the way to the edge of the clearing, where a wide brook babbled over craggy rocks.

Bambi's fascination with the hopping leaf faded as he approached the brook. Water cascaded smoothly over the rocks, bubbling and frothing in shallow pools. He took a step closer and felt his foot touch a rock at the edge of the water.

Suddenly, the rock moved! It shuffled towards the water and then – *plop!* – jumped right in and swam away.

Bambi was dumbfounded as he watched it dive beneath the surface and vanish. He stared at the spot where the rock had been for a moment, and then stooped down to have a drink, widening his stance in order to do so.

Suddenly, he jumped back in alarm. There in the water, staring right back up at him, was a little deer! Cautiously he approached again, and there it was!

Bambi turned and bounded back across the clearing to his mother.

"Mama! Mama!" he cried breathlessly. "You will never guess what I have seen!"

His mother lifted her head and gazed at him with her clear, bright eyes.

"First," he said, "first I saw a jumping leaf. Then, I saw a rock with legs that walked right into the water and swam away! And then," he he continued in amazement, "and then I saw a little deer who lives right in the water! He's right over there, Mama!"

His mother nuzzled her son, thinking over what he had said. Then she laughed gently.

"Darling," she said. "I think you have just seen your first grasshopper, your first turtle and your very own reflection!"

Disney · PIXAR
FROM THE MOVIE **INSIDE OUT**

No More Goofing Around

Things were not going well inside Riley's Mind World. Sadness had touched a happy memory, changing it to a sad one – and made Riley cry in front of her new classmates! Even worse, Joy, Sadness and Riley's core memories had accidentally been sucked out into Riley's Mind World and ended up in Long Term Memory. They had to get the core memories back to Headquarters quickly before Riley forgot about everything she loved!

While Riley was having dinner with her parents, Anger, Fear and Disgust were up in Headquarters trying not to panic. Disgust was driving the console, trying her best to keep Riley acting normal.

"I've found a junior hockey league," Mum said to Riley. "And get this: try-outs are tomorrow after school. What luck, right?"

"Oh yeah," Riley said sarcastically. "Sounds fantastic."

Mum looked at Riley in shock. In Mum's Headquarters, her Emotions figured out something must be wrong.

"How was school?" Dad asked.

"It was fine, I guess. I don't know…." Riley answered grumpily.

Riley's parents were surprised. They couldn't understand why their daughter wasn't her usual happy self.

"Riley, is everything okay?" Mum asked.

"Ugghh!" Riley sighed.

"Riley," Dad said sternly, "I do not like this new attitude."

Inside Headquarters, Anger took over the console. "Oh, I'll show you attitude," he said, pushing buttons and levers.

At the dinner table, Riley lost her cool. "Just leave me alone!" she screamed.

"That is it!" Dad shouted, pounding the table. He pointed upstairs. "Go to your room! Now!"

Riley stormed upstairs.

Later, there was a knock on Riley's door. Dad opened it and stepped into her bedroom. Riley was lying on her sleeping bag in silence.

"Do you want to talk about it?" asked Dad.

Riley said nothing.

Dad tried to start up their goofball act, making noises like a monkey, but Riley simply turned away. Giving up, Dad left the room.

In Riley's Mind World, Goofball Island made a terrible groaning noise. It was collapsing! Riley had stopped goofing around with her dad – that part of Riley's personality was crumbling away!

Joy and Sadness ran back to the solid ground of Long Term Memory. They watched as Goofball Island fell into the darkness.

Then it was gone.

Follow the Microbot

Hiro was in mourning. His brother and best friend, Tadashi, had died while trying to rescue his teacher, Professor Callaghan, from a fire at SFIT's Tech Showcase. Nothing could make Hiro feel better – not even Tadashi's greatest invention, Baymax the caregiving robot. Seeing Tadashi's robot made Hiro feel sad yet happy at the same time. It was confusing.

Hiro took a step backwards, trying to get away from the robot, and fell on the floor. He found himself staring under the bed at the hoodie he had worn at the showcase. And in its pocket was the microbot that Alistair Krei had been holding! Krei – the owner of a large technology company – had offered to buy the microbots from Hiro that night. But Hiro remembered how Callaghan had convinced him not to sell, and that Krei was bad news.

The microbot vibrated in Hiro's hand. "Dumb thing's broken," Hiro sighed, putting the bot in a Petri dish.

"Your tiny robot is trying to go somewhere," Baymax observed as the microbot rattled against the wall of the Petri dish.

"Oh yeah?" said Hiro. "Why don't you find out where it's trying to go?"

So Baymax did just that! Realizing Baymax had gone, Hiro ran to his window and saw the robot was outside, following the microbot!

Hiro ran downstairs, startling Aunt Cass. "Are you registering for school?" she asked. "Uh, yes," Hiro fibbed. He hugged his aunt and ran outside. He couldn't let anything bad happen to his brother's robot.

Hiro finally caught up with Baymax outside an old warehouse.

"I have found where your tiny robot wants to go," said Baymax.

The microbot was pointing at the warehouse. Hiro and Baymax climbed through an open window. Hiro was astonished at what he saw. Someone was building thousands of his microbots!

Suddenly, the microbots swarmed – and attacked! A masked man stood on a platform above. Hiro realized the man must have a transmitter behind his mask, just like the one Hiro had in his headband at the showcase!

Hiro and Baymax turned to run but the swarm followed. Eventually, the microbots pushed them out of the window, but Baymax's inflated body cushioned Hiro's fall.

"Come on! Let's get out of here!" Hiro shouted as he jumped up and started running, with Baymax following behind. Hiro was angry. He decided they should go to the police. After all, the man in the mask had stolen his invention and something had to be done about it!

Disney·PIXAR
MONSTERS, INC.

A Mother's Touch

Work was piling up in the offices of Monsters, Inc. Celia was off with the flu, and there was no one to cover for her.

Sulley, the president of Monsters, Inc., knew he had to act fast. "Who can we get to fill in?" he asked.

"I know!" answered Mike. "I'll call my mum. She'd love to help out."

And so, later that day, in walked Mrs Wazowski. Sulley and Mike went off to discuss some new plans for the laugh factory, while Mrs W. made herself at home – *very* at home. When Sulley and Mike returned at lunchtime, they scarcely recognized the reception area. Mike's mum had hung ruffled curtains and scattered fluffy rugs everywhere. Mike gave Sulley a weak smile.

"We'll change it back when she leaves," he whispered.

Later that day, Mike rehearsed some new comedy routines. "What do monsters eat for breakfast?" asked Mike. "Anything they want!" Sulley and Mike laughed until their sides hurt.

"I couldn't help but overhear," said Mike's mum. "It might be funnier if you wore a silly hat."

Sulley shot Mike a look. "Thanks, Mum," said Mike. "That's a very helpful suggestion. Say – isn't that the phone I hear ringing?"

A little while later, Sulley and Mike summoned her over the intercom to come to the Laugh Floor. "Um, Mum, do you know anything about this?" Mike asked nervously. He pointed to the card keys, which were now filed by colour, making it impossible for anyone to know which card belonged to which door.

"I certainly do!" Mrs W. replied proudly. "I have an 'eye' for organization, if I do say so myself."

Sulley turned and spoke to Mike through gritted teeth. "She's *your* mother. Do something!"

Just before the day was over, Mike went to the front desk, sat down and took his mother's hand. He'd never fired his mother before. This wasn't going to be easy! "Mum, you know I love you. And you make a terrific receptionist, but – "

Just then, Celia walked through the front door. "Schmoopsie-Poo!" called Mike.

"Googly Bear!" Celia cried.

"What are you doing here?" Mike asked. "You're supposed to be home in bed."

"I couldn't stand being away from you one day longer," Celia gushed.

Mrs Wazowski beamed. "He *is* irresistible – isn't he? That's because he takes after my side of the family. Well, I guess my work here is done!" she said, gathering up her things.

Suddenly, Mrs W. stopped. "Oh, Mikey, what were you about to tell me?"

"Not a thing, Mum," said Mike as he gave her a kiss. "Not a thing!"

Undercover Mater

Lightning was in Italy, competing in the second event of the World Grand Prix. He had lost the first race after Mater had confused him over the headset. Lightning didn't realize Mater had been mistaken for an American secret agent – and was now caught up in a mission with two British agents, Finn and Holley!

Little did Lightning know, Mater was nearby. With a new disguise provided by the British agents, Mater had made it into a meeting of Lemons – bad cars that don't work properly – at a casino. Holley and Finn were positioned outside, listening in through Mater's headset.

A wanted criminal named Professor Z introduced the Lemons to their Big Boss, who appeared on a TV screen. But only his engine was visible – the same engine the real American agent had photographed! The Big Boss said that once a new alternative fuel named Allinol was proven lethal, all cars would use gasoline again. Then the Lemons, who owned the oil, would be rich and powerful!

As the Big Boss spoke, Professor Z's goons, Grem and Acer, were at the next race. They aimed a special TV camera at Carla Veloso, the race car from Brazil. Finn and Holley watched from their lookout point as Carla's engine exploded on the racetrack! Finn raced to the top of the tower to stop Grem and Acer. But a helicopter captured him with a giant magnet!

Finn was taken away and Grem and Acer continued to harm more race cars. Their next victim was Shu Todoroki, the racer from Japan. Shu's engine exploded, causing him to crash into another car. Soon, there was a pile up!

At the finish line, Lightning won. By now, everyone thought Allinol was to blame for the crashes. But Lightning insisted he would still use Allinol in the final race. The Big Boss heard Lightning's statement, and gave the order to destroy Lightning at the next race! Mater tried to leave and warn his friend, but his disguise disappeared! Luckily, he escaped using his new spy gear.

When Mater finally arrived at the race track, he saw Lightning surrounded by a crowd. Lightning thought he could hear Mater calling to him, and turned to look for his friend. But before Lightning could spot him, the Lemons pulled Mater away.

The next thing the tow truck knew, he, Finn and Holley were tied up inside a giant clock called Big Bentley! They were in London, England, the location of the final race! How would Mater save Lightning now...?

Potion Commotion

Emperor Kuzco's royal adviser, Yzma, was down in her secret laboratory, mixing potions. She had enlisted her enthusiastic but dim-witted right-hand man, Kronk, to help her in her work.

"Kronk, I need spider legs, one eye of newt and elderberry juice … and quickly!" Yzma directed.

"Legs, eye, juice," Kronk repeated. "Right." He hurried across the laboratory to the cupboard that contained all of Yzma's potion ingredients. Inside were hundreds of glass jars, some filled with coloured liquids and powders, others holding creepy-looking body parts of various insects and lizards.

"Let's see," Kronk said to himself as he pored over the containers. "Legs, eye, juice. Legs, eye, juice." He found the 'legs' section. "Newt legs! Check!" Kronk said to himself, confusing Yzma's instructions.

Then he found the 'eye' section. "Spider eyes! Got it!" he said, grabbing the jar. He hurried back to Yzma with the two containers.

"Kronk!" shouted Yzma. "I said spider legs and newt eye! Not newt legs and spider eye! And where's the elderberry juice? Hurry, hurry!"

Kronk hurried back to the cupboard. "Spider legs … newt eye … spider legs … newt eye," he recited as he went. This time, he managed to remember them and took down the right containers from the cupboard. But what was that third ingredient? "Juice!" Kronk cried. "Berry juice." He found a small vial of blueberry juice and took everything to Yzma.

"Not blueberry juice, you numbskull!" Yzma screamed. "ELDERBERRY!"

"Right," Kronk said.

He hurried back across the laboratory and quickly located the 'juice' section. "Boysenberry … cranberry …" he read, moving alphabetically through the containers.

"ELDERBERRY!" Yzma shouted at him. "Get it over here! *And step on it!*"

Kronk finally located the right bottle. "Got it!" He rushed it across the laboratory. Yzma reached out to take the bottle from him.

But Kronk didn't hand it to her. Instead, he gently placed the bottle on the floor.

Then he lifted his right foot and stomped on it – hard – shattering the bottle and splattering juice everywhere.

"KRONK!" Yzma screamed in surprise. "What are you doing?"

Kronk was confused. "I did just what you said," he explained. "I got the elderberry juice. And I stepped on it."

Yzma let loose a hair-raising scream of frustration and collapsed in a heap on the laboratory floor.

THE JUNGLE Book

Snake Eyes

"I'm ssstarved," hissed Kaa the python as he slithered across the jungle treetops. "I need a sssnack...."

Suddenly, Kaa noticed a small figure relaxing on the ground below. It was Mowgli. Kaa slithered over to him.

"Are you feeling ssssleeepy?" hissed Kaa. "You look sssleeepy; jussst look into my eyesss...."

Mowgli tried not to look into the snake's eyes, but it wasn't easy. When he turned one way, Kaa was there. When he turned another, Kaa was there too!

"Sssslip into ssssilent ssslumber," Kaa hissed. "And sssleep ... sssleeep ... sssleep...."

Before Mowgli knew it, his body went completely limp. Kaa had hypnotized him!

Thank goodness Mowgli's friends walked by at that very moment.

"Look!" cried Bagheera the panther. "Kaa's after Mowgli again."

"Get over there and do something," Baloo told Bagheera.

"The last time I interfered with Kaa, he hypnotized *me*," said Bagheera. "*You* do something."

Kaa's fangs watered as he coiled his long body around Mowgli. Then Kaa opened his giant python mouth above Mowgli's head and – hey! Someone had jammed a stick into his jaws!

"Hello there, Kaa," said Baloo, leaning one big paw against the tree.

The python's powerful jaws snapped the stick. "You sssshould not insssert yourssself between a sssnake and his sssnack," he hissed.

"Oh! Sorry!" said Baloo. "I was just admiring how very talented you are."

"Talented?" Kaa said.

"Sure!" said Baloo. "I'm very impressed how you hypnotized Mowgli there. I bet you could hypnotize almost anything in the jungle. Almost...."

"What do you mean *almost*?" said Kaa.

Baloo coolly polished his claws against his fur. "Well, let's see," he said. "I bet you can't hypnotize ... a fish." Baloo pointed to the pond.

"Jusssst you watch me," Kaa told Baloo as he slithered towards the pond.

Hanging his head over the water, Kaa hissed, "Jussst look into my eyesss. You feel ssssleeepy ... ssssleeepy ... ssssleeepy...."

Suddenly, Kaa stopped hissing. Or moving. He just stared into the water.

Bagheera stepped up to Baloo and whispered, "What's the matter with him?"

Baloo just laughed. "Kaa was so determined to prove me wrong, he didn't even notice the water was reflecting back his image. That crazy snake hypnotized himself!"

Donald Takes Flight

"Daisy, I have a surprise for you," said Donald Duck one clear spring day. "I've been taking flying lessons."

"That *is* a surprise," said Daisy Duck.

Donald took Daisy to a nearby airport. On the runway sat an old-fashioned plane with open-air seats. Together they climbed into the small plane. Then Donald started the engine.

"Up, up and away!" he cried as they took off.

"Can you do any tricks?" shouted Daisy.

"Sure!" called Donald. He steered the plane into a loop-the-loop.

"You're a very good pilot, Donald!" Daisy cried, clapping her hands.

Donald was so proud of himself, he told Daisy he would fly wherever she wanted to go.

Daisy thought it over. "Let's go to Paris, France!" she said. Donald was so eager to impress Daisy that he didn't think twice. "Paris, here we come!" he cried. Before long, however, the plane's engine began to cough and choke.

"Uh-oh," Donald said to himself as the plane began to drift towards the water.

"Is anything wrong?" asked Daisy.

Donald knew they were running out of fuel. But he didn't want Daisy to find out.

"Everything is fine, Daisy," Donald said nervously.

Just then, he saw something floating below them. It looked like an airport runway. But what would a runway be doing in the middle of the ocean?

As the plane drifted closer to the water, Donald realized he had no choice. He'd have to land his plane on the floating runway.

Just before he landed, Donald's eyes nearly popped out of his head. It wasn't a runway at all. It was the top deck of a huge ocean liner!

"Duck!" yelled one of the ship's passengers, and a dozen people scattered.

Donald zoomed over their heads and landed the plane on the long, wide deck.

"Hey, it really *is* a duck!" cried one of the passengers.

Just then an announcement came over the ship's speakers. "Good evening, ladies and gentlemen. Dinner is served!"

Donald helped Daisy out of the plane. He was sure she would be upset. But she wasn't. "Dinner on a cruise ship!" she cried. "Donald, you're just full of surprises, aren't you!"

"Yes, indeed," said Donald with a huge sigh of relief. "And here's one more surprise: I think this ship's on its way to France!"

"Oh, Donald, you're the best," said Daisy.

No, I'm not, thought Donald, as Daisy hugged him. What I really am is one lucky duck!

Pinocchio
Look Sharp, Jiminy!

"Gosh." Jiminy Cricket scratched his head between his antennae and yawned a big yawn. Climbing into his tiny matchbox bed, he gazed again at the wooden boy, who was fast asleep.

Jiminy still could not believe his eyes – or his luck. It had been a miraculous night. Not every cricket got to witness a wish granted by the Blue Fairy and see a puppet come to life. And not every cricket was chosen to be somebody's conscience!

Jiminy hopped out of bed. It was pointless to try to sleep. He already felt like he was dreaming. Being a conscience was a big job, but he was just the bug to do it. "Right and wrong." Jiminy looked from one of his hands to the other. "Sure, I know the difference. All I have to do is tell Pinoke. It'll be a snap." Jiminy snapped his fingers. "And I'll even look good doing it."

Jiminy ran his hands down the new jacket hanging by his bed. He picked up the hat and twirled it. "My, my," he said, shaking his head. Then he could not resist any longer. He put on his new shirt, coat, hat and shoes. Then he hopped over to Cleo's fishbowl to see his reflection.

Jiminy whistled low. "Don't you look smart," he told his reflection. "Smart enough to help that wooden boy. Except for that smudge." Jiminy leaned down to inspect a dull spot on his shoe.

He breathed on it and rubbed it with his sleeve. Soon it was shining like new. He looked like a million dollars!

Suddenly Geppetto snored loudly. Jiminy jumped and looked up. Outside the sky was starting to lighten.

"Would you look at that?" Jiminy knew he had to get to bed. A conscience needed to be alert! He hurried out of his new clothes, hung them up carefully, and tucked himself back in bed. "Big day tomorrow." He yawned. "Very big day." A moment later the little cricket was chirping in his sleep.

Jiminy woke to the sound of hundreds of cuckoo clocks. He sat up and rubbed his eyes. He barely remembered where he was. Then the events of the evening before flooded back. Why, he had work to do!

"Get up, Pinoke!" Jiminy called towards the big bed. But Pinocchio was already gone. The bed was made and Geppetto and Figaro were gone too!

Cleo swished nervously in her bowl and pointed towards the door.

"I must have overslept!" Jiminy pulled his new clothes on quickly. "I can't let Pinoke start school without me. You don't have to be a conscience to know that's wrong!" And, quick as a flash, Jiminy hopped out of the door.

A Shock Discovery

That night, Dusty joined his Mexican friend, El Chu, at Rochelle's hangar. El Chu was still chasing after his crush, Rochelle, the Canadian plane who he had spotted on the first day of the race. Dusty thought about how he could help El Chu catch her eye. He coached his friend on how to sing a love song! El Chu followed his advice – and finally got Rochelle's attention!

"I am in your debt, compadre," El Chu told Dusty. He was delighted.

The next morning, the racers took off over the Pacific. They rose above the clouds, leaving Dusty in the fog below, just as had happened the first time over the Atlantic. Dusty worried that the same thing was going to happen all over again. He could end up back in last place – or maybe not make it at all!

While Dusty was worrying about the weather, Zed, Ripslinger's teammate, sneaked up on him and broke off his antenna. Without it, Dusty lost all radio contact! He quickly flew off course. Now he was really in trouble!

Dusty flew farther and farther. There was no land in sight – and worse still, he was running out of fuel. Suddenly, two navy fighters pulled up beside him. They told him to follow them – he could land on their aircraft carrier.

Dusty couldn't believe it! It was the U.S.S. Dwight D. Flysenhower – Skipper's old ship from his days in the navy!

Skipper must have radioed ahead and asked these guys to keep an eye out for me! Dusty thought to himself.

Dusty braced himself as he looked down at the moving runway. This was a new challenge! The navy planes, Echo and Bravo, talked him through the landing. He touched down on the deck and bounced into a barricade. Everyone erupted into cheers!

On board the ship, Dusty was looking at all of the photos on the Jolly Wrenches Wall of Fame. He found Skipper's photo, but things weren't as he expected – there was only one mission listed for his coach.

"Is it true?" he asked Skipper on the radio. Had Skipper been lying to them all about all the experience he had with the Jolly Wrenches?

Skipper admitted that it was true, but there was no time to explain right now. A storm over the ocean was getting worse. Dusty had to leave the aircraft carrier straight away!

Dusty had fuel and a new antenna for his journey. He was as ready as he was ever going to be. It was time to face the storms head on! The navy crew catapulted him off the ship.

Dusty was back in the race!

RATATOUILLE
(rat·a·too·ee)

A Rave Review

A young chef named Linguini had just discovered that the great chef Auguste Gusteau had been his father. Gusteau's restaurant now belonged to him and was getting very popular. Remy the rat was helping Linguini by hiding in his hat and controlling the cooking – Remy was the one with the true talent.

But Linguini was enjoying his success a bit too much. He had stopped paying attention to food, and Remy didn't like it.

Suddenly, the famous critic Ego – the very same critic who had once ruined Gusteau's – arrived and gave his warning: "I will return tomorrow night with high expectations."

After Ego's announcement, Remy was furious that Linguini wasn't more worried about cooking, and he yanked Linguini's hair, hard. Linguini got angry. He took Remy out to the back and said, "You take a break, Little Chef. I'm not your puppet."

Remy was cross with Linguini and, later that night, Remy told the entire rat colony to take whatever they wanted from the restaurant's refrigerator. That's when Linguini returned to apologize.

"You're stealing from me?" Linguini furiously asked. "I thought you were my friend. I trusted you! Get out and don't come back!"

But Remy did come back. He felt horrible. Plus, Ego had come to review the restaurant. Remy knew his friend Linguini needed help. Boldly, Remy walked alone through the doors, into the bustling kitchen.

"Rat!" shrieked the chefs in unison.

"Don't touch him!" shouted Linguini. "The truth is, I have no talent at all. But this rat – he's the cook."

From the shadows, Remy's father watched the human defend Remy!

Still, the cooks walked out. Only Remy and Linguini were left.

"I was wrong about you. About him," Remy's father told him. He had never trusted humans before. "I'm proud of you."

Django whistled, and rats instantly filled the kitchen. After going through the dishwasher to clean themselves, the rats began to cook. Even Colette came back.

Linguini, acting as waiter, served a delicious dish of ratatouille to Ego. The taste brought back a warm, comforting memory from Ego's childhood. When Ego asked to meet the chef, Linguini and Colette waited until all the other customers left the restaurant, then they brought out Remy. The next morning Ego gave the restaurant a rave review!

Disney
101 DALMATIANS

Patch and the Panther

One dark night, 15 Dalmatian puppies sat huddled around a black-and-white TV set. They watched as Thunderbolt, the canine hero, creeped through a deep, dark jungle.

Thunderbolt suddenly pricked up his ears. The puppies held their breath. Two yellow eyes peered out of the bushes. It was a panther!

"Thunderbolt, look out behind you!" Penny barked at the television.

"How will brave Thunderbolt escape the hungry panther?" the TV announcer asked. "Don't miss next week's exciting episode!"

"Aww!" the puppies groaned, disappointed that their favourite show was over.

"I'll bet Thunderbolt tears that ol' panther to pieces," said Patch.

"I'd be scared to fight a panther," said his brother Lucky.

"Not me!" cried Patch.

"All right, kids. Time for bed," Pongo said, shutting off the television with his nose. He watched as the puppies padded upstairs and settled down in their baskets.

"Good night, pups," Pongo said.

"Good night, Dad," the puppies replied.

Pongo switched off the light. Moments later, the sound of soft snores filled the room. The puppies were fast asleep.

All except for one. Patch was wide awake. He was still thinking about Thunderbolt and the panther.

"I wish an ol' panther would come around here," Patch said to himself. "I'd teach him a thing or two."

Just then a floorboard creaked. Patch pricked up his ears. Then he crawled out of his basket to investigate.

The floorboard creaked again. What if it's a panther? Patch thought with a shiver. But I'm not scared of any ol' panther, he told himself.

Suddenly Patch saw a shadow flicker across the doorway. The shadow had a long tail. Panthers have long tails. Just then two yellow eyes peered out of the darkness.

"Aroooo!" Patch yelped. He turned to run, but he tripped on the rug. In a flash, the panther was on top of him. Patch could feel its hot breath on his neck. He shut his eyes….

"Patch, what are you doing out of bed?" the panther asked.

Patch opened his eyes. It was Pongo!

"I – I was just keeping an eye out for panthers," Patch explained.

Pongo smiled. "Why don't you get some sleep now," he suggested. "I can keep an eye out for panthers for a while."

"Okay, Dad," Patch said with a yawn.

Pongo carried Patch back to his basket. And in no time at all, the puppy was fast asleep.

Woody's Decision

Buzz had led a rescue mission to Al's Toy Barn to save Woody – the cowboy doll had been stolen by the shop's owner. Al wanted to sell the whole *Woody's Roundup* gang to a Japanese museum, for a lot of money!

Buzz had just been accidentally left behind by the rest of the toys. A brand-new Buzz Lightyear toy had come to life and caught Andy's Buzz, and tied him inside a box before joining the rest of the toys!

Old Buzz struggled free from his box just in time to see his friends head out the front door, inside Al's bag! Racing to catch up, he crashed into the automatic doors as they slid shut.

To make the doors re-open, Buzz knocked a nearby pile of toy boxes onto the sensor mat. One box remained stuck between the doors. Opening and closing, the doors hit the box over and over. At last, the box popped open, and a dark figure rose up. It was the evil Emperor Zurg! He took one look at Buzz and growled, "Destroy Buzz Lightyear!"

Outside, the toys had hoped to hitch a ride in Al's bag to wherever Woody was being kept. But at his building, Al jumped out of the car, leaving his bag – and the toys – behind.

"No time to lose!" New Buzz shouted. Quickly, he led everyone into the building through an air vent. Then, because he thought he was a real space ranger, he tried to fly up to the top floor! Luckily, the lift came by just in time and carried everyone up instead.

Sneaking through the vents, the toys reached Al's flat. They charged into the room, knocking down Jessie and Bullseye, then grabbed Woody and ran. Everything was very chaotic – especially when the real Buzz showed up as well!

Finally, things got sorted out, and everyone figured out who was who. But that still left one problem.

"Woody, you're in danger here," said real Buzz. He knew that Al wanted to send Woody to Japan. "We need to leave now."

But Woody didn't want to leave. The *Roundup* gang needed him to make a complete set for the museum. Besides, what if Andy didn't want Woody anymore? Al had fixed Woody's arm when his shoulder had ripped, but what if he broke again?

"You're a toy!" Buzz said. "Life's only worth living if you're being loved by a kid."

"This is my only chance," Woody said.

"To do what?" Buzz replied. "To watch kids from behind glass and never be loved again? Some life."

Sadly, Buzz had to leave Woody behind.

Disney · PIXAR
BRAVE
Mend the Bond Torn by Pride

Princess Merida was an adventurous teenager, who lived in the Scottish Highlands with her family. Her father, King Fergus, was missing a leg – he had lost it when he fought a huge bear called Mor'du.

Merida's mother, Queen Elinor, wanted her to marry in order to keep peace in the land. But Merida wasn't ready to give up her freedom. Elinor told Merida about an ancient prince who had broken tradition and split from his three brothers. Their kingdom had then fallen to ruin.

Feeling angry with her mother, Merida slashed the family tapestry with her sword. Soon afterwards, Merida stumbled upon a witch. She asked for a spell that would change her mother.

The Witch told Merida about a prince who, long ago, had asked for the strength of 10 men. She showed Merida the ring the prince had given her. Two crossed axes were carved into it. Merida would get a similar spell.

The spell had changed Queen Elinor ... into a bear! Now Elinor-Bear and Merida were searching for something to break the spell. But all they had found was a riddle: "Fate be changed, look inside, mend the bond torn by pride."

Soon, they came upon an old stone arch with crossed axes carved on it – just like the Witch's ring. It led to an ancient ruin.

As they explored, Merida fell through a hole. She was in the throne room of a ruined castle. Merida saw a stone engraved with the pictures of four princes. The stone had been split in two – the fourth prince was broken off from the rest. "Split," Merida said. "Like the tapestry."

Suddenly, Merida realized that the Witch's prince had lived here – and he was the same prince of her mother's legend. "The strength of 10 men," she said, seeing that the room was covered in claw marks. "The prince became ... Mor'du!"

At that moment, Mor'du appeared. The demon bear lunged at Merida, but Elinor-Bear pulled her to safety just in time. They raced away from the ruins. Mother and daughter ran until they came to the Ring of Stones.

"I know what to do now," Merida said. She had to find the family tapestry that she had slashed and "mend the bond torn by pride."

The Witch's spell had shown Merida that she must learn to understand her mother's wishes, and fix what had broken between them.

DUMBO

The Best Gift Ever

Apart from Dumbo's mother, Mrs Jumbo, all the elephants at the circus made Dumbo feel like a nobody. They laughed at Dumbo's large ears and said that he would never amount to anything.

But Timothy Q. Mouse was different. Since the day he and Dumbo had met, Timothy had encouraged Dumbo. Dumbo was so happy to have a friend like Timothy. He wanted to do something nice for him.

So, one afternoon, Dumbo decided to give Timothy a gift. At feeding time, Dumbo put aside a bale of hay. Then he lugged the hay behind the Big Top and looked around for Timothy. Dumbo found him lounging in the shadow of the lion cage and plopped the hay bale down.

"Hiya, Dumbo!" said Timothy. "What's with the hay?"

Using his trunk, Dumbo nudged the hay bale closer to Timothy.

"For me?" Timothy said. "Wow. Uh … thanks. I, uh, wonder what I'll do with it all."

Dumbo's heart sank as he realized that mice didn't eat hay. And he wanted to give Timothy something he'd really like.

The next day, Dumbo came upon a patch of flowers growing just outside the elephants' tent. He picked a nice big bouquet and took it behind the Big Top to Timothy.

"Shucks, Dumbo," said Timothy. "You shouldn't have." Tiny Timothy took the flowers from Dumbo's outstretched trunk and promptly fell over, dropping the flowers everywhere.

"Oh dear, look what I did," said Timothy.

But Dumbo thought *he* was the one who should feel bad. The bouquet was too heavy for Timothy to enjoy.

The next day, under the Big Top, Dumbo spotted a bunch of balloons tied to a seat, left behind by one of the children. Balloons! thought Dumbo. Why, those wouldn't be too heavy for Timothy. They stayed up all by themselves. So Dumbo untied them and brought them to Timothy.

But, when Timothy took hold of the balloon strings, the helium-filled balloons lifted him right off the ground! Quickly, Dumbo reached out with his trunk, grasped Timothy around his waist, and placed him gently on the ground.

Then, with a disappointed sigh, Dumbo took the balloons back. Would he ever find a good gift for Timothy? he wondered.

"Dumbo," Timothy said, "I wanted to thank you for giving me the best gift ever."

Dumbo's eyes widened in surprise. What could Timothy mean? Every gift he had tried to give him had been all wrong.

"You're my best friend," Timothy said. "And that's the best gift I could ever ask for."

GREAT MOUSE DETECTIVE
Basil Saves the Day

It was Olivia Flaversham's birthday, and she was celebrating with her father. Suddenly, there was a knock on the door. It was late, and Mr Flaversham felt uneasy. He told Olivia to stay in a cabinet. Olivia peeked out and saw a scary bat. Soon she heard a commotion and ran out. But Olivia's father had been kidnapped!

Meanwhile, Dr David Q Dawson had just travelled to London. He heard someone weeping.

"Are you all right, my dear?" asked Dawson. Olivia explained she was looking for Basil, the great mouse detective.

"Come with me," said Dawson. "We'll find him together." The two mice soon found Basil and explained that Olivia needed help finding her father. Basil knew that the bat, named Fidget, was employed by his arch enemy, Professor Ratigan!

Later that evening, Basil paced back and forth. Just then, Olivia screamed! Fidget had appeared in the window. Basil, Olivia and Dawson raced outside and followed him to a toyshop. Basil noticed that mechanical parts were missing from many of the toys. Olivia wandered over to a pretty doll cradle. Curious, she peeked inside. Suddenly, Fidget jumped out and stuffed her into a bag and flew away! Now they had to save Olivia and her father!

Dawson showed him a piece of paper that Fidget had left behind. He discovered it came from the riverfront. They went there, spotted Fidget and followed the bat all the way to Ratigan's secret lair.

But Basil had walked right into a trap! Ratigan tied Basil and Dawson to a mousetrap. Ratigan left. He was sure the mice wouldn't escape.

Basil thought hard. He calculated the timing of the trap and came up with a brilliant idea that would save them.

"Ready … steady … now!" yelled Basil to Dawson. They escaped!

Basil and Dawson found Olivia and raced to Buckingham Palace. There they discovered what Ratigan was up to: he had forced Olivia's father to build a robot replica of the queen. Then Ratigan had replaced Queen Moustoria with the robot.

A huge crowd was listening to the robot queen. It was announcing that Professor Ratigan was her new royal consort! The crowd gasped in horror.

Offstage, Basil and Dawson finally took control of the robot queen. Ratigan's plan was foiled!

Basil rushed onstage and yelled, "Arrest that fiend!" Ratigan was defeated. Best of all, Olivia and her father were reunited.

A Deal with Vanellope

Wreck-It Ralph was in a racing game called *Sugar Rush*. He had just lost a race to a little girl called Vanellope, and she won his Heroes Medal from him! Ralph had left his own game and got the medal from a game called *Hero's Duty*, to try to prove that he was a Good Guy. In his own game, he was the Bad Guy … and he was fed up of it.

Inside Game Control, the Good Guy from Ralph's game – *Fix-It Felix, Jr* – was trying to find Ralph. He was with Sergeant Calhoun, the leader of the soldiers from *Hero's Duty*. Felix and Calhoun followed Ralph's trail of destruction into the tunnel leading to *Sugar Rush*.

Felix needed to bring Ralph home so that their game wouldn't be unplugged. Calhoun needed to capture the cy-bug that had escaped from *Hero's Duty* with Ralph – even one loose bug could endanger the entire arcade!

At the Sugar Rush Stadium, the Random Roster Race was about to begin! King Candy explained that each racer needed a coin to enter. The top finishers would appear as game characters in the arcade the next day. Vanellope stepped out of the shadows, and tossed Ralph's medal into the pot. She held her breath.

Vanellope's name appeared on the list of racers! The crowd gasped in shock. To them, Vanellope was a 'glitch', a mistake in the game's programming. No one wanted Vanellope and her rickety little kart to race. Quickly, King Candy ordered the Doughnut Police to take her away.

Just then, Ralph burst onto the track, desperate to find his medal. "Thief!" he cried at Vanellope. He chased after her, accidentally wrecking everything in his path.

Vanellope escaped, but Ralph was taken to King Candy's castle. The King told Ralph that the medal would belong to the winner of the next Random Roster Race, to be held later that night, once the racetrack was fixed. Then he ordered Ralph to leave *Sugar Rush*. But Ralph had other plans….

Ralph tracked Vanellope through the Lollistix Forest. But just as he was about to confront her, a group of other racers arrived. They demanded that Vanellope drop out of the race. Then they smashed her kart and tossed her in the mud! That made Ralph mad! He chased the mean racers away.

Afterwards, Vanellope promised that if she won the race, she'd give Ralph back his medal. But to win, she would need a new kart. Reluctantly, Ralph agreed to help … would he finally get his medal back…?

Paradise Falls

Carl had wanted to be an explorer ever since he was a child. So had his friend and wife, Ellie. He had promised Ellie that he'd take her to see Paradise Falls in South America one day.

But they were never able to save enough money to go. When they grew older, Ellie sadly passed away, and Carl was told he had to move out of his house.

But Carl decided he had to keep his promise to Ellie. He tied thousands of balloons to their little house and slowly it lifted into the sky.

Carl steered the flying house using ropes attached to the weather vane. He checked his compass and map, and set a course to Paradise Falls in South America.

"We're on our way, Ellie," he said happily.

Suddenly, there was a knock at the door. Carl was shocked. He was thousands of feet up in the air! Who could be at his door?

It was Russell! A Junior Wilderness Explorer who had knocked on his door a few days before. Carl had told him to find a Snipe – a bird that didn't really exist – just to get rid of him. Russell had been under Carl's porch, looking for the snipe, when the house lifted off.

"Please let me in!" Russell begged.

What choice did Carl have? He let Russell come inside.

Carl hated to stop, but he knew he had to land and send Russell home. He started to cut some of the balloons free.

Meanwhile, Russell was watching the clouds out of the window. "There's a big storm coming," he said. But Carl didn't hear him.

A flash of lightning lit up the room. Carl quickly tried to steer the house away from the storm, but it was too late. The little house tossed in the wind. Carl ran this way and that, trying to save Ellie's belongings. Finally, exhausted, he fell asleep.

When Carl woke up, the storm was over. "I steered us down," Russell told him proudly. "We're in South America."

As Carl and Russell stepped out onto the porch, the house crash-landed and sent them both flying. "My house!" Carl cried as it started to drift away from them. Grabbing hold of the garden hose, he and Russell managed to pull the house back down. Just then, the fog cleared. There, a short distance ahead, was Paradise Falls! It looked just like Ellie's picture!

"We made it!" Carl shouted. "We could float right over there!"

Carl was amazed. He had finally made the trip he and Ellie had always dreamed about.

Disney · PIXAR
FINDING NEMO

Finding Ne-who?

"The coral reef is falling down, falling down, falling down."

Nemo was home, brushing up against the anemone, when the most awful singing he ever heard in his life made him cringe. He swam deeper into the anemone, but it didn't help. The song went on.

"My fair octopus."

And there was something familiar about it…. Still cringing, Nemo poked his head out of the golden tentacles to see who was making the awful racket.

"Dory!" Nemo should have known. How could he have forgotten that voice? Nemo swam as fast as he could towards the regal blue tang fish. "Dory! Where have you been?" It seemed like a whale's age since Nemo had seen the fish that helped his dad rescue him from the dentist's fish tank. And he couldn't wait to give her a big hug!

When Nemo got closer Dory stopped singing. That was good. But when she looked at him her face was blank. That wasn't so good.

"Did you say something, kid?" she asked.

"Dory, it's me. Nemo," he replied.

"Ne-*who*?" She looked at Nemo blankly. "Sorry, kid, don't know you. I was just swimming by, minding my own business, singing a song. Hey, why was I singing? Am I famous? Maybe that's how you know me."

"Dory! We're friends, remember?" Nemo had been missing Dory a lot. She just *had* to remember who he was.

"Friends? I just made friends with a hermit crab … I think." Dory swam in a circle looking for the crab, but got distracted and started chasing her tail.

"Please try to remember, Dory," Nemo asked again. "You helped save me. You helped me find my dad. You know my dad. Big orange guy? Three white stripes? Looks kind of like me?"

"My dad? Looks like you? Sorry, kid, you don't look anything like my dad." Dory looked at Nemo like he was crazy and began to swim away.

Nemo swam after her. "Just think about it for a second," he pleaded. She *had* to remember something. "I'm Nemo!"

Dory did not turn around but she slowed down. Swimming in a wide circle, she came back. She looked at Nemo sideways, and then started laughing so hard bubbles came out of her nose.

"Had you going, huh?" Dory gave Nemo a big hug and smiled at him slyly. "That was just my little joke. You know I could never forget you!"

Nemo giggled and swam circles around his friend. "Good one, Dory!" He grinned.

Dory smiled back. "Good one, *who*?"

Nemo groaned. That Dory!

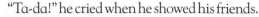

Simba's Thank You Present

Simba lounged in the jungle, feeling happier than he'd felt in ages. After the terrible stampede near Pride Rock, he didn't think he'd ever be happy again. But his new friends Timon and Pumbaa had helped him feel better.

"I should do something to thank them," Simba told himself as he watched his friends in the river nearby. "Something really special!"

He decided to make them a present. When he saw a piece of bark lying on the ground, he had an idea.

"Ta-da!" he exclaimed a while later, leading his friends to the gift.

Pumbaa blinked. "Thanks," he said. "Er, what is it?"

"A scratching spot," Simba said, flexing his claws. He'd used vines to attach it to a thick tree trunk at shoulder height.

"Gee," Timon said. "Nice thought and all, Simba. But it's a little high for me." He stretched to his full height but could barely reach it.

Pumbaa nodded. "And I don't scratch." He held up one foot. "Hooves, you know."

"Oh." Simba hadn't thought of that.

"Thanks anyway, kid," Pumbaa said.

Simba decided to try again by building them a nice, soft bed to sleep in. He dug a cosy hole in the ground, then filled it with soft things – feathers, sand and bits of fur.

"Ta-da!" he cried when he showed his friends.

Timon sighed. "What are you trying to do, kill us? Prey animals here, remember? If we sleep on the ground, we become somebody's midnight snack!"

Simba sighed as they left again. Why couldn't he think of a present they would like?

"I would've loved that scratching spot," he mumbled. "The bed, too."

Suddenly he sat up straight, realizing what he'd just said. All this time he'd been thinking of presents HE would like – but the presents weren't for him.

"I've got to think like they think," he whispered. Slowly, a smile spread across his face….

A little while later he called them over. "I've got something for you." He pointed to a pile of palm fronds. "I think you're really going to like it. Ta-da!"

He pulled back the leaves. Underneath was a mass of wriggling, squirming, creeping, crawling creatures – bugs and grubs and worms of every shape and size … and flavour.

Timon and Pumbaa gasped with delight. "Simba!" Timon cried. "You're a prince! It's just what we always wanted!"

"Yeah, thanks," Pumbaa mumbled through a mouthful of grubs. "You're a real pal!"

Simba smiled. "No," he said. "Thank *you*. Both of you. *Hakuna matata!*"

Mater Saves the Day

Two British secret agents, Finn and Holley, had mistaken Mater for an American secret agent, and he was helping them track the activities of a criminal, Professor Z. The professor was blowing up racecars that used the new alternative fuel, Allinol, so that everyone would go back to using oil. This would mean the Lemons – bad cars who ran the oil reserves – would be rich and powerful!

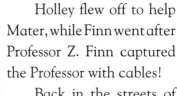

Lightning McQueen was taking part in the World Grand Prix, and races had already taken place in Japan and Italy. Lightning and Mater had argued after the first race. Mater had left to go home, but instead he had gone with Finn and Holley – now the three of them were tied up inside a huge clock called Big Bentley in London!

Professor Z's goons, Grem and Acer, told Mater that they had planted a bomb inside Lightning's pit at the final race. Lightning was using Allinol, so they wanted to blow him up. After the pair left, Mater escaped and rushed to save his friend. Finn and Holley soon broke free, too. Then they realized the bomb was actually on Mater!

As Mater arrived at the pits, Finn radioed the tow truck to tell him the bomb was on him. Mater tried to leave the pits to save his friend, but Lightning was so happy to see Mater, he hooked himself onto his buddy. Mater rocketed off before Professor Z could set off the bomb.

Holley flew off to help Mater, while Finn went after Professor Z. Finn captured the Professor with cables!

Back in the streets of London, Grem and Acer were about to crash into Mater and Lightning. Holley rammed into the bad cars, who went flying into the air! Finn arrived with Professor Z and ordered him to deactivate the bomb on Mater. Professor Z told Finn that only the one who activated the bomb could turn it off – and that was not the Professor.

Other Lemons arrived to get rid of Finn, Holley, Mater and Lightning for good. But the Radiator Springs crew came to the rescue!

Just then, Mater figured out who the Lemons' Big Boss must be. He flew straight to Buckingham Palace with Lightning attached to his tow hook! Mater explained that Miles Axlerod had invented Allinol and made it look dangerous so everyone would go back to using gas. Then Axlerod and all the Lemons who owned the supply of oil would get rich! Axlerod was trapped, and had no choice but to deactivate the bomb. Mater had saved the day! No one was prouder of him than Lightning.

Street Cats

"Oh, Mama!" said Marie dreamily. "Paris is so pretty in the morning! May we please go explore just a bit?" The kittens and their mother had spent the previous night in Mr O'Malley's swinging bachelor flat, and were now making their way through the streets of Paris back to Madame's house.

"All right, darlings," their mother replied. "But just for a few minutes. Madame must be missing us terribly. Be sure to stick together!"

They passed a doorway to a jazz hall, where the previous night's party appeared to be still in full swing. "Oh, yeah!" said Toulouse as he danced in the doorway to the swinging beat.

"Come on, Toulouse," said Berlioz crossly. "I'm hungry!"

A few steps down the block, a fishmonger was just setting out his wares in the window of his shop. The three kittens put their paws on the windowsill, licking their lips as they watched him lay out the gleaming fish. The fishmonger smiled at them through the window, then came out of his shop and tossed them each a sardine. "Here you are, my pretty cats!" he said to them.

Yum! Sardines! The three meowed back a thank you and gobbled up the tasty treat.

"The streets of Paris are the coolest place on Earth!" said Berlioz as they continued walking. "I don't want to go back to Madame's house!"

"Berlioz! You mustn't speak like that!" said Marie. "You know how much Madame needs us…." Suddenly, she broke off. Her brothers followed her gaze, which was directed at the window of a fancy pet shop. "Oh, my!" she cried out delightedly. "Look at those!" In the window of the shop were several jewelled cat collars, all in different shades of the finest leather. Marie thought they were simply beautiful – especially the pink one. "I must say, the streets of Paris are a wonderful place!" Marie said dreamily.

Just then, they heard a deep barking. A moment later, a huge dog came bounding around the corner. The kittens froze in fear for a moment. Then all three of them turned and scampered back down the street in the direction of their mother and Mr O'Malley, with the dog hot on their heels.

"Paris is a fine city," said Berlioz, panting, as he raced down an alleyway. Darting behind some dustbins, the kittens were able to lose the snarling dog.

"Yes," replied Marie. "But I'm not sure how I feel about the Parisians – particularly the canine kind!"

DISNEY·PIXAR
MONSTERS, INC.
Monster Day Care

Mike always arrived at Monsters, Inc. at half past eight, put his lunch box in his locker and promptly reported to his station on the Laugh Floor. But one morning, as he came out of the locker room, there was Celia. "We have a little problem, Mike," she said. "The day care teacher is sick today, so we need a sub. And seeing as how you've already met your laugh quota for the month, I thought maybe *you –* "

"Day care!" cried Mike. "Wait just a – "

Just then Sulley stepped in. "Happy to do it, Celia," he interrupted. "Day care, here we come."

"Are you crazy?" Mike grumbled.

"What's the big deal?" Sulley shrugged. "We handled Boo, didn't we? What's a few more kids? We'll eat a few snacks. Watch a few videos. Play a little peekaboo. It's like having a paid holiday, Mike, my man!"

But the minute they opened the day care room door, they both knew Sulley was wrong....

There were monster children everywhere! Swinging from the ceiling. Slithering up the walls. Bouncing from corner to corner. Mike's and Sulley's jaws dropped open. What were they going to do?

Sulley took a deep breath. "We just have to let them know who's in charge, is all," he told Mike. "Okay, kids!" he announced. "Uncles Sulley and Mike are here. It's time to settle down."

But, instead of settling down, the little monsters dived for Sulley and Mike, yelling, "Horsey rides! Yeah!" and "Play ball!"

"I think they know who's in charge," Mike said as an oversized, six-handed monster child scooped him up and tossed him to his twin. *"Help!"*

Sulley quickly intercepted Mike and set him back down on his feet.

"'Paid holiday', my eye," muttered Mike.

"All we need to do," said Sulley calmly, "is get their attention. Let's see … a video?" But the TV was too covered with monster slime and finger paint for anyone to watch it.

A snack? No. Every cracker and fright roll-up had been gobbled up long before.

A story? Of course! Except a four-eyed toddler seemed to be happily tearing the pages out of each and every book.

"How about a song?" said Mike finally.

"Great idea!" said Sulley. And do you know what? It was! They sang "The Huge Gigantic Spider" and "The Wheels on the Monster Bus". Before long even Mike was having fun.

"What did I say, Sulley? I said it'd be like paid holiday, and it is! I don't understand why you were so reluctant," Mike said.

Sulley rolled his eyes. "Whatever you say, Mike."

HERCULES

Bring a Friend

Hercules was training to be a hero, and it was a lot of work. One day, Phil, his coach, set up a practice course for Hercules and then tied his student's hands behind his back. Herc had to run the course with no hands!

Phil had put a doll at the end of the course. He said it was a "practice damsel in distress," and Hercules was supposed to rescue it. So the hero-in-training rushed into the first section of the course – a darkened cave. Herc plunged into darkness and fell headlong into stagnant water.

"Yech!" Hercules spat out the putrid water and scowled. He wanted to be a hero more than anything. But sometimes Phil made things a little more difficult than necessary.

Feeling his way in the darkness with his feet, Herc noticed something slithery slipping around his ankles. Snakes!

Herc shook several of the water snakes out of his sandals. He hurried towards the other end of the cave and dived into the daylight, shaking the last snake off his feet. Panting, Herc lay down on the grass to rest for a moment.

"Rest later!" Phil shouted.

Herc rolled slowly over. The doll had to be around here somewhere. Behind him Hercules heard more stamping hooves and turned around. A huge ox was thundering towards him!

Herc jumped to his feet. He dodged the ox, but another was on his heels. Spotting the damsel at last, Herc leaped over the second ox. The doll was sitting 20 feet above him on the edge of a steep cliff.

At least Phil had left him a rope. In fact, it looked as though Phil had left two. Gripping the first rope in his jaws, Herc inched steadily upward. He was about halfway up when Phil lit the end of the second rope, which was soaked with oil! The fire raced up the rope towards a stack of dry wood under Herc's damsel.

Hercules threw himself the last few feet. He tackled the damsel, rolling away from the stack of wood, which was now blazing merrily away.

Breathing hard, Hercules finally relaxed.

"And another thing …" Phil's gruff voice echoed up to him from the base of the cliff. Hercules held his breath, but not because he was waiting for Phil's next words. Herc was holding his breath because he had spotted a scorpion next to his foot. The insect was poised to sting!

Crunch. Hercules' winged horse Pegasus used his hoof to flatten the creature.

Hercules smiled at Pegasus as Phil's final words of advice reached his ears. It was the best tip yet: "Always bring a friend!"

Disney
Lady and the TRAMP

Howling at the Moon

Lady had been having a really bad day. First, she'd had a run-in with two nasty cats. Then, she'd been put in a horrible muzzle. But, because of Tramp, everything had changed.

"It's amazing how a day can start off terribly but end wonderfully," Lady told Tramp as they trotted through the moonlit park. "Thank you for helping me escape that terrible muzzle – and for dinner at Tony's."

"Aw, shucks, don't mention it!" said Tramp. "Hey, you wanna have some real fun?"

"I don't know," Lady said cautiously.

While she was very fond of Tramp, she also knew they were very different dogs. Tramp was used to life on the streets. So his idea of 'fun' might be very different from hers.

"Don't worry," Tramp teased. "This is something I think you'll enjoy."

"What is it?" asked Lady.

"Well, for starters, you have to look up," said Tramp.

Lady did. The sky was filled with stars and a big, bright moon.

"What am I looking for?" she asked.

"The moon, of course!" cried Tramp. "Haven't you ever howled at the moon?"

Lady laughed at Tramp's suggestion.

"What's so funny?" asked Tramp.

"I'm a practical dog," explained Lady. "I bark politely when the situation calls for it, but I don't see any point in howling at the moon."

"Why not?" asked Tramp.

"Well," said Lady, "what's the use of it?"

"You know, Lady," said Tramp, "a thing doesn't have to be useful to be fun. You like to chase a ball, right?"

"Right," said Lady.

"So, there you go," said Tramp. "Sometimes it's good to chase a ball. And sometimes it's good to just let go and howl at the moon, even for no reason."

Lady thought it over. "Okay," she said. "What do I do?"

"First, sit up real straight," said Tramp. "Then, look up at the moon, take a deep breath, and just let all the troubles of your day disappear in one gigantic howl!" He demonstrated: "Ow-ow-OWWWWWWW!"

Lady joined Tramp and howled as loudly as she could.

"You're right!" she cried. "It does feel good to howl at the moon!"

"Stick with me, kid," said Tramp. "I know what's what."

Lady suspected Tramp did know what was what, but there was an even better reason for her to stick with him. He'd become the very best friend she'd ever had.

Peter Pan

The Lost Boys Get Lost

The Lost Boys were walking single file through the woods of Never Land, on their way home after an afternoon of adventure-seeking, when Slightly, who led the way, stopped in his tracks on the bank of Mermaid Lagoon.

The others – Rabbit, the Raccoon Twins, Cubby and Tootles – came to an abrupt halt behind him.

"Wait a minute," said Slightly. "We already passed Mermaid Lagoon. What are we doing here again?"

Behind a bush, Tinker Bell giggled as she watched the Lost Boys looking around in confusion.

Tink had spotted them on their march and had not been able to resist playing a joke. So, she had flown ahead of them and used her fairy magic to enchant various landmarks on their route home. She had made Bald Rock look like Spiky Rock, causing the Lost Boys to make a right turn where they should have turned left. Then she had enlisted the help of the sparrows, convincing them to move from their usual perch in the Sparrow Bird Grove to another group of trees, thus tricking the Lost Boys into making another right turn too soon. And finally, she had enchanted the Towering Elm Tree to look exactly like the Weeping Willow, and the Lost Boys had made yet another wrong turn, thinking they were nearly home.

But now, here they were, walking past Mermaid Lagoon, when Slightly remembered passing the same spot a good while back.

"I think we're walking in circles!" Slightly proclaimed. "Lost Boys, I think we're … lost!"

Tinker Bell overheard and tried desperately to stifle her laughter. But, before she could contain it, one giggle exploded into a fully fledged laugh and –

"Hey!" said Cubby. "Did you hear that?"

He darted over to a bush growing alongside the path and moved a branch to one side. There was Tinker Bell, hovering in mid-air, holding her stomach and shaking with laughter.

"Tinker Bell!" cried Tootles.

It didn't take them long to work out that Tinker Bell was laughing at *them* – and that she was the cause of their confusion.

Still laughing, Tinker Bell flitted away, taking her normal route home to the fairy glade: left at the Weeping Willow Tree, right just before Sparrow Bird Grove, right again at Spiky Rock, and on towards the Sparkling Stream, which led to Moon Falls and the fairy glade entrance.

But – wait a minute! After turning right at Spiky Rock, Tinker Bell saw no sign of the Sparkling Stream anywhere. Where was she? She had got completely lost.

Do you know how?

The Prospector

Buzz had organized a rescue mission to Al's Toy Barn to save Woody – the cowboy doll had been stolen! Al wanted to sell the whole *Woody's Roundup* gang to a Japanese museum, for a lot of money!

But after meeting the rest of the *Woody's Roundup* gang, Woody had started to think that maybe he'd be better off at the museum. Soon, Andy might stop loving him and playing with him. Sadly, Buzz and Andy's other toys were forced to leave Woody behind.

Soon after, though, Woody realized Buzz was right – he belonged with Andy. He ran to the vent and called for his friends to return. Then he turned to the *Roundup* gang.

"Come with me," he said. "Andy will play with all of us, I know it!"

Jessie and Bullseye were excited … but the Prospector blocked their path! After a lifetime in his box, he was determined to go to the museum. "And no hand-me-down cowboy doll is gonna mess it up for me now!" he shouted.

Suddenly, they heard footsteps – Al was coming! The toys stopped moving.

Al packed Woody and the *Roundup* gang into a case, and dashed out of the door. He was late for his flight to Japan.

"Quick! To the elevator!" Buzz shouted, hoping to catch up. But on the roof of the lift, Emperor Zurg refused to let them pass! As Zurg attacked the group with his blaster, Rex turned away, terrified – and knocked Zurg off the lift with his tail!

"I did it! I finally defeated Zurg!" Rex cried happily.

The moment Zurg was gone, the toys rushed to the lift's emergency hatch. Looking down, they saw Al, still inside the lift.

While Buzz held onto his legs, Slinky stretched down to Al's case. Swinging closer, he undid the latches and grabbed hold of Woody's arms.

But then the Prospector popped up – and yanked Woody back down again! A moment later, the elevator doors opened at ground floor. Al hurried outside, with the *Roundup* gang still in his case.

Andy's toys sprinted into the car park, but Al had already jumped into his car and driven off. How would they rescue Woody now?

New Buzz had just discovered that Zurg was his father, so he decided to stay behind with his dad. But everyone else hopped into an empty Pizza Planet delivery van that was nearby. Real Buzz handled the steering while Rex navigated and Slinky accelerated.

Soon they were swerving through traffic, hot on the trail of Al's car!

Baloo's Secret Weapon

Mowgli and his pal Baloo were taking a lazy afternoon stroll through the jungle. Suddenly, Mowgli stopped in his tracks. "Did you hear that?" he asked.

"Hear what, little buddy?" Baloo asked.

"It sounded like twigs snapping," Mowgli said. "I think somebody might be following us!"

"That was just your old Papa Bear's stomach growling," Baloo told him. "It's time for some lunch."

"And I know just where to get it," announced Mowgli. He shimmied up a tree, plucked a bunch of bananas, and tossed them down to the bear.

"That's my boy!" Baloo cried proudly.

But, as he was scrambling back down, Mowgli spotted a flash of orange and black.

"Shere Khan!" Mowgli whispered to Baloo. "We've got to get out of here!" The tiger had been after Mowgli ever since the boy had first set foot in the jungle.

The two friends didn't know which way to turn. Now that Shere Khan had their scent, it would be almost impossible to lose him. Then they both heard a lively beat drumming its way through the jungle.

"Oh, no," said Mowgli. "King Louie and his crazy band of monkeys. That's all we need!"

Baloo's eyes suddenly lit up. "That's *exactly* what we need, Little Britches!"

Still clutching the bananas, Baloo and Mowgli ran towards King Louie's compound. When they arrived, Baloo disguised himself as a monkey. The orang-utans were so busy dancing and singing they didn't notice his disguise. Then the bear quickly found a huge empty barrel, and filled it with the bananas.

"Look!" cried Baloo, peering into the barrel. "Lunch!" The monkeys ran over and jumped right into the barrel! They greedily ate the feast, tossing peels out as they made their way through the bunch.

Baloo signalled to Mowgli, who came out of hiding. "Come and get me, Shere Khan!" the Man-cub taunted.

Within seconds, the tiger appeared in the clearing, a fierce gleam in his eye. "Hello, Stripes," Baloo greeted him cheerfully. Then the bear picked up the barrel, heaved it, and sent King Louie's troop flying at Shere Khan. The orangutans landed on the tiger's back, where they frantically jumped up and down, pulling on his tail and ears. Mowgli and Baloo watched as Shere Khan raced back into the jungle, trying to free himself from his shrieking passengers.

"Like I always say," Baloo declared as he grinned at Mowgli, "there's nothing more fun than a barrel of monkeys!"

Monster Truck Mater

One day outside Flo's V8 Café, Lightning McQueen pointed out a monster truck that was driving by.

"I used to wrestle trucks bigger than that," Mater said. He began to tell Lightning about the time he was a wrestler called The Tormentor. His first match was in an arena filled with cheering fans. Mater wore a blue-and-red mask.

An ice cream truck with monster wheels rolled into the ring. The Tormentor wasn't sure how to wrestle such a big truck. So he put on a cap, hoping to trick his opponent instead. "Can I have one double-dip sundae, please?"

"Huh?" said the I-Screamer. "Oh, sure." When the ice cream truck reached for a sundae, The Tormentor grabbed his bumper with his tow hook and flipped him. The referee announced that The Tormentor had won.

After his first win, The Tormentor just couldn't stop winning, and soon he made it all the way to The World Championship! He was feeling confident until he saw ... Dr Frankenwagon's Monster! Just one of the Monster's tyres was bigger than the Tormentor. He had a giant scoop on one side and a claw on the other. The wrecking ball on his back could crush a truck with one direct hit.

Back in Radiator Springs, Lightning interrupted the story. "Whoa!" he cried. "What did you do?"

Mater looked over at his friend. "Don't you remember nothin'? We was a tag team."

Mater continued his story, except this time, Lightning was also in the ring, wearing his own wrestling outfit.

"Tag, you're it!" said Mater, touching Lightning with his tyre. The Monster lunged for the race car, ignoring the tow truck.

Lightning saw their opponent coming straight at him. Lightning raced around the ring to avoid the Monster's wrecking ball. When the Tormentor heard Lightning call for help he ducked back into the ring. Luckily, the Tormentor had a plan.

While the Monster's wrecking ball was on the ground, the Tormentor quickly snagged it with his tow hook. Then he zipped under one side of the ring and out the other. With a wink at his fans, the Tormentor yanked his towline. He flipped the entire ring – trapping the Monster underneath!

"The winners!" the referee announced. "The Tormentor and ..." He turned to Lightning. "What's your name?"

"Lightning McQueen," he replied.

"And Frightening McMean!"

Funny Faces

Hugo, Victor and Laverne were gargoyles at the great Cathedral of Notre Dame. Most of the time they were stone, but they came to life in the presence of Quasimodo, the bell ringer at Notre Dame. Although they were all good friends, Hugo and Victor were always finding something to bicker over, and today was no exception.

"That's ridiculous!" Hugo snapped at Victor.

"No, *you're* ridiculous!" Victor shot back.

Victor had suggested that Quasimodo tell Frollo, the Minister of Justice and Quasi's master, that he wanted to take some time off. Hugo had pointed out that Frollo would sooner become a gypsy than give Quasimodo a holiday. Then the argument had really taken off.

"Well, you started it," Hugo told him.

"I started it?" Victor asked.

"That's right, stone face!" Hugo shouted.

"Who are you calling stone face? Blockhead!" Victor fought back.

Suddenly, a loud whistle interrupted them.

"May I have your attention, please?" Laverne said. "I would like to propose a way for you to settle this dispute like gentlemen."

"What is it?" Quasi asked.

"A face-making contest," Laverne said. "Here are the rules. You two take turns making faces at each other, and the first to make the other laugh, wins!"

"I'm going first!" declared Hugo, sticking his tongue out at Victor.

"Child's play," said Victor scornfully. He crossed his eyes at Hugo.

"Ha!" said Hugo. "Try resisting *this*!" Hugo crossed his eyes, flared his nostrils, and stuck his lower jaw out, baring a crooked row of teeth in a hideous grimace.

Victor managed to keep a straight face at this, but Quasimodo couldn't help but laugh out loud.

"Shh!" Laverne said. "Frollo's coming!"

"Frollo?" Hugo and Victor grew pale and quickly turned back to stone.

Just then, Frollo marched in. "What's going on up here?" he asked Quasimodo.

"Nothing, sir," Quasi said, trying not to laugh. He was having a hard time keeping a straight face because, behind Frollo, Victor and Hugo were still busy making faces at each other, each trying to make the other laugh.

"Hmm," said Frollo suspiciously. As he turned to go, Victor and Hugo stopped making faces at each other, and began making funny faces at Frollo's back. When he was out of sight, all four friends collapsed with laughter.

"You know what," Quasi told them. "I have so much fun with you guys, it beats going on holiday!"

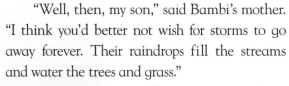

Bambi

Rain, Rain, Go Away

Rrrrumble, rrrrumble, *BOOM!* The loud clap of thunder startled Bambi and his friends.

"I don't like thunderstorms!" cried Thumper, looking a little scared.

"I don't like them either!" exclaimed Flower.

"Bambi!" called his mother as the clouds grew dark and the rain began to fall. Bambi followed his mother out of the open meadow and into the woods. From their warm, dry thicket, Bambi watched sheets of rain pour down.

"I don't like thunderstorms," he told his mother, echoing Thumper's words. "I wish the storm would go away and never come back again."

"Oh, my," said his mother. "Do you mean you never again want to drink the cool, fresh water from the forest stream?"

"Well, no," said Bambi.

"Then, do you want the big trees to go thirsty? Their leaves to wither and branches to become brittle?" asked his mother.

"No! Of course not!" cried Bambi. "The trees give us shelter, and their branches give the birds a place to make their nests."

"Then, do you want the sweet grass to turn brown?" asked his mother.

"No," said Bambi. "We eat the grass. We'd go hungry if that happened!"

"Well, then, my son," said Bambi's mother. "I think you'd better not wish for storms to go away forever. Their raindrops fill the streams and water the trees and grass."

"But storms are so scary," Bambi said.

Just then, the rain began to let up, and Bambi's friends scampered through the underbrush and into Bambi's thicket.

"Look at the pond!" cried Flower.

Bambi peered through the thicket. The pond was alive with activity. The frogs were leaping and playing. And a family of ducks was shaking their feathers and waddling into the water.

"Uh-oh," said Thumper. "That old bullfrog's gonna get a surprise."

Bambi watched the lily pad with the big bullfrog drift closer and closer to the line of ducklings. The last duckling wasn't paying attention. The sudden collision sent the frog toppling off its lily pad with a startled *croak!* and surprised the duckling so much it did an underwater somersault!

Bambi, Thumper and Flower laughed.

"I guess I like thunderstorms after all," Bambi told his mother.

"You didn't like thunderstorms?" said Thumper. "That's silly! Why would you ever say a thing like that?"

Disney·PIXAR

MONSTERS, INC.

The Spooky Sleepover

It was a quiet morning at Monsters, Inc. Sulley had arrived early to catch up on paperwork when he got a phone call from dispatch. "Annual slumber party at Shannon Brown's house. Waxford is out sick. We need a replacement."

"I'll get right on it," replied Sulley. He knew there would be a lot of kids at the party, and he wanted to make sure he had a monster there to tell jokes and capture laughs. Who better for the job than his one-eyed pal, Mike?

Mike was in the locker room getting ready for work when Sulley entered and explained the situation.

"Piece of cake," Mike said as a door slid into his station on the Laugh Floor. Then Mike walked through the wardrobe in Shannon Brown's room. It was empty. "Uh ... hello?" Mike called. Just as Mike started to leave, he heard the sound of laughter.

Just then, thunder cracked across the sky. Mike ran to the wardrobe door to return to the factory. He jiggled the doorknob, but it just opened into the wardrobe, not the Laugh Floor at Monsters, Inc.!

Mike soon realized that lightning must have struck the door and broken it. He took a deep breath and headed into the hallway.

Meanwhile, back at Monsters, Inc., Sulley was working on the Laugh Floor. The floor manager came running over. "Sulley!" he shouted. "Mike hasn't returned from the slumber party. He's never been gone this long!"

When Sulley went to check on the door, he saw it had broken and brought someone in to fix it. After a few hours, the door was working! Now it would open into a different room at Shannon's house.

Back at Shannon's, Mike heard laughing down the hall. When he found the right room and went in, it was quiet. Slowly, Mike entered the dark, silent room. All of a sudden, a light went on! Mike jumped. Shannon Brown and all her friends started roaring with laughter! They thought Mike looked funny sneaking into the room. Mike screamed in fright.

At that exact moment, the wardrobe door opened and Sulley burst into the room. Sulley was so surprised to find Mike screaming that all he could do was scream too! Then he and Mike huddled in fright. Shannon and her friends laughed even harder.

"Looks as if our work here is done," Sulley said to Mike.

"I was never scared for a second," said Mike.

"Me neither, buddy," Sulley replied, his fingers crossed behind his back. "Me neither."

Flik Wings It

Flik knew that Hopper and his gang of hungry grasshoppers would soon come to steal all the food from the peaceful ants of Ant Island. So Flik headed off to the big city to find warrior bugs to help fight the grasshoppers.

On his way, Flik saw a shiny dragonfly flutter across the sky.

"Wow, I wish I could fly like that!" he exclaimed.

Suddenly, Flik had an idea. "I built a harvester that harvests pretty well. I wonder if I could invent a flying machine?"

Flik got to work. He gathered sticks and vines and leaves. He found a mushroom cap to use for a seat, and a long red feather for a tail.

When he had gathered all the parts, Flik began to strap the pieces together.

After lots of hard work, Flik took a step back and studied his invention.

"Well, it certainly *looks* like it could fly," Flik said finally. "It has wings that flap and a long red tail."

The frame of Flik's flier was made of twigs, and the wings were made of leaves. The whole machine was tied together with strong vines.

"Time for a test flight," Flik decided.

He climbed onto the mushroom cap seat and used a vine as a safety belt. Then he put his feet on the little pedals and started to pump. Faster and faster, the green wings began to flap. Soon, Flik's flier began to rock; then it leaped into the sky!

"It's working!" Flik cried. He was flying! With the air racing between his antennae, Flik watched the world flash under his feet. He saw frogs and turtles and other creatures that ate ants.

"Flying is so much safer than walking," said Flik.

But he spoke too soon, for high in the sky above Flik a mother bird was teaching her three little hatchlings how to fly. She spied Flik's strange-looking contraption and thought one thing – dinner!

Flik looked up and saw the mother bird and her babies coming down on him like dive bombers!

"Test flight over!" Flik cried.

Pedalling faster, Flik steered his flier through the limbs of a tall tree. The mother bird and two of her babies were blocked by the branches. But the third baby bird raced between the leaves and caught up with Flik.

Pecking wildly, the little bird ripped a wing from Flik's flier. Spinning out of control, the machine crashed to the ground.

Luckily for Flik, he had also invented a parachute out of a spider's web, and he made a soft landing in the middle of a daisy.

"Another failed invention," Flik said with a sigh. "Maybe someday I'll have a chance to make a flying machine that really works!"

An Ice Skating Game

Mickey woke up and looked outside. It had snowed last night! "It's a perfect day for ice skating!" he cried. "I'll invite all my friends to come."

On the way, Mickey picked up Goofy, Donald, Daisy, Huey, Dewey, Louie and Minnie. When they got to the pond, everyone laced up their skates and made their way to the ice. It was as smooth as glass. The friends began skating around and around.

"Hey, I have an idea!" shouted Mickey. "Let's play crack the whip!"

Nobody else knew how to play, so Mickey explained the game. "I'll start out as the leader," he said. "We all join hands and form a line. Then we all skate around and around in a big circle. Once we get going, the skater at the end of the line lets go!"

"That sounds like fun!" said Goofy.

"Cool!" cried Huey, Dewey and Louie.

They all joined hands and began skating in a circle. Around and around and around they went. Donald was at the end of the line.

"Okay, Donald, let go!" shouted Mickey. Donald let go and went sailing away.

Around and around and around the rest of the gang went.

"Now, you go, Daisy!" cried Mickey. Daisy let go and went flying away across the ice.

Next went Huey, then Dewey, and finally Louie. Goofy followed them.

Now just Mickey and Minnie were left. Around and around they skated. Then Mickey shouted, "Let go, Minnie!"

Minnie let go and zoomed off with a squeal.

Mickey was having a fine time. Now all alone, he began to spin around and around and around. When he finally came to a stop, it took quite some time for his head to stop spinning. "Wasn't that fun, guys?" he said. "Want to do it again? Guys? Where is everyone?"

Mickey looked around. Where had everyone gone? And then he saw them. Seven pairs of ice skates at the ends of seven pairs of legs were sticking out of seven different snowbanks, kicking away.

"Uh-oh," said Mickey. He dashed over to the side of the pond and, one by one, he pulled all of his friends out of the snow.

"Gee, sorry about that," said Mickey.

Goofy shook his head, and snow flew everywhere. "That was fun!" he said cheerfully. "But I sure could use a cup of –"

"Yoo-hoo!" came a cheerful cry. It was Grandma Duck, standing at the edge of the pond. She was carrying a flask filled with hot chocolate!

"Hooray!" cried all the friends.

Disney·PIXAR

MONSTERS, INC.

Tough Audience

The sticker on the door read: ENTER AT YOUR OWN RISK. But Mike wasn't scared. He always collected the most laughs on the floor and he had never met a child he couldn't crack … up. Tossing his microphone from one hand to the other, Mike sauntered through the wardrobe door to face his audience.

"Hey, how ya doin' tonight?" Mike greeted the child. The boy in the racing -car pyjamas just glared. "Did you hear the one about the monster who made it in show business? He really clawed his way to the top." Mike paused for a laugh, but the boy was silent. "Talk about making a killing!" Mike added. Still he got nothing.

"All right. I can see you're a tough audience. Enough of the B material." Mike pulled out the stops. He told his best jokes. He worked the room. He was on the stool, off the stool, hanging on the curtains, standing on the bedstead. But the child didn't even crack a smile.

Mike prepared to let the one about the seven-legged sea monster fly, when he heard tapping on the wardrobe door.

"You know you really ought to get that checked." Mike pointed at the wardrobe. "You could have skeletons in there." The child didn't blink.

Mike pulled the door open a crack. "I'm working here," he whispered.

Sulley poked his head in. "Mikey, you're dying. You've been on for 20 minutes and you're getting nothing. There are plenty of other kids to make laugh tonight. You can come back to this one later."

"No way," Mike hissed. "He loves me. When he laughs he's going to laugh big. I can feel it." A teddy bear sailed through the air and hit Mike in the eye. "See? He's throwing me presents."

"Cut your losses, Mikey. Let this one go." Sulley put a large hairy paw on Mike's head and urged him back through the door.

"I'm telling you, I've almost got him," Mike spoke through clenched teeth, and barely flinched when the unamused boy tossed a banana peel at him.

"And I'm telling you to give … it … up." Sulley pulled harder on Mike. Mike grabbed the door frame and braced himself. Suddenly Sulley lost his grip, and Mike flew backwards, skidding on the banana peel and falling flat out.

"Why, I oughta…." Mike leaped to his feet ready to charge Sulley but was interrupted by the sound of laughing. In fact, the child was laughing so hard tears streamed down his face. Mike high-fived Sulley. "You know, some kids just go for the physical comedy," he said with a shrug.

Friends to the End

Dusty's race over the Pacific had been filled with danger. His antenna had been broken, so none of the other flyers or race officials knew where he was!

Meanwhile, the other racers had already arrived in Mexico. One reporter asked Ripslinger what he thought about the fact that Dusty had disappeared.

"Dusty was a nice guy who flew the challenge and pierced the clouds of mediocrity," Ripslinger replied. "We're all going to miss him."

Dusty was fighting his way across the Pacific. Rain pounded down on him and lightning flashed in his path. He was flying so low that a wave crashed over him. He made a desperate call for help before he was swept underwater!

A Mexican navy helicopter arrived just in time. After pulling him out of the water, the helicopter brought a battered Dusty to the hangar in Mexico. Dusty was in really bad shape. His worried friends, who had come to Mexico to see him, surrounded him.

Dusty looked at Skipper. During his flight, Skipper's navy friends had come to Dusty's rescue and Dusty had found out that Skipper had lied about his past. "One mission? So much for 'Volo Pro Veritas'," Dusty said.

That was the motto that Skipper had taught him. It meant 'I fly for truth'.

Skipper asked everyone to leave. Then he told Dusty about his one mission. He had lost his whole squadron during it. After that, he was too afraid to fly again – the memories were just too horrible.

Dusty felt upset and betrayed by his coach. All this time, Skipper had been lying to Dusty.

"At least *you* were honest," Dusty told Dottie, his mechanic. "You said I wasn't built for this."

Dottie told him that she was wrong. "You're a racer," she said. "And now the whole world knows it!"

Dusty couldn't fly in the bad condition he was in. But his competitors had grown to love Dusty and they decided they didn't want to race without him. To his surprise, they brought him the parts he needed. Ishani even gave him the new propeller she had received from Ripslinger! Dottie got out her tools and set to work. Soon Dusty was better than ever and ready to race again.

Meanwhile, Chug was watching race footage of Ripslinger. He noticed something that he thought could help Dusty win. Dusty was grateful for the tip!

The race was on!

Miss Bianca's First Rescue

The headquarters of the Rescue Aid Society was buzzing with activity. Mice from all over the world had gathered together for an emergency meeting. The Chairman of the Society had to shout to be heard over the hubbub.

"Attention, delegates!" he cried. "I have called this meeting because a canine urgently needs our help." He clapped his hands. "Mice scouts, bring in the distressed doggie!"

Two mice workers hurried into the room, leading a small dog with a long body and short little legs. His head was stuck inside a dog food can.

"*Mama mia!*" cried the mouse from Italy.

"Arooooo!" howled the dog.

The mouse from Yemen suggested pulling the can off the dog. Four muscular mice set to work, pulling and tugging. But it held fast.

The mice finally decided that the can would have to be removed by mechanical means. The Zambian delegate suggested using a can opener.

Suddenly the door to the meeting room flew open. There stood a pretty little mouse. She wore a fashionable coat and expensive perfume.

"Oh, excuse me," she said. "I seem to be in the wrong place. I'm looking for Micey's Department Store?

"Dear me," she said, noticing the delegate with the can opener, "what are you doing to that poor dog?"

"The dog is quite stuck, I'm afraid," the Chairman told her. "But the situation is under control."

The glamorous mouse pushed up her sleeves and marched over to the dog.

She kicked the top of the can three times. Then she gave it a swift twist to the left. And the can popped off!

"Hooray!" the mice all cheered happily.

The little mouse smiled. "That's how I open pickle jars at home," she explained. "Well, I'd best be on my way."

"Ah, Mr Chairman?" a voice piped up from the corner of the room. It was the Zambian delegate.

"Yes?" said the Chairman.

"I'd like to nominate Miss ... uh, Miss ..." The delegate looked at the pretty mouse.

"Miss Bianca," she told him.

"I'd like to nominate Miss Bianca for membership in the Rescue Aid Society," he said.

The Chairman turned to the rest of the mice delegates. "All in favour say, 'Aye!'"

"Aye!" all the mice cried.

"Woof!" the dog barked happily.

Miss Bianca smiled. "Well," she said, "I suppose Micey's can wait for another day."

A Bear-y Tale

It was time for Mowgli, Bagheera and Baloo to go to bed.

"Good night, Man-cub," purred Bagheera.

"But I'm not sleepy yet," protested Mowgli. "I need a bedtime story."

"Bedtime story?" said Bagheera. "At this hour?"

Mowgli turned to the big bear. "Please, Baloo?"

"A bedtime story, huh ... " said Baloo. "Now, how do those things begin?"

"Once upon a time ..." purred Bagheera.

"Oh, right ... Once upon a time ... in a house not far from this very jungle, there lived a clan of men," Baloo began.

"Real men?" asked Mowgli.

"Yep," said Baloo. "A father and a mother, and a little cub, just like you. Well, now, this clan, they cooked their food, and one day, don't you know, they made a mighty tasty stew ... only thing was, when they sat down to eat, it was just too hot. So the mother got an idea. They'd go for a walk in the jungle and, by the time they got back, their stew would be nice and cool. But do you know what happened next?"

"No," Mowgli said.

"Well, that family had barely been gone a minute, when an old bear came wandering up, and stuck his nose into the Man-house."

"He did?" gasped Mowgli.

"Well, now, can you blame him? That stew just smelled so awfully good. And the next thing you know, he was tastin' it – startin' with the biggest bowl, but that was still too hot. So next he tried the middle bowl, but that was too cold. So – he tried the littlest bowl, and, don't you know, it was just right! That old bear didn't mean to, but he ate the whole thing right up!"

"What happened next?" said Mowgli.

"Oh, well, after that, this bear, he started to get tired. Real tired. And, don't you know, Little Britches, that right there in that house, looking so soft and comfortable, were three cushy-lookin' pads ... I think men call them 'beds.' Anyway, that bear, he had to try them, too. Naturally, he laid down on the biggest one first. But it was too hard. So he tried the middle one, but that was much, much too soft. So, he tried the littlest one, and, son, let me tell you, that thing was so comfortable, he fell asleep right then and there! And he would have slept clear through the next full moon ... if only that family hadn't returned and ..."

"And what?" Mowgli asked breathlessly.

"And startled that bear so much, he ran back into the jungle ... full belly and all."

Mowgli smiled and tried to cover a big yawn. "Is that a true story, Baloo?"

The bear grinned. "Would I ever tell you a tall tale, Little Britches?"

An Airport Rescue

Driving wildly in a Pizza Planet delivery van, Buzz and the gang were following the owner of Al's Toy Barn, who was taking Woody and the *Roundup* gang to the airport! Al wanted to sell them to a museum in Japan.

At the airport, Buzz spotted a pet carrier. The toys piled inside, sticking their legs through the bottom. Moving as quickly as they could, they followed Al and his green case, and climbed onto the luggage conveyer belt.

"Once we go through, we just need to find that case," Buzz explained, nodding at the door to the baggage area.

The toys gasped as they entered a huge room full of conveyer belts and chutes. Buzz finally found Al's case, but when he opened it – the Prospector jumped out and punched Buzz!

"Hey! No one does that to my friend," Woody yelled, tackling the Prospector.

With his pickaxe, the Prospector started to rip open Woody's shoulder! He was about to drag Woody back into the case, but the rest of Andy's toys arrived just in time. Bullseye also kicked free as a conveyer belt carried them outside, but Jessie was stuck!

"Ride like the wind, Bullseye!" Woody yelled as he and Buzz jumped on the little horse's back. They chased the baggage truck.

Woody finally scrambled onto it, but by then, the green case was already being loaded into a plane! Woody hid inside another bag and was tossed onto the plane, too. He found the scared cowgirl. "C'mon, Jess," he said. "It's time to take you home."

Just then, the plane's doors closed! They crawled through a hatch, down to the wheels. The plane was already speeding down the runway – and Woody slipped! Jessie caught him, but his arm was starting to rip again. Woody lassoed his pull string onto the wheels. Then he held Jessie's hand and, together, they swung down and landed right behind Buzz, who was galloping along on Bullseye!

Everyone was safe. Watching the plane take off into the sky, the toys cheered.

When Andy arrived home from Cowboy Camp, he was surprised by what he found. "New toys!" he cried. "Thanks, Mum!"

Jessie and Bullseye had joined all his favourites, welcoming him home. Andy couldn't wait to play with everyone … right after he sewed up Woody's shoulder.

Someday Andy would grow up, and maybe he wouldn't always play with toys. But Woody and Buzz knew there was no place they'd rather be. Besides, they'd always have each other – for infinity and beyond!

Disney · PIXAR

FROM THE MOVIE **INSIDE OUT**

Goodbye, Friendship

With Joy and Sadness lost in Long Term Memory with the core memory spheres, Anger, Fear and Disgust had been trying to take care of Riley on their own. But, after Riley's argument with her parents, all they could do was watch as Goofball Island collapsed inside Riley's mind.

To get back to Headquarters, Joy realized that she and Sadness would first have to weave through the endless maze of shelves full of memory spheres in Long Term Memory. They had to get Riley's core memories back to Headquarters before more Islands of Personality collapsed!

Sadness did not like Joy's plan. She thought they would get lost.

"Think positive," said Joy.

"I'm too sad to walk." Sadness moaned from the floor. "Just give me a few … hours."

Joy didn't have a minute to lose, so she picked up one of Sadness's legs and dragged her along.

They met a couple of Mind Workers, called Forgetters. It was their job to dispose of memories Riley didn't need anymore. They vacuumed old memories from the shelves and sent them down to the Memory Dump below, where the old memories would fade away into mist. Joy watched the Forgetters with a great deal of concern. She and Sadness had to get back to Headquarters before Riley stopped caring about everything and the core memories were lost forever!

At that moment, Riley was chatting to her best friend, Meg, on her laptop. Meg lived back in Minnesota.

"Do you like it there?" asked Meg.

But before Riley could reply, Meg started telling her about a brilliant new girl on their hockey team.

"We can pass the puck to each other without even looking!" said Meg.

Riley missed playing with her old team, so hearing about this made her feel angry.

In HQ, Anger took charge of the console.

"Hey, hey," said Disgust. "We do NOT want to lose any more islands!" But Anger had already pushed a button.

"I gotta go," Riley said and slammed her laptop shut. It sounded like her old friends didn't miss her at all.

In Riley's Mind World, Joy and Sadness heard a horrible groaning sound. They both watched, helplessly, as Friendship Island toppled and fell into the dark dump below.

"Ohh, not Friendship!" Joy exclaimed.

"Goodbye friendship," Sadness sighed. "Hello loneliness."

Pinocchio
Fish Food

Figaro the cat was scared. He was also hungry. But he knew there wouldn't be any dinner. Figaro, Geppetto and Cleo the goldfish had just been swallowed by a whale!

"Don't worry, Figaro," Geppetto said, seeing the cat's worried look. "We'll get out of here somehow – and when we do, we'll keep searching for Pinocchio."

That Pinocchio! Figaro growled. After all that Geppetto and the Blue Fairy had done for Pinocchio, he had run away from home without a care in the world. That was how they ended up inside the whale! Now what would become of them?

Figaro decided then and there that if they ever found Pinocchio, he was going to use both of the wooden boy's legs as scratching posts. It would serve him right.

Meanwhile, Geppetto was peering into the puddle of water at the bottom of the whale's stomach. Figaro watched curiously.

"Let's see," Geppetto murmured, bending over and poking at the water. "There must be something in here…."

"Aha!" Geppetto cried happily. He was clutching a small, soggy clump of seaweed.

Figaro blinked. Seaweed?

A moment later, Geppetto bent down again. "Aha!" he cried once more.

The little cat began to purr, imagining that Geppetto had caught a wonderful snack. But when he peered into Geppetto's hand, all Figaro saw was – more seaweed.

Seaweed was *fish* food, Figaro thought with a scowl. Surely Geppetto didn't expect *him* to eat that for dinner.

But, as he watched, Geppetto carefully divided the seaweed into three portions. He placed one portion in Cleo's bowl. He set one portion in front of Figaro. The third he kept for himself.

"Let's eat!" Geppetto said, smiling bravely.

Figaro sniffed his seaweed. He stirred it around with his paw. But he just couldn't eat the seaweed. With a twitch of his tail, Figaro turned away.

Geppetto watched the little cat with sad eyes. Figaro sighed. He couldn't help but feel ungrateful.

Reluctantly, Figaro turned back to his dinner. He nibbled at the seaweed. It was cold. It was slimy. But it tasted like – *fish*!

Figaro gobbled down the rest of his meal. With his belly full, the little cat felt better. He decided that if they found Pinocchio, he would only use *one* of the puppet-boy's legs to sharpen his claws on.

Probably.

Unidentified Flying Mater

In Radiator Springs, a hubcap flew past Mater and Lightning McQueen. "Hey, look, a UFO!" Mater shouted. "And I know, 'cause I seen one once."

Mater began to tell his friend a tale about the time he saw a spaceship. He had pulled up to a railroad crossing in the desert when suddenly he saw a UFO floating right in front of him! "Well, hey there," he said. "My name is Mater."

"My name is Mator," the UFO replied.

That sounded a lot like his own name, the tow truck thought. "Should I take you to my litre?"

"Your leader," the UFO echoed. Mater led the UFO to the spot where he kept his oil cans. "Here are all my litres," he said.

The UFO looked excited. Mater grabbed a can and drank the oil through a straw. When he glanced over, the UFO was slurping from a large oil drum. Later, Mater showed his new friend around. They did all of Mater's favourite things, including tractor tipping. Then his new friend taught Mater how to fly! "We're going to be best friends forever!" Mater exclaimed.

Suddenly, a giant magnet dropped from the sky. ZINGGGG! It grabbed the UFO and pulled him upwards. Three military helicopters were hovering overhead.

"Mator! I'll save you!" Mater yelled.

He secretly followed the helicopters through the desert to a military base and sneaked inside. Several military and science vehicles were examining the UFO. "Dadgum!" the UFO exclaimed.

"He's trying to communicate!" one of the scientists said. "Where's Dr Abschleppwagen?"

Mater quickly put on a scientist disguise. "Here I am!" he announced.

"What does 'dadgum' mean?" asked one scientist.

"It means …" Mater began. Then he flicked a switch, turning off the magnet! Mater and Mator flew away at top speed. Everyone from the military base chased after them….

In Radiator Springs, Lightning interrupted. "Do you expect me to believe that?"

"You should," Mater said. "You was there, too!" Then he continued his story. Except this time, Mater described how Lightning was zooming across the desert too. Suddenly, an enormous mother ship appeared. It pulled Mater, Mator and Lightning aboard in a beam of light. Then the ship blasted into space. After a quick ride through space, it was time for Mater and Lightning to get back.

"Thank you!" Mater called when they were safely home. He would miss his new friend, Mator, but he was glad the little UFO was safe.

Disney's The Fox and the Hound

A Party of Three

The Widow Tweed hummed cheerfully as she decorated her cottage. Tod, the little fox she had adopted not long ago, watched with excitement. This was his first birthday in his new home!

"Now, Tod," said the widow, "who shall we invite to your party?"

Tod jumped on the windowsill and looked over at Amos Slade's farm. The Widow Tweed knew what that meant: Tod wanted his friend Copper the hound dog to share in the celebration. "I know Copper is your friend," she said, "but what if Amos catches him over here? There's no telling what that old coot might do!"

Tod jumped on the kind woman's lap and gazed up at her with big, sad eyes. "Oh, Tod! Stop looking at me like that. Well – all right! You can ask Copper over just this once!"

"I'm not supposed to leave the yard," Copper explained when Tod invited him. "I'll get in trouble with my master."

"Don't worry," Tod said. "I've got it all figured out." He lifted up one of the hound dog's enormous, floppy ears and whispered his plan.

Soon Tod showed up in Amos Slade's chicken yard. He ran among the birds, causing them to flap their wings and cluck in panic. That was Copper's signal to bark as loudly as he could. Amos burst out of the cabin just in time to see Copper chasing Tod into the woods.

"Follow me!" yelled Tod to Copper. He led his friend through a series of hollow logs, and then through a long, underground burrow. When the two pals emerged above ground, they were right outside Tod's back door. The Widow Tweed was waiting.

"Quick, scoot!" she said, shooing the two into the cottage.

While Amos Slade wandered around the woods trying to find Tod and Copper, the party festivities at the Widow Tweed's were just beginning. The three played hide-and-seek, pin-the-tail-on-the-donkey and drop-the-clothespin-in-the-jug. Tod won every game. Finally, it was time to cut the cake. After everyone had seconds, the widow spied Slade coming out of the woods. She let Copper out through the back door, where he stood barking ferociously.

"Good tracking, Copper!" Slade cried. "Did you chase that no-good fox all the way through the woods?" Copper looked up at his master and wagged his tail. "Copper," Slade said, "what's that on your face?" The hound turned his head and quickly licked the cake crumbs off his muzzle. "Hmmm," said Slade. "Must be seeing things. Let's go home then."

Inside the cosy cottage, Tod smiled. It had been a wonderful birthday – and sharing it with his best friend had definitely been the icing on the cake!

BIG HERO 6
New Moves

After discovering that a mysterious masked man had stolen his microbot invention, Hiro tried to explain everything to the police – but they didn't believe him.

Feeling fed up, Hiro and Baymax left the police station. When they got home, Hiro slowly opened the front door. He couldn't let Aunt Cass see Baymax – she'd ask questions he didn't have time to answer. Luckily, she was in the kitchen preparing dinner. Hiro waited until her back was turned, then beckoned Baymax to come in. But the friendly robot wanted to meet the boys' aunt.

"We jumped out of a window!" Baymax chirped. His battery was almost empty and he was having trouble controlling himself. Hiro quickly steered Baymax towards the stairs and rushed the robot up the steps.

"Hiro? You home sweetie?" Aunt Cass called, turning towards the stairs.

"Uh, that's right!" Hiro yelled down, shoving Baymax into his room.

With Baymax finally in his charging station, Hiro collapsed on to his bed. He needed to think. None of this made any sense.

"Tadashi," said Baymax.

Hiro sighed. "He's dead, Baymax."

Baymax filtered this news. He scanned Hiro and gave him a diagnosis: grief.

"Treatments for personal loss include contact with friends and loved ones. I am contacting them now," Baymax said, sending a message to Tadashi's school friends. Then Baymax gave Hiro a big hug. "I am sorry about the fire," he said.

"It was an accident," Hiro said, quietly. Then he continued, "Unless … unless it wasn't! At the showcase that guy in the mask stole my microbots. Then set the fire to cover his tracks!" Hiro realized the masked man must have been responsible for Tadashi's death. "We've gotta catch that guy," he decided. But first, Baymax needed some upgrades: a suit of armour and some serious battle moves. But most of all, he needed the motivation to fight.

Hiro got to work straight away. He programmed a red computer chip with martial arts moves, and created green body armour with his 3D printer. He placed the fighting chip in Baymax's chest, next to Tadashi's nurse chip. The robot began to show off his new moves. Baymax could now break through a door with one mighty kick. After all his hard work, Hiro was pleased with the new and improved Baymax. The robot was definitely ready to face the masked man. Now all they had to do was track down their enemy!

101 DALMATIANS

Lucky's Last Laugh

It was getting quite late at Pongo and Perdita's house, but their darling little puppies were still not asleep. Not that they didn't want to go to sleep. At least most of them. No, the problem was that one of them wouldn't let them go to sleep – Lucky!

"And then, don't you remember, you guys, the part at the very beginning, when Thunderbolt jumped across that canyon? Whoosh! Like a rocket! Clear to the other side!" Lucky said.

"Yes, Lucky, we remember," his sister Penny said with a groan. "How could we forget? You've reminded us 101 times!"

"Yeah! It was so great! And then there was that part when – "

"Lucky!" wailed Rolly. "We all watched the same episode of Thunderbolt tonight. You don't have to tell us about it."

"Yeah, I know, but I just wanted to tell you about the part when Thunderbolt found the little girl, then ran back to tell the sheriff – "

"Lucky! It's late! We want to go to sleep!" barked Patch.

Lucky laid his head on his paws. "Okay," he said. "I'll be quiet."

All the puppies closed their eyes.

"Oh! But what about the part when the sheriff told Thunderbolt to climb up that cliff, and he got to the top, and he grabbed that rope with his teeth, and he pulled up the little girl – "

"Lucky!" yelped Pepper. "We don't care about Thunderbolt. We want to go to bed!"

"Right." Lucky sighed, lying down once again. "Wait a sec!" He sat up. "Don't care about Thunderbolt? How could you not care that he carried that little girl across that broken bridge and through those raging rapids?"

"We mean," said Freckles, "we want you to be quiet so we can go to sleep!"

"You mean," said Lucky, "you don't want me to tell you about the last part where Thunderbolt ran back to the mountains and into that cave, and found that amazing thing?"

"Yes!" Lucky's brothers and sisters shouted together.

"Why didn't you say so?" said Lucky. "Good night."

And with that, Lucky closed his eyes. For a minute, everyone enjoyed the silence. Then Penny sat up.

"Hey, wait a minute," she said. "What thing did he find?"

"Yeah," said Patch. "I missed that part."

"Me, too," said Rolly. "What was it exactly that he found, Lucky? Tell us."

But there was no answer. Lucky was fast asleep. And now the *other* Dalmatian puppies were wide awake!

Disney·PIXAR
MONSTERS, INC.
Bedtime for Billy

Mike the one-eyed monster and his friend, Sulley, were excited about their evening. They were monster-sitting for Mike's nephew, Billy. Billy's mother told her son to be good, and he said that he would.

"Everything will be fine, sis," said Mike. "Sulley and I will take good care of the little guy. You don't have to worry about a thing."

Billy's parents kissed him good bye and hopped in the car. The three monsters went inside and ate pizza and popcorn while they watched classic movies like Gross Encounters of the Kid Kind. After the movies were over, the three monsters listened to music, sang and danced. Billy and Mike even had a video game contest! The night flew by and soon it was bedtime.

"It's time for some shut-eye, Buddy," said Mike with a yawn. But putting Billy to bed wasn't going to be that easy. There was one very important detail that Billy's mother had forgotten to tell her monster-sitters. Billy was scared of the dark!

"Aaaaaaahhhhh!!!!" screamed Billy.

"Wh-wh-what is it?" shouted Mike as he and Sulley ran back into the bedroom.

"There's a kid hiding in the c-closet …" stammered Billy. "It wants to g-get me!"

Mike and Sulley searched for human children. They checked the whole room, once with the lights on and twice with the lights off.

"There aren't any kids in the closet," said Mike.

"All clear under the bed," announced Sulley.

"See, there's nothing to worry about," Mike said. "You can go to sleep now."

But Billy was still frightened. Mike and Sulley quickly realized they had to come up with another plan. How could they show Billy that children weren't scary?

"I've got it!" exclaimed Mike. "The scrapbook!"

"You're a genius, Mikey!" declared Sulley.

The three monsters looked through the scrapbook. It was filled with photographs of monsters with children, newspaper clippings of them together and laugh reports.

"See, Billy," said Mike. "Human kids are not dangerous, and they love to have fun just like you."

"And they help us!" added Sulley. "Their laughter powers our city!"

"You know, Billy, sometimes human kids get scared of us," said Mike. "But once they see that we're funny and friendly, they realize there's no reason to be scared of monsters."

Billy soon fell fast asleep as Mike and Sulley watched from the doorway. "Another job well done, Mike," said Sulley.

Disney · PIXAR

WALL·E

A Robot Kiss

When WALL·E met EVE, he had fallen in love. He had latched onto the spaceship that came to take her away from Earth. Now, the spaceship was docking inside an enormous ship called the Axiom. This was where all the humans from Earth now lived.

The Captain's robot assistant, Gopher, wrapped EVE in energy bands and drove her away. WALL·E raced after her. And M-O, a cleaner-bot, chased WALL·E. (M-O was programmed to clean, clean, clean. WALL·E, the little trash-compacting robot from Earth, was his biggest challenge ever.)

As WALL·E chased EVE, he accidentally disabled a human passenger's electronic system. The human blinked and looked around. She saw the world around her, instead of viewing it digitally over her holo-screen. She liked it!

Meanwhile, EVE was finally ready to give the plant she had found among WALL·E's treasures to the Captain. By doing so, she would prove that Earth was clean enough that a plant could now grow there. That meant everyone could return to the planet.

But EVE's compartment was empty. The plant had disappeared!

Disappointed, the Captain sent EVE to the repair ward, along with WALL·E. When they got there, WALL·E thought some orderlies were hurting EVE. So he helped her escape, along with all the reject-bots from the repair ward.

But there was a problem. Once they ran, they looked like convicts. A warning broadcast their escape throughout the Axiom. The ship's stewards tried to catch them.

To avoid being captured, EVE took WALL·E to an escape pod. She would send him to Earth where he would be safe, and then she could find the plant. Instead, Gopher appeared. He had the plant! He put it in the escape pod, and WALL·E and the plant were launched into space – not towards Earth, but far into outer space! WALL·E panicked and pushed a lot of buttons.

WALL·E pushed the wrong button. The pod exploded! WALL·E managed to escape, and EVE went to try to help him. *Whoosh!* WALL·E zoomed up to EVE and showed her that he had saved the plant. Delighted, she leaned in towards him, and an arc of electricity passed between their foreheads – a robot kiss.

Soon they were floating in space, dancing and giggling, excited about taking the Earth plant back to the Captain.

'Ears a Job for You, Dumbo!

It had been a hard day for little Dumbo. It was bad enough that everyone made fun of his ears except his mother, but then they had put his mother in a cage, so Dumbo couldn't even be with the one person who loved him and treated him decently.

What made things even worse was that Dumbo didn't have anything to do. It seemed that he was the only creature in the circus who didn't have a job. Everyone had a purpose except Dumbo. All he could do was feel sad and be laughed at.

Dumbo heaved a sigh and went for a walk through the circus tents. Soon, he found himself among the refreshment stands. Everyone here had a job too. Some were squeezing lemons to make lemonade. Others were popping popcorn or roasting peanuts. Wonderful smells filled the air.

Finally, Dumbo came to a little candyfloss wagon. The puffy cloud of sugar looked tempting, and Dumbo wanted a taste, but there were so many customers he couldn't get close enough.

Suddenly Dumbo heard a loud buzzing. Then all the customers waved their hands over their heads and ran away.

The smell of sugar had attracted a swarm of nasty flies!

"Scat!" cried the candyfloss man. "Go away before you scare off my customers."

Dumbo reached out his trunk to smell the delicious candyfloss.

"Not you, Dumbo!" the candyfloss man cried. "It's bad enough chasing flies. Do I have to chase elephants too?"

Poor Dumbo was startled. With a snort, he sucked candyfloss right up his nose.

Ahhh-choo! When he sneezed, Dumbo's ears flapped, and something amazing happened.

"Remarkable!" the candyfloss man cried. "All the flies are gone. They think your ears are giant fly swatters!"

The candyfloss man patted Dumbo's head. "How would you like a job?"

Dumbo nodded enthusiastically and set to waving his ears. Soon, the candyfloss stand was the most popular refreshment stand in the circus – and had the least flies. But, best of all, Dumbo now had something to do to take his mind off his troubles. He was still sad, but things didn't seem quite so bad. And, who knows, perhaps soon he'd have his mother back.

"I wonder what other amazing things those big ears can do?" said the candyfloss man, giving Dumbo a friendly smile. "I'll bet they carry you far...."

Hide, Dude!

"**C**ome on, Squirt!" Nemo cried happily. "Race you to the coral shelf!"

Nemo took off, pumping his mismatched fins as hard as he could. His young sea turtle friend laughed and swam after him.

Squirt was visiting Nemo at his home on the reef. "This way, dude!" Squirt yelled, flinging himself through the water. "I'm catching some rad current over here!"

Nemo hesitated for just a second, watching as his friend tumbled along past some stinging coral. Squirt was so brave! Even after all that Nemo had been through – being captured by a scuba diver, then escaping from a tank to find his way home again – he still got scared sometimes.

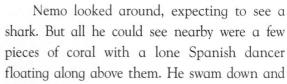

With a deep breath, he threw himself into the current. He tumbled after Squirt, fins flying as the water carried him along. Finally, he came out the other end of the current, landing in the still ocean beside Squirt.

He giggled. "Hey, that was fun!" he cried. "Let's do it again! Squirt? Squirt, what's wrong?"

The sea turtle was staring into the distance, his eyes wide. "Hide, dude!" Squirt cried.

Before Nemo could respond, Squirt's head and legs popped into his shell and he landed on the sea floor with a flop.

Nemo started trembling. What had scared Squirt so much?

Nemo looked around, expecting to see a shark. But all he could see nearby were a few pieces of coral with a lone Spanish dancer floating along above them. He swam down and tapped on Squirt's shell. "Hey," he said. "What is it? There's nothing scary here."

"Whew!" Squirt's head popped out. He looked around, then gasped and hid again. When he spoke, his voice was muffled. "It's totally still there!"

Nemo blinked and looked around again. Again, all he saw were the coral and the Spanish dancer.

"Hey, wait a minute," he said, suddenly realizing something. "Haven't you ever seen a Spanish dancer before?"

"A – a Spanish wha-huh?" Squirt asked, still muffled.

Nemo knocked on his friend's shell again. "It's a kind of sea slug," he explained. "Don't worry, Spanish dancers are nice – you don't have to be scared. I promise."

Finally Squirt's head popped out again. He smiled sheepishly at Nemo.

"Sorry, dude," he said. "I never saw one of those before. It totally freaked me out."

"It's okay." Nemo smiled back. He already knew that new things could be scary – and now he knew he wasn't the only one who thought so. "Come on, let's go play," he said.

Disney

THE
LION KING
The Best Fisherman of All

Simba and his friends Timon and Pumbaa were hungry. They wandered through the forest until they came to an old, rotten tree. Timon knocked on the trunk.

"What's it sound like, Timon?" Pumbaa asked.

"Like our breakfast!" Timon replied.

He yanked at the bark and hundreds of grubs slithered out.

Timon handed Simba a grub.

"No, thanks." Simba sighed. "I'm tired of grubs."

"Well, the ants are tasty," said Timon. "They come in two flavours. Red and black."

Simba shook his head. "Don't you eat anything but bugs?"

"Fish!" Pumbaa declared.

"I love fish!" Simba exclaimed.

"Why didn't you say so?" said Timon. "There's a pond at the end of this trail." The three friends started off down the trail.

"What now?" asked Simba when they arrived at the pond.

"That's the problem!" said Timon. "We're not the best fishermen in the world."

"I'll teach you!" Simba said.

The lion climbed up a tree and crawled onto a branch that hung over the water. Then he snatched a fish out of the water.

"See!" Simba said, jumping to the ground nimbly. "Not a problem. Fishing's easy."

"Not for me!" Timon cried. He dangled from the branch, but his arms weren't long enough to reach the fish.

Simba laughed. "Better let Pumbaa try."

"What a joke!" cried Timon. "Pumbaa can't even climb this tree."

"Want to bet?" asked Pumbaa.

"Stay there," Timon warned. "I don't think this branch is strong enough for both of us."

With a hop, Pumbaa landed on the branch next to Timon. The limb started to bend.

"Yikes!" Timon cried as he leaped to another tree.

Crack! The branch broke under Pumbaa. With a squeal, he landed in the pond. The splash was enormous!

Simba, sitting on the bank, was soaked. Timon was nearly blasted from his perch. Pond water fell like rain all around them.

Simba opened his eyes and started to laugh. So did Timon.

Pumbaa was sitting in a pool of mud where the pond had been. He'd splashed so much of the water out that dozens of fish squirmed on the ground, just waiting to be gobbled up.

"Wow!" Timon cried. "I think Pumbaa is the very best fisherman of all!"

Rescue Squad Mater

Red the fire truck was watering some flowers in front of the fire station. "I used to be a fire truck," Mater said, out of the blue. Then he began to tell the story of Rescue Squad Mater....

Rescue Squad Mater was at the fire station when an emergency call came in. "Fire in progress at 120 Car Michael Way."

Rescue Squad Mater recognized that address. "That's the old gasoline and match factory!" he exclaimed. He zoomed out of the station and roared down the street. Moments later, Rescue Squad Mater sped up to the burning building. Rescue Squad Mater aimed a water hose and started spraying. He bravely battled the flames, ignoring the danger.

"Mater," Lightning said, stopping the story. "I can't believe you were a fire truck."

"You remember," Mater replied. "You were there, too!" Then he went on telling his tale. The fire had spread through the entire factory, but Rescue Squad Mater still continued to battle it. Suddenly, a frightened voice called out. "AAAh! Help! Help!" Lightning was stuck on the top floor of the burning building!

The rescue truck began to raise his ladder towards the top floor. Soon the ladder was right beneath Lightning. Would there be enough time for Rescue Squad Mater to get him to the ground – before the factory exploded? The crowd watched, waiting on the edges of their tyre treads.

KA-BLAM! The factory blew up in a huge explosion! Luckily, Lightning was out of the building by then. Mater used his ladder to lift him into an ambulance. Finally, Mater turned towards the crowd and smiled.

When Lightning arrived at the hospital, he was rushed into the operating room. A whole team of nurses was there, too. Lightning looked around. Where was the doctor? Then he heard a nurse's voice over the loudspeaker. "Paging Dr Mater."

Lightning blinked. Had he heard that right? Seconds later, the doctor rolled in. Lightning could hardly believe his eyes. It was Mater! "Mater, you're a doctor, too?!"

"That's right, buddy," Dr Mater replied.

Lightning spotted Dr Mater's diplomas on the wall. "Clear!" Dr Mater called out as he swung the arm of a scary-looking medical instrument towards Lightning. Then Mater stopped telling his story.

"What happened?" Lightning asked.

"I saved your life," Mater said.

"Whaaa...?" Lightning was pretty sure he would remember something like that.

Survival of the Smallest

It was the first day of summer, and Dot and the other Blueberries were getting ready for a big adventure. They were heading out for the First Annual Blueberry Wilderness Expedition. Their journey would take them to the thicket of tall grasses next to the ant colony. It was only a few yards from home – but, to a little ant, it seemed like an awfully long way.

As the group prepared to leave, some boy ants arrived to tease them.

"How do you expect to go on an expedition without supplies?" asked Jordy.

Dot put her hands on her hips. "For your information," she said in a superior tone, "the whole point is to survive using our smarts. Whatever we need, we'll make when we get there."

The Blueberries hiked a few yards from the ant colony, then Dot consulted her survival manual. "Okay," she said, "the first thing we need to do is build a shelter from the sun."

"I know!" Daisy volunteered. "We could make a hut. All we have to do is stick twigs into the dirt side by side to make the walls, then lay leaves over the top for the roof."

The rest of the Blueberries decided this was a great idea. With a lot of teamwork and determination, they completed a shelter to comfortably hold the troop.

"Now," said Dot, looking at the manual again, "it says here we need to protect our campsite."

So the girls dug a narrow trench in front of the hut, just as the manual instructed.

The girls gathered some seeds and went into their home-made hut to have some lunch. A short while later, they heard a scream. When they went to investigate, they discovered Reed, Grub and Jordy at the bottom of the trench.

It was clear to the Blueberries that the boys had been up to no good.

"Girls," said Dot, pointing to the boys, "observe one of the Blueberries' most common natural enemies – though certainly not one of the smartest."

When it was time for the Blueberries to pack up and hike home, the boys were still stuck in the trench. "Say the magic words and I'll get you out of there," said Dot.

"Okay, okay!" Reed, Grub and Jordy agreed.

"Well?" demanded Dot.

"Blueberries rock," the boys admitted.

Dot lowered down a ladder she had expertly made of sticks. "You bet we do!" she said. "'Cause if we can survive you, we can survive anything!"

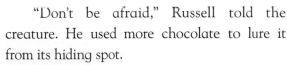

Strange Animals

Carl Fredricksen and a Junior Wilderness Explorer named Russell had just arrived in South America! Carl had dreamed of seeing Paradise Falls his whole life. He had promised his wife, Ellie, that he'd take her there one day. Sadly, Ellie had died before they could take the trip.

When Carl was told he had to move out of their home, he decided it was time to keep his promise to Ellie. He tied thousands of balloons to their house, and it lifted up into the air!

But Carl hadn't planned on taking a companion along – a boy called Russell had been on Carl's porch when the house took off!

They had hit a storm and crash landed very near Paradise Falls. There was just one problem: the crash had sent them flying out of house, and now they couldn't get back in – it was hovering too high off the ground.

Russell had an idea: they could walk the house to the Falls. They made a harness out of the garden hose and pulled the house along.

"This is fun already, isn't it?" Russell said as they trudged along. "Don't you worry. I'm gonna assist you every step of the way."

After a while, they stopped to take a break. As Russell nibbled a chocolate bar, a beak poked out of the bushes and began to nibble it too!

"Don't be afraid," Russell told the creature. He used more chocolate to lure it from its hiding spot.

When the creature emerged, Russell gasped. It was the biggest bird he had ever seen! The bird liked chocolate. It liked Russell, too. Russell named the bird Kevin. He couldn't wait to show his new friend to Carl! But Carl yelled with fright when he saw the bird.

"Can we keep him?" Russell asked.

"No," said Carl.

Carl and Russell set off again. But Russell didn't want to leave Kevin behind, so he dropped a trail of chocolate for the bird to follow.

They hadn't gone far when they met a dog. "Hi there," said the dog. "My name is Dug." A talking dog? Carl and Russell were stunned! "My master made me this collar so that I may talk," Dug explained. "My pack sent me on a special mission. Have you seen a bird? I want to find one. I have been on the scent."

Suddenly, Kevin flew out of the bushes and tackled Dug. "Hey, that is the bird! May I take your bird back to camp as my prisoner?" Dug asked Carl.

"Yes! Yes! Take it!" Carl told him. He didn't want to deal with all these strange animals – he just wanted to reach Paradise Falls. But would he ever get there?

A Big Imagination

Desperate to get Riley's core memories back to Headquarters, Joy led Sadness through the maze of Long Term Memory in Riley's mind. They had already lost two Islands of Personality – Goofball and Friendship – they couldn't afford to lose any more or Riley would forget everything about herself!

Soon, they ran into a funny-looking creature. It appeared to be made from candyfloss, but was shaped like an elephant crossed with a cat and a dolphin! Joy recognized the creature immediately. "You're Bing Bong!" she said. "Riley's imaginary friend!"

When Riley was little, she and Bing Bong used to play together. They put on concerts where they banged pots and pans, and they had a rocket wagon which would take them to the moon when they sang a special song! But, over the years, Riley had forgotten her imaginary friend.

Bing Bong's dream was to rocket to the moon with Riley, so Joy suggested he come to Headquarters with them.

"Ha ha!" Bing Bong cried, dancing around.

Bing Bong offered Joy a satchel so she could carry the core memories.

"Thanks!" she said. "This'll make it a lot easier to walk back to Headquarters."

"Walk?" asked Bing Bong. "We're not walkin'! We're taking the Train of Thought!"

He pointed to a train speeding towards Headquarters. Joy couldn't believe she hadn't thought of that.

"There's a station in Imagination Land," Bing Bong explained. "Come on, this way!"

Imagination Land was full of crazy places that Riley had imagined. Joy and Sadness were amazed by what they saw. They passed through French Fry Forest, where Bing Bong stopped every now and again to munch another chip. Then there was Trophy Town, filled with medals, ribbons and certificates, followed by Cloud Town! Joy leaped on to a small chunk of cloud and floated into the air. "Ha ha!" she cried. "It's so soft!"

Suddenly, a handsome teenage boy rolled towards them on a conveyor belt. A Mind Worker explained that the boy was an Imaginary Boyfriend who Riley had created in her mind.

"I would die for Riley," the Boyfriend said.

"Oh, gaa!" Joy said. She was not impressed.

"Anyway," said Bing Bong, as they walked past the Boyfriend, "This way, through Preschool World! We're nearly to the train!"

"Riley, here we come!" Joy said, happily.

They didn't have time for any more distractions. They had to get the core memories back to Headquarters – and fast!

Andy's All Grown Up

There was a train robbery underway, and Sheriff Woody had to work quickly! Standing on top of the moving train, Woody confronted One-Eyed Bart. But Bart threw Woody off the train, then escaped in a getaway car driven by Aliens! Luckily, Woody was caught by the brave cowgirl Jessie, galloping nearby on Bullseye. Still, the train plunged over a cliff – until Buzz Lightyear lifted it to safety! The battle continued, good guys vs. bad, until the evil Dr Porkchop finally cornered Woody and his crew.

"Buzz, shoot your laser at my badge!" Sheriff Woody ordered. Buzz's laser bounced off the badge and up at Dr Porkchop's spaceship. ZAPPPP!!! The bad guys were no more. It was another thrilling adventure for the toys in Andy's room.

With Andy, the toys felt as if anything was possible. Maybe they'd be villains trying to take over the world – or maybe they'd be the heroes who would save it. For years, the toys could do anything Andy's imagination dreamed up. They loved every single day with Andy, and they all agreed: being loved and played with by a kid – by their kid – was the best feeling in the world.

But lately, the toys had been spending more time in the toy box. Andy hardly ever took them out. The toys decided to take action.

"All right, guys, we've got one shot at this," said Woody, gathering everyone together. Sarge and two of his men appeared in Andy's room, dragging a mobile phone behind them. "Mission accomplished!" Sarge reported.

"Make the call," Woody ordered.

Jessie dialled some numbers on a cordless phone. The other toys were very nervous. The mobile phone began to ring. "Just like we rehearsed it, guys," instructed Woody.

Hearing the phone ring, Andy entered the room and looked around. He went to the toy box, lifted the lid and stuck his hand inside, rummaging around. Finally, he found the mobile phone wedged between Rex's arms.

"Hello?" Andy said into the phone. "Hello … anyone there?" But no one answered.

"Molly, stay out of my room!" he yelled, clicking the phone off.

"I wasn't in your room!" his sister shouted.

Andy just rolled his eyes. He glanced at Rex for a moment, then dropped the dinosaur back into the toy chest and closed the lid.

The toys were disappointed. They knew the truth: Andy was a teenager now, and he didn't want to play with toys anymore.

Lady and the TRAMP

In the Doghouse

"Good morning, Tramp," said Lady, with a yawn and a stretch. She rolled over on her silk cushion. "Wasn't that just the most wonderful night's sleep?"

But Tramp's night's sleep had been far from wonderful. In fact, he hadn't had much sleep at all. The past night had been Tramp's first sleeping in Lady's house … or in any house, come to think of it.

"How do you do it?" he grumbled. "That bed is so soft, I feel like I'm sinking in a feather pool. And between Jim Dear's snoring and the baby's crying, I could barely hear the crickets chirping."

"Oh, dear," Lady said, feeling truly sorry for her mate. "I know!" she exclaimed. "Jim Dear and Darling love you so – I'm sure they'd let you sleep up on their bed tonight. There's nothing in the world better than that!"

But Tramp shook his head. "I'm afraid it's the outdoors I need," he explained. "I mean, I know you grew up this way and all … but it's just so much fun to sleep under the stars. And the moon too. There's nothing to howl at in this bedroom."

"You can see the moon out the window," Lady told him.

But Tramp shook his head. "It's not the same. You know," he went on, "we've still got that fine doghouse in the yard. What do you say we go back out there tonight? It'll be like a honeymoon!"

"Well …" Lady looked at Tramp's tired eyes. "Okay."

And so that night, as soon as the sun set and the moon began to rise, Lady and Tramp went out to the garden.

Happy at last, Tramp turned three times and then plopped down. "Oh, how I love the feel of cool dirt on my belly!" he said with a dreamy smile … while Lady gingerly peeked into the dark and slightly damp kennel. The stars were not even out, and already she missed the comforts of Jim Dear's and Darling's room.

Tramp watched as Lady stretched out on the kennel floor, then got up and moved outside, then back in once again. It was plain to see: try as she might, Lady just could not relax on the cold, hard ground.

"Don't worry," Tramp announced, "I have an idea."

And with that, he ran into the house … and in seconds reappeared with Lady's cushion in his teeth. Carefully, he swept the kennel with his tail, and laid the cushion down just the way Lady liked it.

Lady smiled and lay down. And, do you know what? That night, they both had the sweetest dreams either one had ever had.

Peter Pan
A 'Snappy' New Ship

"My ship, my beautiful ship!" Captain Hook moaned. It had not been a good day for the pirate. Peter Pan and the Darling children had stolen his ship. And now, Hook was stranded on an island with Smee and the other pirates, their rowing boat having been chomped to bits by the crocodile.

"It's a nice island, Captain," offered Smee, trying to cheer up his boss. "And you could use a holiday. Why, look at those dark circles under your eyes."

Captain Hook turned to Smee with a furious look on his face. "Pirates don't take holidays!" Hook boomed. "Pirates seek revenge! Which is precisely what we are going to do, as soon as we have a new ship to sail in."

Smee looked around. "Where are we going to find a ship around here, Sir?" he asked.

"*We* aren't going to find one," Captain Hook answered. "You and the rest of this mangy crew are going to *build* one! And I don't mean a little one either. I mean a big, menacing, fit-for-a-magnificent-pirate-like-me one!"

For weeks, the pirates chopped trees and cut them into planks for the ship. They whittled thousands of pegs to use for nails, and crushed countless berries to use for paint. "You're not moving fast enough!" Hook complained as he sat in the shade, sipping juice out of a pineapple.

Finally, an exhausted Smee fetched Hook as he awoke from his afternoon nap.

"It's ready, Captain!" he announced.

Even Hook had to admit the ship was magnificent. Shaped like a gigantic crocodile, it was painted a reptilian shade of green. "No one will dare come near this ship. Not even that pesky crocodile. He won't want to tussle with anything this terrifying," Smee assured him.

Captain Hook was delighted. "We set sail tomorrow!" he crowed.

That night, Smee couldn't resist putting one more finishing touch on the ship. He painted a row of eyelashes on the crocodile's eyelids.

The next morning, Captain Hook and the crew climbed aboard and pushed off. The ticking crocodile soon appeared.

"Smee!" yelled a terrified Captain Hook. "I thought you said he wouldn't come near us!"

"But look how calm he is," said Smee, puzzled. "He's even smiling!"

Smee leaned over the side of the railing. "You know, it might be those eyelashes I painted. Maybe the croc thinks the ship is its mother."

Hook lunged at the roly-poly pirate. "You made my ship look like a *mother* crocodile? This vessel is supposed to be terrifying!"

"Mothers *can* be terrifying, sir," said Smee. "You should have seen mine when I told her I was going to become a pirate!"

BIG HERO 6

A Team Effort

Hiro had realized that the masked man who had stolen his microbot technology at the Tech Showcase must have also started the fire in the hall – the fire that had killed Hiro's brother, Tadashi.

Hiro was determined to unmask the mysterious villain so he upgraded his brother's best invention – Baymax – turning him into a fighting machine.

Hiro and Baymax went back to the warehouse where they had first seen the masked man. At the dock, Hiro's last microbot escaped from the Petri dish and soared out over the water. He saw it join a swarm of microbots that were transporting a huge piece of equipment – and the masked man! Hiro and Baymax dived out of sight.

Meanwhile, Wasabi, Honey, Go Go and Fred – Tadashi's school friends – had received a message from Baymax telling them Hiro needed help. But when they arrived at the warehouse, Hiro told them to leave – he didn't want them to get hurt. They refused and pulled Hiro into their car, just as the masked man spotted them.

"Hiro. Explanation. Now!" Go Go demanded as the car sped off. Hiro reluctantly told his friends all about the masked man.

"That mask. Black suit. We're under attack from a super-villain, people!" Fred said.

The villain pursued them, throwing cars and other obstacles in their path, but Go Go swerved around them all … until the man used the microbots to build a road which curved into a tunnel around the car! Go Go accelerated hard as the tunnel's exit closed up in front of them.

"We're not going to make it!" shouted Wasabi.

They just made it through the tunnel, but Go Go couldn't stop the car from plunging right into the bay! The friends screamed as the car hit the water, and the bad guy retreated in triumph.

Underwater, the friends struggled to escape. But Baymax saved them by shedding his armour and floating them to safety.

Soaking wet and shivering, the gang followed Fred to his parents' mansion.

With no time to waste, Hiro got to work. "The guy in the mask was carrying something with this symbol on it," Hiro said, pointing to a sparrow he had drawn.

"Alistair Krei!" Fred suddenly shouted.

"What?" asked Hiro.

"Think about it. Krei wanted your microbots, and you said no – but rules don't apply to a man like Krei!" Fred explained.

Hiro found it hard to believe that Krei was behind all this. The group decided to call the man 'Yokai' – Japanese for 'bad guy' – until they unmasked him. But no matter who it was, they all wanted to find him.

Aladdin

Market Day

"What's wrong, Abu?" asked Aladdin. The normally lively little monkey hadn't been himself lately. Abu sat at the window gazing longingly towards the village. "You're right," Aladdin said. "A trip to the marketplace is exactly what we need. Let's go right now!"

The pair had a wonderful afternoon visiting old friends. Abu played with Salim the goat, joked with Kahlil the ox and teased Gamal the camel. He and Aladdin stopped at each vendor's stall to say "hello." Aladdin saw how happy Abu was in the hustle and bustle of the marketplace.

"You know, Abu," said Aladdin that night, "you can invite your friends from the marketplace to the palace anytime you'd like." The monkey jumped up and down, hugging Aladdin and knocking off his hat. "Okay! Okay! You're welcome!" Aladdin laughed.

The next day, Abu disappeared first thing in the morning. When he returned, Salim and Kahlil were with him. "Welcome," said Jasmine. "Please make yourselves at home." But they already had. The goat was chewing on the curtains, and the ox was wandering in the garden, eating the tops off the flowers.

"We can always buy new curtains or plant new flowers. The important thing is that Abu is happy again," Aladdin said to Jasmine, who sighed and agreed reluctantly.

The following day, Gamal and several other camels arrived. Jasmine was not pleased when they spat on the new carpet. "Think of Abu," Aladdin told her.

The day after that, the fruit seller rolled through the palace with his cart. Another vendor came with a pile of smelly fish. Next came the lady who sold dates, and the man who sold pottery.

"Isn't it wonderful that Abu has so many friends?" said Aladdin.

"It is," Jasmine agreed. "But have you noticed that we only see his friends coming and not going?"

"Now that you mention it, I have," Aladdin replied. "Let's find out what's going on." The couple followed Abu as he led his guests out to the garden. What they saw made them gasp. There was the entire marketplace! Aladdin burst out laughing. "I guess the next time Abu is feeling homesick, he doesn't need to go any farther than his own backyard!"

Jasmine sighed. "Aladdin, these people can't stay here." But, when Jasmine saw the sad look on Aladdin's face, she added, "Well, maybe they could come back next month."

And so began a new tradition – "Palace Market Day," which happened once a month. And *that* made little Abu *very* happy!

101 DALMATIANS

The Twilight Bark

Rolly, Patch, Lucky and the rest of the puppies were watching the end of *The Thunderbolt Adventure Hour*. As the credits began to roll, Pongo turned off the TV.

"Aw, come on, Dad!" Patch complained.

"We let you stay up late to watch the whole show," Pongo said.

Lucky sat staring at the blank television screen, hoping it would magically turn itself back on.

Perdy licked his face encouragingly. "Sit down, children," she said. "Your father and I need to speak with you."

"Uh-oh," Penny said worriedly.

"Oh, it's nothing like that," Pongo assured her. "We just think it's time to tell you about the legend of the Twilight Bark."

"Sounds cool!" Pepper cheered.

"What's the Twilight Bark?" Freckles asked.

"Legend has it," Perdy began, "that there's a special way that dogs can send each other messages. It stretches from the farthest side of the city all the way to the countryside."

"Wow!" Penny gasped. "Why would you need to do that?"

"Sometimes," Pongo began, "you need to communicate information from one place to another quickly, and you don't have time to go to the other place yourself."

"I don't need any Twilight Bark!" Patch said. "I can take care of myself."

"Fat chance!" Lucky said under his breath.

"What do you know?" Patch barked.

"If you ever get into any trouble," Perdy told the pups, "just go to the top of the highest hill you can find and bark out your message, and the members of the Twilight Bark will pass it along until someone can come and help you."

"That sounds like a bunch of baloney," Patch told his parents.

"Patch!" Pongo scolded his son. "That isn't very nice."

Just then, Lucky started howling at the top of his lungs.

"What's got into you?" Perdy asked.

"I'm trying out the Twilight Bark," Lucky said. "To get us rescued from Patch."

"Lucky," Perdy scolded him, "apologize to your brother."

"That's okay," Patch said. "I don't need his apology. I was right anyway. All that howling and no word from the Twilight Bark."

Just then, the doorbell rang. All of the puppies gasped and turned to look at Patch.

Perdy and Pongo smiled at each other, knowing it was actually Roger returning from the shop with milk for tomorrow's breakfast.

Something for Felix to Fix

Wreck-It Ralph, who was the Bad Guy from the computer game 'Fix-It Felix, Jr', was in a racing game called *Sugar Rush* – where everything was made of sweets. Ralph had left his own game to find a medal and prove he was a Good Guy, but had ended up far from where he belonged!

He had agreed to help his new friend Vanellope to make a new cart – she was a racer in *Sugar Rush* and wanted to win. If she did, she promised she would give back Ralph's medal, which he had lost to her.

Elsewhere, Felix from Ralph's game and Sergeant Calhoun from *Hero's Duty* were searching for Ralph. When Ralph crashed in *Sugar Rush*, he had accidentally set free a dangerous cy-bug! Felix was looking for Ralph, and Calhoun was looking for the cy-bug. Calhoun asked Felix why Ralph would leave his own game.

"I wish I knew," Felix replied. "I never thought he'd go Turbo…."

Years ago, there had been a racing game in the arcade called *Turbo Time*. Its star, Turbo, was very popular … until a newer racing game arrived. Overcome with jealousy, Turbo left his own game and tried to take over the new one. But when Turbo appeared in the wrong game, everyone thought it was broken!

In the end, both games were unplugged and hauled away.

"I've got to fix this mess and get Ralph home, or the same thing's going to happen to my game," said Felix. Together, the two headed further into Sugar Rush. Calhoun was determined to find that cy-bug before it could multiply.

Not far away, Vanellope led Ralph to the Sugar Rush kart bakery. The two sneaked inside and baked a kart … Vanellope loved it!

Just then, King Candy – the King of Sugar Rush – arrived. Vanellope and Ralph ran away! Vanellope led Ralph through a secret entrance into Diet Cola Mountain. She lived inside, near a hot spring of fizzy soda. Now and then, a few mint sweets fell into the spring, causing a boiling hot explosion.

Ralph wrecked the rocks around the lake, to create a practice racetrack. Soon Vanellope was speeding along! Ralph thought Vanellope might be a natural, if only she could stop all the twitching and glitching that she did.

Vanellope was excited. She and Ralph were heading for the big race! She was happy to have a friend, at last. The other racers thought she was just a glitch in the game, but she was going to prove them wrong!

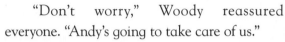

Packing for College

Woody, Buzz and the rest of Andy's toys were sad. They knew the truth: Andy was a teenager, and he didn't want to play with toys anymore.

"Andy's going to college any day now," Woody said. "We all knew this day was coming. Every toy goes through this."

Buzz noticed Sarge and his men climbing up to the windowsill. "What are you doing?" he asked.

"We've done our duty," Sarge replied.

"And," added another soldier, "when the trash bags come out, we army guys are the first to go." They parachuted out of the window.

"We're getting thrown away?" cried Rex. Then everyone started squeaking and shouting. No one wanted to get thrown away!

"Whoa! Hold on!" shouted Woody. "Through every yard sale, every spring cleaning, Andy held on to us. He must care about us, or we wouldn't still be here. You wait – Andy's going to tuck us in the attic …"

"And we'll be together," added Buzz. "Let's get our parts together, get ready and go out on a high note."

"I'd better find my other eye," said Mrs. Potato Head. She could still see images through the lost eye, remotely – and wherever it was, it was seeing a lot of dust.

"Don't worry," Woody reassured everyone. "Andy's going to take care of us."

Just then, the toys heard footsteps in the hall. They scrambled back into the toy box as Andy returned to the room. And his mum was right behind – carrying black plastic bags. "Okay, let's get to work here," she said. "Anything you're not taking to college either goes in the attic, or it's trash."

Andy's mum suggested Andy donate his old toys to the daycare centre. But Andy shook his head. "No one's going to want those," he told her. "They're junk."

Inside the toy box, the toys gasped!

"Fine," Andy's mum replied. "You have 'til Friday. Anything that's not packed for college or in the attic is getting thrown out."

Andy opened the toy box. He scooped up Rex, Hamm, Slinky and Mr. and Mrs. Potato Head – and dumped them into a rubbish bag!

But when Andy came to Woody and Buzz, he paused. They had always been his two favourite toys. He looked at each, then made his decision: Buzz went into the rubbish bag, and Woody went in the box bound for college.

Buzz lay on top of the other toys, feeling shocked. Had he really been dumped? What were they going to do now?

Disney · PIXAR

BRAVE

Choose Your Own Fate

"**M**end the bond torn by pride." That was what Princess Merida needed to do.

Merida's mother, Queen Elinor, had wanted her daughter to marry a son of a local lord in order to keep peace in their Scottish kingdom. The clans had all come to the castle and the sons had taken part in an archery competition to win the princess's hand.

But Merida wasn't ready to marry.

Determined to choose her own fate, Merida had picked up her bow and beat all three of the sons in the competition!

Queen Elinor was upset with Merida, and Merida was angry with her mother. She slashed the family tapestry with her sword.

Upset, Merida rode her horse into the forest and came upon a witch. She asked for a spell to change her mother's mind. But, instead, the spell had changed her mother into a bear!

Merida and Elinor-Bear needed to break the spell, and the only clue they had was a riddle from the Witch: "Fate be changed, look inside, mend the bond torn by pride."

Merida now realized what this meant – she needed to mend the tapestry. She took her mother, the bear, back to their castle.

Inside the Great Hall, they found Merida's father, King Fergus, and the other clans locked in battle – all because Merida refused to marry one of the sons!

Merida looked to her mother for help. But there was nothing Elinor-Bear could do. It was up to Merida to stop the fight.

Merida marched into the centre of the room. She was just about to agree to marry one of the lords' sons, when, from the shadows, her mother stopped her.

Elinor-Bear mimed what she wanted Merida to say. "The queen feels … that we should … find love in our own time," Merida translated.

"A grand idea!" Young Macintosh exclaimed happily.

The other lords' sons agreed. They all wanted to be able to choose their own fates. Everyone cheered.

"That settles it," Lord MacGuffin said. "Let these lads try to win her heart before they win her hand."

Elinor-Bear felt very proud of her daughter, and Merida realized the importance of what her mother had wanted her to do. It had taken a spell that turned Queen Elinor into a bear … but they finally understood each other.

Now, surely, the spell would be broken?

Bambi

Sweeter than Clover

"Hi, Bambi," said a soft voice.

Bambi looked up from the grass he was eating, and his friend Flower stopped searching for berries. Standing there was the pretty young fawn Bambi had met that spring.

"Hi, Faline," Bambi said. "It's nice to see you!"

"It's nice to see you too," Faline said shyly.

"Faline!" a young male deer called across the meadow. "Come over and play with me!"

Bambi's eyes narrowed. He didn't like the idea of Faline going off to play with someone else.

Faline blinked in confusion. "Do you want me to go?" she asked Bambi.

"No, don't go," said Bambi. But what could he say to make her stay? he wondered. Suddenly, Bambi had an idea.

"I want to show you something special," he told her.

"Something special?" asked Faline.

"I know where to find the sweetest clover you'll ever taste," Bambi bragged. Thumper had shown him exactly where to find it.

"Where?" asked Faline.

"Just follow me!" exclaimed Bambi.

He led Faline across the meadow to the babbling brook. Then he followed the brook all the way up a steep grassy hill.

Finally they came to a big waterfall.

"The sweet clover is right here by this weeping willow tree," said Bambi.

Bambi couldn't wait to share it with Faline. But, when he got to the tree, there wasn't one single clover blossom left.

"Oh, that Thumper!" complained Bambi.

"What's the matter?" asked Faline.

Bambi shook his head. He felt very silly. He'd brought Faline all this way, and now he had nothing special to share with her! But, just then, Bambi looked up.

"Look," he whispered. "Up in the sky."

Faline looked up and gasped.

Shimmering bands of colour had formed an arch over the waterfall.

"It's so beautiful," whispered Faline. "I've never seen anything like it."

"Neither have I," said Bambi. "But I remember hearing my mother talk about it. I think it's called a rain … bow."

"It's wonderful!" cried Faline.

"I'm glad you think so," said Bambi, a little relieved. "But I'm sorry you came all this way for no clover."

"Oh, Bambi," said Faline. "I came because I wanted to be with you. And, besides, a rainbow is a much sweeter surprise than some silly old clover, anyway!"

Welcome to Sunnyside

"Have you all lost your marbles?" Woody asked the toys. Andy was leaving for college and the toys had accidentally been put out with the rubbish! Andy had decided to put them in the attic but, because he put them in a rubbish bag, his mum had thrown them out.

Woody knew the truth and he tried to explain the mistake to the other toys, but they didn't believe him. Jessie had convinced the others that they should go to Sunnyside Daycare – the nursery to which Andy's mum was donating some old toys. They were in the boot of the car, in the box marked 'Sunnyside Daycare' when suddenly, Andy's mum shut the boot, got in and pulled the car out of the driveway. Woody instantly began planning their return to Andy's house. "We'll hide under the seats ..." he began.

The others didn't think it was a good idea. "He left us on the kerb!" Jessie pointed out.

Woody insisted the toys would be sorry. "Daycare is a sad, lonely place for washed-up old toys who have no owners," he said.

But when they arrived, Sunnyside Daycare didn't look sad or lonely at all. It looked cheerful and colourful! Inside, Andy's mum greeted the receptionist and the woman's young daughter, Bonnie. The receptionist took the box of toys right to the Butterfly Room.

The children were outside playing, but Andy's toys couldn't contain their excitement. They accidentally knocked over the box and spilled out onto the floor. The room looked wonderful to them. And the daycare toys were friendly – they cheered when they saw Andy's toys.

Friendliest of all was a big, pink bear who smelled like strawberries. "Welcome to Sunnyside!" he called warmly. "I'm Lots-o'-Huggin' Bear! But, please, call me Lotso!"

Lotso's smile was comforting. "You've been through a lot today, haven't you?" he asked. "Just you wait – you'll find being donated is the best thing that ever happened to you."

"Mr Lotso," asked Rex. "Do toys here get played with every day?"

"All day long. Five days a week," Lotso answered.

"But what happens when the kids grow up?" Jessie asked.

"When the kids get old, new ones come in," Lotso replied. "You'll never be outgrown or neglected. Never abandoned or forgotten. No owner means no heartbreak."

To Andy's toys, daycare was sounding better and better! Woody still wanted to go home to Andy, but no one would listen. Maybe the daycare centre would be okay, after all?

DISNEY·PIXAR
MONSTERS, INC.
Mike's Dog Problem

It was business as usual at the new Monsters, Inc. Mike Wazowski was one of the top Laugh Collectors. He told funny jokes and made children giggle a lot, but lately, he was having trouble on the job.

"Oh, no, this kid has a dog!" Mike groaned as he read the paperwork for his next assignment. Mike was terrified of dogs, but no one else knew. He was too embarrassed to say anything.

Mike was pacing the Laugh Floor, trying to come up with a good excuse to skip work, when his friend Sulley arrived.

"What are you waiting for, buddy?" asked Sulley.

Mike couldn't think of an excuse, so reluctantly he walked into the boy's bedroom He saw the dog straight away and jumped up on a stool to get away from it … but this was a playful dog. It ran up to the stool and sat in front of Mike, who got so nervous he couldn't remember his jokes!

The boy didn't laugh at all, and Mike was very upset. He just couldn't relax when dogs were around. He would have to go back to work without any laughs.

The next day, Mike was assigned to the same room because he hadn't collected enough laughs. Sulley noticed that Mike didn't want to go, so he snuck in behind him to find out why.

Once inside, Mike tried to tell a joke – but he was so nervous that he froze with fear.

Watching from outside, Sulley suddenly realized that his friend was afraid of dogs! That day after work, he asked Mike about it.

"I feel like a giant chew toy when I'm near them, like any second they might bite me!" cried Mike.

"Don't worry, pal," Sulley said. He then taught Mike all about dogs.

They read stories and watched videos together about friendly dogs. "Remember Mike," Sulley said. "Even though dogs slobber, have big teeth and make loud noises, that doesn't mean they're scary."

The next day, Mike and Sulley went to a room with a dog. Mike remembered what Sulley had taught him – to stay calm and let the dog sniff him. He took a deep breath. The dog bounded over and sniffed Mike, who tried to relax. The dog was friendly and Mike began to feel comfortable. Soon he was telling one joke after another! Thanks to Sulley's help, Mike became the top Laugh Collector again – and he even grew to like dogs.

"Maybe I'll get a dog," declared Mike.

"Maybe you should start with a hamster," Sulley said with a chuckle.

Disney MICKEY & FRIENDS
How to Unpack for a Vacation

One morning, Donald Duck heard a knock at the door. When he opened it, he found his friend Mickey Mouse standing there.

"Today is the day!" exclaimed Mickey.

"Today is *what* day?" asked Donald with a yawn.

"Don't you remember?" said Mickey. "You're driving me, Minnie and Daisy to the beach for a week's vacation." Mickey held up his suitcase. "I packed last night. Aren't you packed too?"

"No," said Donald. "I thought we were leaving next week!"

"No," said Mickey. "We're leaving today. And Minnie and Daisy will be here in an hour."

"Oh, no!" cried Donald.

"Calm down," said Mickey. "You have time to get ready. Just pack your things now."

While Mickey relaxed on the porch in a rocking chair, Donald went back inside.

"What do I pack?" Donald muttered to himself as he raced through his house. "I'll need my toys, of course, in case I get bored." Donald ran to his playroom and placed all his toys in boxes.

"What else should I pack?" Donald asked himself. "Clothes!" He ran to his bedroom and took out every suitcase he owned. Then he emptied all his drawers and filled his suitcases.

Finally, Donald calmed down. "That should do it," he said with a sigh of relief.

Mickey couldn't believe his eyes when Donald began packing up his car. Just then, Minnie Mouse and Daisy Duck arrived. They each had one small suitcase.

Minnie and Daisy took one look at Donald's car and gasped. Boxes and baskets were crammed into the back and front seats. Daisy opened the boot and found it overflowing with Donald's suitcases.

"There's no room left for *our* suitcases!" cried Daisy.

"Forget our *suitcases*!" exclaimed Minnie. "There's no room for us!"

Mickey put his arm around Donald.

"It's okay, Donald," he said. "It's hard packing for a vacation. You have to leave some things behind – even some of your favourite things. But they will all be here when we get back. I guarantee it!"

"And besides," added Daisy, "don't you want to leave room in your car to bring back souvenirs, like seashells and T-shirts and salt-water taffy?"

Donald brightened. "Seashells and T-shirts and saltwater taffy!" he cried excitedly. "Oh, you bet!"

"Good," said Mickey. Then he pointed to Donald's overflowing car. "Now let's all help Donald *un*pack for this vacation!"

The Finish Line

Finally, it was time for the last leg of the Wings Around The Globe Rally.

"We'll see you in New York!" cried Dottie the mechanic as she waved to her friend. She had fixed Dusty up as good as new after the dangerous last leg. The whole gang had come to Mexico to make sure Dusty was ready to finish the race.

Dusty was ready. He blasted off the runway and quickly overtook the other planes. This time he meant business. Out over the desert, he zoomed up right behind Ripslinger, the race champion!

"Let's end this," Ripslinger called to Ned and Zed, his teammates, as soon as they were out of camera range. He was really unhappy that a little plane like Dusty was so successful and stealing all the attention away from him. There was no way Ripslinger was going to let Dusty win! Ripslinger manoeuvred Dusty towards the rocks. He wanted Dusty to crash.

Suddenly, Dusty's coach Skipper came roaring out of the sky! He flew into Ripslinger's path and saved Dusty. Dusty couldn't believe his eyes – Skipper was flying for the first time in years! "Go get him!" Skipper hollered to Dusty as Ripslinger zoomed off.

Dusty knew there was only one way to get ahead of Ripslinger: fly high and use the tailwinds for speed, just like Skipper had taught him. There was only one problem – Dusty was afraid of heights! But this time he wouldn't give in to it. He fought through his fear and punched through the clouds! Dusty whooped with delight as the tailwinds rocketed him forwards. Soon he caught sight of Ripslinger below him.

Ripslinger approached the finish line. He didn't know it, but Dusty was gaining on him. Ripslinger tilted towards the cameras for a photo. Earlier, Chug had told Dusty that Ripslinger always slowed to pose for the cameras – that meant Dusty could pass him at the finish line! Dusty dived and shot past Ripslinger, straight over the line. Dusty won!

Dusty's friends pushed through the reporters to congratulate the new champion. They were all so proud of him! Dusty thanked them for their help along the way.

He was most grateful to Skipper – the old fighter had faced his biggest fear to save Dusty. Because of him, Dusty's lifelong dream had come true! Before going home, Dusty and Skipper attended a special ceremony on Skipper's old navy ship. Then they were both launched off the deck. The friends soared high into the sky. Their adventures together had just begun!

Disney · PIXAR
FINDING NEMO

Nemo's Day Off

Nemo liked lots of things. But there was one thing he didn't like – rules. He thought his dad, Marlin, had way too many: don't play outside the neighbourhood. Never have more than one after-school snack. Do your homework as soon as you can. Go to bed at a reasonable hour.

"I wish I could have a day without any rules!" Nemo said one morning.

"The rules are for your own good, Nemo," Marlin replied. "Someday, you'll thank me."

Just then, Dory swam up and Marlin had an idea. "Dory is going to babysit you for a while, Nemo."

When Nemo told his friend Sheldon, he got very excited. "This means no rules!"

"Hey, Dory!" Sheldon said. "My friends and I are going to the coral reef to play hide-and-seek. Can Nemo come?"

"Sounds like fun!" Dory said cheerfully.

Nemo was having a great time until he tried to hide in a grumpy moray eel's home!

"Moray eels are not as friendly as I expected," said Dory, ushering Nemo away.

Then it was time for an after-school snack. "How about plankton pizzas?" Dory said.

"All right!" Nemo and Sheldon shouted.

A few minutes later, Dory exclaimed, "You boys haven't had your after-school snack yet! How about some seaweed sandwiches?"

Then a little later she added, "Anyone for kelp cookies? Sea-grass smoothies?"

After all that, Nemo and Sheldon felt ill. Nemo knew he should be doing his homework.

"Oh!" Dory said. "I just remembered something. I think it's time to –"

"– play kick the clam!" said Sheldon.

"Yes," said Dory. "That must be it!"

"Now I think it's time to –" Dory began.

"… play splash tag with Bruce!" Nemo suggested.

"Now I'm pretty sure it's time to …" Dory said after Bruce had left.

Nemo and Sheldon looked at each other. They had run out of ideas.

"… play toss the sea disc!" shouted Dory.

A few hours later, Nemo was ready to go home. But Dory was still having fun. "I think it's time to go home for real," he told Dory.

When they got home, Nemo was sleepy.

"Well, I guess it's time for bed," he said with a yawn. "Goodnight!"

"Just five more minutes?" Dory asked. "Come on! Please?"

"Nope, it's one of the rules. And sometimes you have to stick to them," said Nemo.

Marlin smiled. "You sound just like me."

"Daddy, I'm so glad you're home!" Nemo cried. He paused. "Maybe … rules aren't so bad after all."

DISNEP·PIXAR
FROM THE MOVIE INSIDE OUT

Hockey Trials

A lot had happened since Riley and her family moved to San Francisco. Inside Riley's mind, two of her Emotions, Joy and Sadness, had accidentally got lost in Long Term Memory with Riley's vital core memory spheres. Now they were travelling through the Mind World, trying to make their way back to Headquarters.

Meanwhile, Riley was at the trials for her new hockey team, and she was feeling more nervous than ever before.

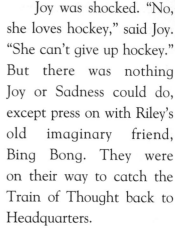

In Headquarters, Riley's other Emotions were trying to hold things together. Fear had recalled every hockey memory Riley had to try to replace the missing hockey core memory, but he could see through the window of Headquarters that Hockey Island was struggling to light up. Two Islands of Personality – which made Riley who she was – had already crumbled into the Memory Dump after Riley had argued with her parents and best friend.

Out on the ice, Riley tried to hit the puck, but missed and fell over.

Hockey Island began to shake. Anger pushed Fear aside and took over the console. Riley immediately threw down her hockey stick and stormed off the ice. Riley's mum stood up, concerned, as Riley joined her in the stands.

"Let's go," said Riley, tugging off her skates.

"Are you sure?" asked Mum.

But Riley was already heading for the exit. Inside Riley's mind, Hockey Island crumbled into the Dump.

Joy was shocked. "No, she loves hockey," said Joy. "She can't give up hockey." But there was nothing Joy or Sadness could do, except press on with Riley's old imaginary friend, Bing Bong. They were on their way to catch the Train of Thought back to Headquarters.

They had almost made it when a Mind Worker accidentally pushed Bing Bong's magical rocket wagon over a cliff and down to the Memory Dump.

"No!" said Bing Bong, starting to cry. Instead of tears, sweets sprang from Bing Bong's eyes – something Riley had dreamed up as a little girl. Joy tried to cheer him up, but nothing worked.

Sadness sat beside Bing Bong. "I'm sorry they took your rocket," she said.

"It's all I had left of Riley," Bing Bong replied, still crying. The pair talked for a bit longer, then Bing Bong stood up and said, "I feel okay now."

Joy was surprised. Sadness had actually made Bing Bong feel better! If only Sadness could make Riley feel better.... Suddenly, Joy heard the train in the distance – they had to hurry!

A New Life

Woody, Buzz and the gang had just arrived at Sunnyside Daycare. Andy would soon be leaving home for college, and had meant to store the toys safely in his attic. But Andy's mum had mistaken the bag of toys for rubbish and thrown them out!

Luckily, the toys managed to escape and jump into a box going to the nursery.

On first impressions, Sunnyside seemed like a pretty great place. A pink teddy bear called Lotso welcomed the new toys.

"Now let's get you all settled in," Lotso said. "Ken! New toys!"

Ken emerged from the doorway of a dollhouse. "Folks, if you want to step right this way…." Then he spotted Barbie. To the two dolls, time seemed to stop. It was love at first sight – they were made for each other!

Lotso broke the romantic spell. "Recess doesn't last forever!" he reminded Ken. The children would soon be coming in from outside. Barbie linked her arm through Ken's, and the toys set off on the Sunnyside tour.

"You've got a lot to look forward to!" declared Lotso. "The little ones love new toys."

Lotso and a doll named Big Baby led the tour around Sunnyside. Lotso nodded towards Big Baby and whispered sadly, "Abandoned by his owner, just like the rest of us."

Finally, Lotso and Ken ushered the group to their new home: the Caterpillar Room.

"Look at this place!" cried Jessie excitedly.

It was time for Lotso, Ken and Big Baby to head back to the Butterfly Room, but Ken hesitated.

"Barbie!" he blurted out. "Come with me. Live in my Dream House!"

Barbie cast a glance at her friends. The toys smiled and nodded their approval, and Barbie joined Ken.

Most of Andy's toys stood in the Caterpillar Room, counting the seconds until the children would arrive. They hadn't been played with in a long time, and they couldn't wait! Woody felt differently.

"It's nice here," said Woody, "but we need to go home now."

"We can have a new life here, Woody," Jessie declared. "A chance to make kids happy again."

The other toys agreed.

"What's important is that we stay together," said Buzz.

"We wouldn't even be together if it weren't for Andy," Woody shot back. He walked to the door. "I'm sorry. I've got to go."

Woody just couldn't abandon Andy. He had to get back to his oldest friend.

Lady and the TRAMP
Lost and Found

Lady stretched and rolled over. It was so cosy up on the window seat. Sunlight shone through the glass and glinted on her diamond-shaped name tag. Lady sighed contentedly. The tag was her most prized possession. Besides her owners, of course.

Jim Dear and Darling were very good to her. Just last night, they had given her and Tramp steak bones to munch on. There were so many, they had not been able to eat them all.

The bones! Lady had almost forgotten them. Leaping off the window seat, she hurried to the kitchen. Luckily, they were still right next to her food bowl.

Lady began to carry the bones into the garden. It took three trips, but soon the bones were lying in a heap on the grass. Then she got to work.

Dig, dig, dig. The soil piled up behind her as Lady dug yet another hole. She carefully nosed the last bone into the hole and covered it with soil. After prancing delicately on top to pat down the soil, she collapsed in an exhausted heap. Burying bones was hard work!

Rolling over, Lady let the sun warm her belly. The garden was the perfect place for a late-afternoon nap. She was just dozing off when, suddenly, her neck itched.

Sitting up, Lady gave it a scratch.

But something was missing.

Lady stopped scratching and gingerly felt her neck. Her collar! It was gone! Panicked, Lady searched the garden for the collar. It was nowhere to be found.

I must have buried it with one of my bones! Lady realized. She looked at all the freshly dug holes. It would take her all night to dig up the bones. But she just had to find her collar!

Tramp will help, Lady thought. She ran inside to get him. He was playing with the puppies, but ran outside as soon as he heard what was wrong. Soon the two dogs were busy undoing all of Lady's hard work.

"I see something shiny!" Tramp called. Lady was by his side in an instant, but it wasn't the collar. It was just an old bottle cap. Lady dropped her head sadly.

Lady and Tramp got right back to digging. And, just as dusk was falling, Tramp found a thick blue band with a golden tag. Lady's collar!

Lady let out a happy bark. Then she carried the collar into the house and sat down at Jim Dear's feet.

"Your collar came off, Lady?" Jim asked as he fastened the collar around Lady's neck. "It's a good thing you didn't accidentally bury it with your bones!"

Pinocchio
A Bright Idea

One day, Geppetto told Pinocchio, "I am off to deliver these puppets. I will be gone for a few hours. Stay out of trouble!" But Geppetto had not been gone for 15 minutes before Pinocchio became bored. "I have nothing to do," he said.

"You could clean the shop," said Jiminy Cricket.

"That's no fun," said Pinocchio. "I'll paint a picture instead."

"Where will you get paint?" Jiminy asked.

"From the workbench," said Pinocchio.

"You know you're not supposed to go near Geppetto's workbench," warned Jiminy. But the cricket's warning came too late.

"Oops!" Pinocchio cried.

He'd spilled red paint all over the workbench. Hurriedly, he grabbed a rag and tried to clean up the mess, but the paint just smeared. He'd made the mess even bigger!

Pinocchio looked around desperately. When he noticed Geppetto's kitten, Figaro, sleeping by the hearth, he had an idea.

"I'll say Figaro did it," Pinocchio said.

Jiminy shook his head. "That would be wrong," he said.

"What else can I do?" Pinocchio asked. "The workbench is ruined, and my father will be furious!"

"Why don't you paint it?" suggested Jiminy.

"That's a very good idea!" said Pinocchio.

So he set to work. First, he painted the bench top bright red. Then he painted the drawers green and yellow. Figaro woke up and investigated, getting paint all over his whiskers.

Soon, the job was done.

"It looks wonderful," said Jiminy.

"Yes, it does," Pinocchio agreed. But he did not feel proud at all.

"It's a work of art!" Geppetto cried when he got home. "It's so colourful it makes the whole shop cheerful."

Then Geppetto saw the paint on Figaro's whiskers. "Did Figaro knock over the paint again?" he asked. "Is that why you painted the workbench?"

"No," Pinocchio said. "I spilled the paint. I couldn't clean it up, so I painted the whole workbench. I'm sorry."

Geppetto was quiet for a moment, and then he said, "I'm proud of you, Pinocchio."

"Because I painted the workbench?" Pinocchio asked.

"No," said Geppetto. "I'm proud of you because you told the truth and apologized instead of telling a lie. That takes courage. Now, every day, when I see my workbench, I'll remember you did the right thing, and that will make the colours seem even brighter!"

Dusty's England Adventure

Dusty Crophopper was in England for his good friend Bulldog's retirement party. Dusty couldn't understand why such a legendary plane would want to retire!

"I'm proud of my racing career," Bulldog explained with a sigh, "but I'm getting older. I don't have all those fancy gadgets that the newer race planes have."

But Dusty knew his friend could outrace almost anyone. "All right," Dusty said with a grin. "But first, let's do some sightseeing."

"That's a smashing idea!" Bulldog said, happily.

They soared over fields to Wingsoar Castle and then Hoverton Court Palace.

Bulldog then took Dusty to Flownhenge. The planes took turns timing each other as they weaved through the ancient stones. Dusty marvelled at how Bulldog always managed to beat the time Dusty had set.

"I don't suppose an old-fashioned plane like yourself would be up for one last race?" Dusty asked.

"You're on!" said Bulldog. "The first plane to land back in Hatfield wins!"

Dusty and Bulldog took off, racing as fast as their engines would allow. Every plane they zoomed by was amazed at the speed of the two racers. Dusty started out in the lead, but then Bulldog swept out ahead of him. By the time they reached the coast, the sun was setting and both racers were nose to nose.

But as the darkness settled in, so did a wall of thick fog. In an instant, the fog became so dense that Dusty couldn't see his navigation instruments. In fact, he didn't have the foggiest idea where he was!

"Uh, Bulldog?" Dusty called out nervously.

Then he heard Bulldog shout, "Pull up, lad! Hurry!"

Dusty reacted quickly to Bulldog's orders and saw he had nearly hit a cliff!

Dusty was thankful to land safely back in Hatfield behind Bulldog. "How did you know I was so close to that cliff?"

"I know the area like the back of my wing," Bulldog said. "I simply used my instincts."

"What good are instincts?" Dusty teased. "Sure, you can navigate mazes, fly through fog like a pro, but you're still grounded without those fancy gadgets and gizmos, right?"

Bulldog chuckled. "Maybe I should reconsider retirement."

All Bulldog's friends came to his party that night. And everyone was overjoyed to discover that the retirement celebration was now a comeback celebration!

The veteran plane made a toast. "Here's to all the racing we've done together and all the racing that's yet to come!"

Not Just a Glitch

Wreck-It Ralph, from the computer game *Fix-It Felix, Jr*, had helped his new friend Vanellope to build a new racing cart, so he could get his Medal of Heroes back – he wanted the medal to prove he was a Good Guy, and Vanellope wanted to win her big race! She was a character in the *Sugar Rush* game.

As the pair headed out to race, Vanellope hit the brakes. "Forgot something!" she said. "I'll be right back."

That's when King Candy, the leader of *Sugar Rush*, arrived. He told Ralph that Vanellope was in danger – that she didn't belong in the game, and if players in the arcade saw her glitching, they'd think *Sugar Rush* was broken and switch off the game. And because Vanellope was a glitch, she wouldn't be able to escape the game – she'd be switched off along with it!

King Candy gave Ralph's medal back and asked for his help. He told Ralph he had to stop Vanellope from racing.

After King Candy left, Vanellope returned with a homemade medal, just for Ralph. On the back, it read: "To Stink Brain" and on the front, "You're MY HERO!"

Then, Vanellope saw the Medal of Heroes in Ralph's pocket. "You sold me out!" she cried.

Ralph tried to explain. He told Vanellope that she would confuse the players if she raced. And if the game were switched off, she would be doomed. Vanellope wouldn't agree, so to save her, Ralph wrecked her kart so she couldn't race.

Sadly, Ralph returned to his own game. Only a character called Gene was still there. Everyone else had fled, believing the game would be scrapped. Gene saw Ralph's medal, but he didn't care. He told Ralph that nothing had changed. Ralph would always be a guy who wrecked things.

Sadly, Ralph took off his medal and threw it against the game's front window. The glass shook and the "Out of Order" sign slipped. Ralph could see the *Sugar Rush* console ... with Vanellope's picture on it! Ralph gasped. Vanellope *did* belong in *Sugar Rush*!

Ralph hurried back to Sugar Rush to get some answers. He found King Candy's sidekick, Sour Bill. Sour Bill explained that King Candy had reprogrammed *Sugar Rush* and stolen Vanellope's computer code. But if she ever crossed the finish line, she'd become an official racer again!

Ralph knew he had to help Vanellope to cross that finish line. He rushed off to find his little friend.

A Summer Day

It was a hot summer day and Mickey Mouse and his friends were relaxing in Mickey's living room. The friends were just deciding what to do with their day when *pop!* Mickey's air-conditioning broke!

"Maybe there will be a breeze outside," said Minnie. But there wasn't.

"What are we going to do now?" asked Daisy.

Minnie looked around. "Hmmm …" she said. "Maybe we could make fans. Or we could try sitting in the shade under the tree…."

"Gosh! Those sprinklers look nice and cool!" said Goofy, pointing at Mickey's lawn.

Donald nodded. "But there isn't enough water coming out of them to keep us all cool!" he said.

As Mickey watched his friends looking at the sprinklers, he had an idea. "I've got it!" he shouted. "Let's go to the lake! There's always a breeze there and there's so much to do!"

"What a great idea!" said Minnie.

Mickey's friends raced home to pack and soon they were on their way. They were really excited about a day at the lake!

"What should we do first?" Minnie asked when they got there.

Before anyone could stop him, Donald raced off towards a little boat. He'd decided he wanted to go fishing.

Donald was about to hop into the boat when Mickey called out to him. "Wait, Donald!" he said. "I don't think we can all fit in the boat. Let's do something together, first."

"But the water looks so nice," said Donald.

"Why don't we go for a swim?" said Minnie. "We can all do that."

Donald really wanted to go fishing, but finally he agreed. After all, they had come to the lake to do something together.

"Aah," said Donald as they got into the water. "You were right, Mickey. This was a good idea!"

Mickey smiled to himself. He was glad he and his friends had found a way to cool off.

"I could stay in this water all day!" Daisy said. And that is just what they did.

As the sun set and the day started to get cooler, Mickey and his friends got out of the water. And Mickey had one last surprise for his friends … marshmallows!

"Gee, Mickey," said Minnie as they roasted the marshmallows over a campfire, "you really do know how to plan the perfect day!"

Finally, it was time to leave. Mickey and his friends packed their bags and got into the car.

"That was so much fun!" said Donald as they drove home. "Let's do it again tomorrow!"

The Flying Blueberries

Everyone in the ant colony was in a good mood. The grasshoppers had been driven off once and for all, and none of the ants had even been hurt. But Flik's amazing fake bird had taken quite a beating, and the Blueberries were determined to mend it.

"Fixing that bird is a big job," said Mr Soil, Dot's teacher, "but I know the Blueberries can do it."

The Blueberries stared at the fake bird. It was a big mess!

"I'll be back in a little while to see how you're doing," said Mr Soil before he left.

"How can we ever fix this thing?" one of the Blueberries cried.

"We can do it!" said Dot. "I bet we can make it even better this time!"

With a cheer, the Blueberries went to work. Some picked new leaves to cover the frame. Others glued those leaves into place with sticky honey.

After hours of hard work, the bird was mended.

"Let's sit in it!" Dot said.

But, just as the Blueberries crawled inside the bird, the wind began to blow. Suddenly, the breeze caught the wings. The bird took off!

It was up to Dot to save the day. She hopped into the pilot seat and took control. The Blueberries flew around Ant Island once, then twice. Soon they weren't afraid any more.

"Look!" screamed Rose. "Real birds are attacking the worker ants!" Dot jiggled the controls. The fake bird dived out of the sky and frightened the real birds away.

"Hooray!" yelled the Blueberries.

"Don't cheer yet!" Dot cried. "This contraption is out of control!"

With a bump and a crash, the bird hit the ground and skidded to a halt.

"Everybody get out!" Princess Dot commanded. One by one, the Blueberries escaped.

"It's wrecked again!" said Rose. "And here comes Mr Soil! He's going to be so mad!"

But, surprisingly, Mr Soil was smiling.

"You're heroes!" he told them. "You saved the worker ants."

"But the bird is wrecked again," said Rose.

"And you can fix it again too," Mr Soil replied.

"Yeah," said Dot, "and when it's fixed again we'll go up for another flight."

"Hooray!" the Blueberries cried.

"And here is a merit badge for you, Princess, in honour of your first flight," said Mr Soil.

Dot was confused. "I've already made my first flight," she said, fluttering her tiny wings.

"Ah, but this is a special badge," Mr Soil replied. "It is for making your first flight not using your wings, but using your head!"

The Caterpillar Room

Andy was soon leaving for college, and he had planned to store his toys in the attic. The toys, however, thought Andy was going to throw them away! They escaped and instead got taken to the Sunnyside Daycare nursery.

Woody knew Andy would never throw them away, and that it must have been a mistake. Most of the toys decided staying at the nursery was for the best. But Woody had to get home. The cowboy doll slipped out of the door just as the caretaker was passing by with his cart. The cowboy hopped a ride into the bathroom, and then made his way up to a window and onto the roof.

From his perch, Woody saw a tall wall surrounding the playground. He wasn't sure how he would get over it ... until he found an old kite on the roof. Grabbing it, he leaped off the building. The kite glided gently over the wall and down towards the ground. But then a gust of wind yanked him back into the air!

The kite soared wildly through the air, then – *SNAP!* – the kite broke, sending Woody hurtling down through a tree outside the daycare centre. Luckily, his pull-string caught on a branch, saving him from a crash.

The nursery receptionist's little girl, Bonnie, was playing outside, and she ran over to see the dangling toy. Just then, her mum honked the car horn. It was time to go home. The little girl grabbed Woody, shoved him into her bag and ran to the car.

"Oh, great!" Woody whispered. He just wanted to get back to Andy!

Back in Sunnyside, in the Caterpillar Room, playtime was about to begin! Andy's other toys waited as footsteps thundered towards them and a crowd of excited toddlers burst into the room. Shrieking with delight, the children grabbed the new toys.

But this playtime was not what the toys expected. The toddlers tangled Slinky's coil, dipped Jessie's hair in paint and covered Hamm with glitter and glue. They hammered with Buzz's head and stuck the Potato Heads' parts in their mouths. The toys couldn't believe it! Andy had never treated them like this!

A toddler tossed Buzz into the air. Buzz flipped onto the windowsill and lay still, looking out of the window ... into the other daycare room, the Butterfly Room.

Inside, Buzz could see a group of older children playing gently with Lotso and the other toys. Buzz wondered: why had he and his friends been put into a room where they were handled so roughly? There must have been a mistake. Buzz knew he'd have to ask Lotso – if he survived the afternoon!

101 DALMATIANS

One Lucky Pup

"Where are we going?" Penny asked. "Why do we have to get in the car? We're going to miss *Thunderbolt!*" Pepper pouted. The puppies all hated to miss their favourite dog hero TV show. They groaned in disappointment.

"This will be even more fun," Perdy said soothingly as she coaxed the puppies into the car. "I promise."

Roger and Anita got into the front seat. It didn't take long to get out of the city. Soon the car was winding down a country lane. The puppies smelled all kinds of good things. They smelled flowers and hay. Then they smelled something sweet – peaches!

"Here we are!" Anita opened the car door.

"Where's here?" Freckles asked Lucky.

"It looks like an orchard!" Lucky yipped. He loved to eat fruit.

Roger stretched. "You dogs run and play," he said. "We'll call you when it's picnic time."

"Don't eat too many peaches," Pongo barked, but the puppies were already running off.

All morning, the puppies romped and played in the grass until Pongo and Perdy came to call them. "Time for lunch!" Pongo barked.

"I'm not hungry," Rolly said, rolling over.

"I hope you didn't eat too much," Perdy said.

The big dogs herded their puppies up the hill towards the spot where Roger and Anita were laying out a picnic.

Perdy scanned the group. "Wait a minute," she said to Pongo. "Where's Lucky?"

The black-and-white pack stopped in its tracks. Pongo counted them. Lucky was definitely missing!

Perdy sighed and began to whimper.

"Don't worry, Mother," Pepper said sweetly. "I have an idea." He turned to his brothers and sisters. "Hey, everyone. Let's play *Thunderbolt!*" he barked. "We have to find Lucky!"

All of the puppies yipped excitedly and tumbled over one another to find Lucky's trail. Soon every nose was sniffing the ground.

Penny sniffed around a tree and behind a patch of tall grass. She'd caught the scent! "Here he is!" Penny barked.

The rest of the dogs gathered around to see the puppy asleep in the grass.

Lucky's ears covered his eyes, but there was no mistaking the horseshoe of spots on his back, or the pile of peach stones by his nose!

"Lucky is lucky we found him," Perdita said with a relieved sigh.

"And," Pepper joked, "he'll be *really* lucky if he doesn't wake up with a tummy ache!"

El Materdor

Mater and Lightning were out for a drive. Mater stopped to look at some grazing bulldozers. "I was a famous bulldozer fighter in Spain," he began. "They called me 'El Materdor'...."

El Materdor stood in the centre of a packed arena. With a nod of his head, he signalled that he was ready. A door at the side of the ring opened, and an angry-looking bulldozer rolled out. El Materdor raised his tow hook. One glimpse of the red cape dangling from it and the bulldozer charged towards the cape. El Materdor stood his ground.

Again and again, the bulldozer charged. Each time, El Materdor dodged him with a last-second move. Until the bulldozer finally surprised him. He came up behind El Materdor and pushed him across the ring, driving him right into the ground! The crowd watched in silence. Then the tow truck's hook poked out from a pile of dirt. At the end of it was El Materdor's red cape. The battle would go on!

El Materdor dusted himself off and bravely faced the huge bulldozer again. Through narrowed eyes, they studied each other. Suddenly, the bulldozer smacked his front blade on the ground. Two doors at the side of the ring opened and two more bulldozers drove out. Now it was three against one!

The bulldozers charged! For a time, El Materdor fought off all of them. But then the three bulldozers circled him and began to close in. There was nowhere for El Materdor to go. Nowhere but up, that is. El Materdor waited until the last moment. Then, with a mighty leap, he jumped out of the path of the charging bulldozers, who collided and collapsed in a heap.

"Olé!" El Materdor cried, landing on top of the wrecked bulldozers. But the celebration was short-lived. Soon more bulldozers rolled into the ring. It turned out that the wrecked ones had some friends.

"There I was, surrounded," Mater told Lightning. "Bulldozers all around me."

"What did you do?" Lightning asked.

"Don't you remember? You was there, too!" Mater said. In the arena, Lightning gasped. His paint job was red – just like El Materdor's cape! The bulldozers revved their engines and began their chase.

Back in Radiator Springs, Lightning interrupted the story. "Mater," he said, "that didn't happen."

"Well, try telling that to them bulldozers," Mater replied, pointing behind Lightning. The bulldozers that had been grazing were now surrounding Mater and Lightning!

DUMBO
Telephone!

"Did you hear the news, my dear?" one of the circus elephants said to another.

"What is it?" the second elephant asked.

The first elephant looked around carefully to make sure that no one was listening. "Well," she whispered in the second elephant's ear. "You know Mrs Jumbo's son, Dumbo, right?"

"Of course," the second elephant said. "The small fellow with the big ears. The one who became a ..." she shuddered with distaste, "... a clown."

"That's right," the first elephant said. "Well, a little bird told me that the first show was a hit! Everyone loved the 'Building on Fire' act. Dumbo leaped off a platform 20 feet high. And they're going to raise it up much higher next time!"

"Oh, my!" the second elephant said.

"But don't tell a soul!" the first elephant warned.

But, as soon as the first elephant turned away, the second elephant turned to another of her friends. "Listen, dear," she said. "You'll never believe what I just heard!"

"What is it, dear?" the third elephant asked.

The first elephant lowered her voice to a whisper. "Oh, you'll never believe it!" she began. "It's Dumbo – 20 clowns had to hit him with a tyre to get him to leap off a platform!"

"Oh, my!" the third elephant gasped. "That is big news!"

"But don't breathe a word to anyone!" the second elephant exclaimed.

"Certainly not!"

Soon, the third elephant was whispering to another friend. The fourth elephant gasped with amazement as she listened.

"... and so Dumbo set the platform on fire, and it took 20 clowns to put out the flames," the third elephant confided.

The fourth elephant told a fifth, and a fifth told a sixth. Soon, the whole circus was buzzing with the news of Dumbo's first clown show.

A little bird was flying over the Big Top when he saw a pair of elephants chattering below.

He flew down to see what was going on, landing on one elephant's trunk. "Good day, ladies," he said. "What's the word around the circus this evening?"

"It's about Dumbo," one elephant said excitedly. "It seems he fell off a platform in the last show, and hit 20 clowns. Now they're talking about setting him on fire next time!"

The little bird didn't stick around to hear the end of the discussion. "I can't wait to spread this news!" he squawked, fluttering back up into the sky. "Wait until everyone hears – they'll never believe it's true!"

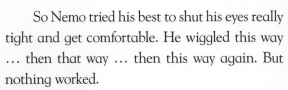

Sleep Tight, Nemo

It was late at night at the bottom of the sea – but little Nemo was wide awake.

"Nemo," said Marlin, poking his head into the anemone, "you should be asleep!"

"But I can't sleep," said Nemo. "I need another story."

"No more stories," said Marlin. "I told you five already."

"Then maybe another snack?" said Nemo.

But Marlin rolled his eyes. "No, Nemo. You just had a plankton snack five minutes ago. What you should do now, young clownfish, is go to sleep!"

"Okay, Dad," said Nemo. Then he did as his dad told him and closed his eyes. But, seconds later, they popped open again.

"Dad!" Nemo called out. "Daaaad!"

"Nemo!" Marlin groaned. "I'm beginning to lose my patience!"

"But, Dad," said Nemo, "I … I … I heard a noise."

"What kind of noise?" Marlin asked.

"Um … a … a spooky noise," answered Nemo.

"Hmph." Nemo could tell Marlin did not like this reason for being awake either. But still, Marlin stopped and listened … and listened … and listened.

"I don't hear anything, Nemo," he said after a moment.

So Nemo tried his best to shut his eyes really tight and get comfortable. He wiggled this way … then that way … then this way again. But nothing worked.

"Daaaaaaaaaaad!" he called out.

"Nemo," Marlin said. "For the last time, it's time to go to sleep. If you call for me again, it had better be a good one or … or … or else. Good night!"

Now, Nemo knew his father well, and he knew when Marlin was just a teeny, tiny, itsy, bitsy bit angry with him. But Nemo also knew that when you can't go to sleep, you can't go to sleep. And no matter how many moonfish or angelfish or sea stars you count; no matter how tightly you close your eyes; no matter how mad your dad gets – you'll never go to sleep until you're absolutely, positively, no-doubt-about-it ready. And Nemo wasn't. But why not?

Suddenly, Nemo bolted up. "Dad!" he shouted. "Dad! Oh, Daaaaad!"

"All right. That's it, Nemo!" Marlin said.

"But, Dad," Nemo said. "There's one more thing I really, really, truly need. Then I promise, I'll go to sleep."

And with that, he snuggled into Marlin's fins for a great big goodnight hug.

"I love you, Dad," he said. "See you in the morning."

Disney · PIXAR

Meeting a Hero

Carl and a young boy called Russell were in South America. They had flown there in Carl's house with thousands of balloons tied to it! Carl had been married to a woman called Ellie for many years. They had always dreamed of becoming explorers and visiting Paradise Falls in South America. Sadly, they were never able to save enough money to take their trip, and Ellie had passed away. But Carl still wanted to make their dream come true.

Since arriving in South America, Carl and Russell had met a strange, huge bird – Russell named him Kevin – and a talking dog called Dug! Dug was on a mission to find Kevin and wanted to take the bird prisoner.

They were walking to Paradise Falls, holding onto the house with the garden hose. That night, they stopped to rest. "Dug says he wants to take Kevin prisoner. We have to protect him!" Russell told Carl while the others slept. Carl agreed that Kevin could come with them to the Falls.

"Promise you won't leave Kevin? Cross your heart?" Russell asked Carl.

Carl thought for a moment. The last time he'd crossed his heart was when he'd promised Ellie he would take her to Paradise Falls.

"Cross my heart," he finally told Russell.

The next morning, they found Kevin perched on the roof of the house. The bird was calling towards the distant rocks. "The bird is calling to her babies," Dug explained.

"Kevin's a girl?" Russell asked in surprise.

Soon Kevin set off for her home. Russell wanted to go with her. But Carl was in a hurry to get to the Falls. "She can take care of herself," he told Russell.

Suddenly, three fierce dogs burst from the bushes. They surrounded Carl, Russell and Dug, and demanded they hand over the bird. The dogs were part of Dug's pack. When they realized that Dug had lost the bird, they wanted to take the travellers to their master.

The dogs led Carl and Russell to a huge cave. An old man stood in the entrance, surrounded by more dogs. When the man saw Carl's house, he laughed. He had thought that Carl and Russell were explorers – but real explorers wouldn't come in a floating house! "My dogs made a mistake," he told Carl.

Carl thought the man looked familiar. "Wait," he said. "Are you … Charles Muntz?"

Carl couldn't believe it – Muntz was his and Ellie's childhood hero! "My wife and I, we're your biggest fans!" he said, shaking Muntz's hand. Carl wished that Ellie was there – he knew she would have been thrilled.

THE LION KING
Runaway Hippo!

One morning Simba, Timon and Pumbaa were eating breakfast.

"Mmm, crispy, crunchy bugs," said Pumbaa.

"Try the big red ones," said Timon. "They have lots of legs. They come with their own toothpicks!"

Suddenly, they heard a sad cry from the jungle.

"Sounds like somebody is in trouble," said Simba.

"The sound is coming from over here," said Pumbaa. He led them to a muddy pond full of thick vines. In the middle of the swamp was a baby hippo. He was tangled up in vines and half buried in mud.

"Help!" the hippo cried as he struggled against the vines. The more the hippo squirmed, the more tangled he became, and the deeper he sank into the mud.

When the little hippo saw Simba, he became very frightened. "Oh, no, a lion! He's going to eat me!" he cried.

"Take it easy," Simba replied. "These guys have got me on an all-bug diet."

Timon grabbed a vine and swung over to the hippo. He began digging the little hippo out of the mud.

Meanwhile Simba jumped onto the hippo's back and began tearing at the thick vines with his teeth.

That made the hippo even more afraid!

"You *are* trying to eat me!" he shouted.

Finally, Simba and Timon got the hippo unstuck. Free at last, the hippo started to cry. "P-p-please don't eat me," he said to Simba.

"I'm not going to eat you, I promise," said Simba. "I just want to know how you got stuck in the mud."

"I was angry at my little brother and I bit his tail and made him cry. I was afraid my parents would be upset so I ran away from home," said the little hippo.

"I'll bet your parents *are* upset," said Simba. "Because you're gone and they're worried about you."

"They won't care," the hippo said.

"Come on," said Simba. He led the little hippo to the edge of the river. When they got there, they could hear the other hippos calling.

"Oyo! Oyo! Oyo!"

"Listen," said the hippo. "Oyo's my name. They're calling me! They miss me!"

"Sure," said Simba. "You can't just run away without being missed. When you're part of a family, no matter what you do, you'll always belong."

"What about *your* family, Simba?" Timon asked as they watched the little hippo rejoin his family. "Do you think they miss you?"

"I didn't used to think so," Simba replied thoughtfully, "but now I wonder...."

Island Adventure

Mickey, Minnie, Donald and Daisy were on their way to their seaside holiday. As soon as they arrived, they put on their bathing costumes and ran down to the beach.

They came to a lovely cove. "I'm going to relax right here!" Minnie declared as she spread out her blanket.

"Me, too," said Daisy, opening her umbrella.

"Those waves are just perfect for surfing," said Donald.

"You boys run along," Minnie said.

"We're happy right here," said Daisy.

Mickey and Donald surfed and swam until the sun went down.

The next day was sunny too. On their way to the beach, Mickey and Donald spied a boat for rent. "Let's go fishing!" cried Donald.

But Daisy and Minnie shook their heads. "We want to relax," they said.

So Donald and Mickey went fishing alone.

On the third day, Mickey and Donald wanted to go for a long swim.

"No, thanks," said Minnie. "I want to take it easy."

"Me, too," said Daisy. "We're going to the cove to relax."

The boys went off to swim. Daisy and Minnie headed for the cove.

While she and Minnie were lounging under the palm trees, Daisy spied a bottle floating in the water. There was a map rolled up inside. She waded into the water to get it.

"It's a treasure map!" she exclaimed.

"The treasure is on an island!" cried Minnie, pointing to an X on the map.

Minnie and Daisy decided to follow the map. They went up one hill and then down another. They crossed a stream and reached a dock with a boat tied to it.

"That's the island," said Daisy, pointing out to sea. They hopped into the boat and started to row.

They rowed and they rowed until they reached the island. Minnie and Daisy were very tired and very hungry.

"Look!" Minnie cried. "I see a fire!"

"Pirates!" exclaimed Daisy.

But there were no pirates. Just Donald and Mickey, waiting for Daisy and Minnie to arrive. A campfire was roaring, and fish sizzled on the grill.

"Looks like they found our map!" Donald exclaimed.

"*Your* map?" cried Minnie.

"It was the only way to get you two to have an adventure with us!" Mickey replied.

"Now, sit down by the fire," said Donald. "Lunch is served!"

DISNEY·PIXAR
MONSTERS, INC.

The Last Laugh

"Feeling funny today?" Sulley asked Mike on the Laugh Floor one morning.

Mike smiled. "You bet!"

Just then, laughter filled the Floor, catching Mike off guard. A group of employees were standing around another monster.

"Who's the comedian?" Mike asked.

"Stan, our newest recruit," Sulley replied. "I'll introduce you."

"Good morning!" Stan said when he saw Sulley.

"Hey, there's someone I'd like you to meet," Sulley turned to Mike. "Mike Wazowski, this is Stanley Stanford. And Mike here is our top Laugh Collector."

Mike and Stan shook hands. "What were you guys laughing about before?" Mike asked.

"I was just telling them about the time I met the Abominable Snowman and his mother. I said to him, 'Hey, Mr Snowman, where's your mother from?' And he said, 'Alaska.' And I said, 'Hey, don't bother. I'll ask her myself!'"

Everyone burst out laughing all over again – everyone except Mike, who couldn't help feeling green with envy. Mike felt like his position as best scarer was being challenged!

"Hey, good one, Stan," Mike said when the laughter had died down. "But have you heard the one about the skeleton who decided not to go to the party?" All eyes turned to Mike. "He had no body to go with!" Mike exclaimed. Everyone laughed. He was back on top!

But Stan had another joke. "That's funny, Mike," he said. "Have you heard the one about the big elephant that wouldn't stop charging? The only way to stop him was to take away his credit card!" Now everyone was laughing at Stan again. Mike knew this was joke war. As the jokes came fast and furious, the employees gathered around the two jokesters.

The joke-off carried on until, in a moment of panic, Mike's mind went blank! He began to jump up and down, hoping to jump-start his brain. Then, in one of his panicky little jumps, Mike landed on the edge of a wheeled trolly.

"Waaaaaaah!" Mike cried as the dolly took off, rolling across the room and carrying him with it! The employees watched as Mike rolled wildly across the Laugh Floor. They fell down, laughing their heads off! When Mike landed in a pile of cardboard boxes, the joke-off was over, and Mike was the winner. "You're a funny guy, Mike Wazowski," Stan said.

Mike smiled. Stan wasn't such a bad guy, after all. And with two hilarious monsters on the laugh team, thought Mike, just imagine all the laugh energy they could collect!

DISNEY · PIXAR

BRAVE
Mending the Bond

Deep in the ancient Scottish Highlands, in a kingdom called DunBroch, Princess Merida lived with her family.

Merida's mother, Queen Elinor, wanted her daughter to marry in order to keep peace in the kingdom. But Merida was an adventurous teenager – she wasn't ready to marry.

The bond between Merida and her mother had broken, because they couldn't understand each other's points of view.

Merida asked a witch for a spell that would change her mother's mind.

But the spell cake changed Elinor into a bear!

Now, Merida was trying to break the spell. She knew she had to mend the family tapestry, which she had slashed in anger.

But King Fergus had found Merida and Elinor-Bear in the castle. Fergus didn't like bears because, long ago, a huge one named Mor'du had taken his leg!

Fergus slashed at Elinor-Bear, not realizing it was actually his beloved wife. And Elinor-Bear was starting to act more like a real bear! She struck back, knocking Fergus to the ground. The noise drew the lords and the rest of the clans, who were visiting the castle.

"Mum, run!" Merida cried.

Elinor ran, with the men in pursuit. Merida tried to explain to her father what had happened, but he didn't believe her. He locked her in the tapestry room for her own safety, and gave the key to the nursemaid. Then he set off to hunt the bear.

Merida was desperate to get out. Through the window in the door, she spotted three little bear cubs. They were her little brothers, the triplets! They'd eaten the rest of the spell cake and turned into bears, too! Merida told the triplets to get the key.

Meanwhile, a terrified Elinor-Bear was running from the hunters. Fergus and the lords were closing in on her....

Freed by the triplets, Merida grabbed the tapestry. She climbed onto her horse and raced into the forest to save her mother. As she rode, Merida mended the tapestry.

Merida finally caught up with the hunters. She saw the king raise his sword to kill the bear. Merida stepped in front of him.

"Are you out of your mind, lass?" Fergus exclaimed.

Gathering all of her strength, Merida swung her sword and chopped off Fergus's wooden leg! King Fergus couldn't understand why his daughter would do such a thing. But Merida was willing to risk everything to save her mother. The bond between them was finally beginning to mend.

PLANES 2

Red Spells Danger

Racing sensation Dusty Crophopper was unstoppable! Three years had passed since he had won the Wings Around the Globe Rally, and Dusty was now a racing legend. He pushed himself hard, race after race, and the fans loved him for it.

But Dusty knew he couldn't have done it alone. "I've had an amazing team supporting me every step of the way," he told reporters.

His greatest thanks had to go to his coach, Skipper, for pushing him higher and faster than he thought he could go. And then there was Chug the fuel truck and Dottie, Dusty's mechanic. They were his biggest fans.

When Dusty wasn't racing, he spent his time in his hometown of Propwash Junction, where the annual Corn Festival was a great event. It was not long until the next one and the banners were flying. The whole town was getting excited.

Remarkably, it had even made the national news! Sparky, Skipper's assistant at the flight school, was reading the paper to Dusty and his friends when he saw the announcement. It was sure to be the busiest and best Corn Festival ever.

Later that day, Skipper was putting Dusty through his paces in a training run. Dusty roared through turns and pulled into a steep climb.

But then Dusty's engine stuttered and he fell into a spin!

"Dusty? Dusty? What's wrong?" Skipper asked worriedly.

Out of breath, Dusty couldn't answer as he began to lose altitude.

"Whoa, steady there!" hollered Skipper.

Dusty managed to regain control just in time and landed safely.

Dottie examined Dusty's instrument panels and checked his engine. She had bad news.

"Your reduction gearbox is failing," she told him. Even worse, they might not be able to find a replacement part – it was out of production.

Dottie explained what it meant to Dusty. Pointing to one of his dials, she showed him there was a green zone, an orange zone and a red zone. "Push yourself into the red," Dottie explained, "you crash." She fitted Dusty with a warning light. "If it comes on, you need to pull power ... slow down," she said.

All of Dusty's friends watched his expression. They knew this was terrible news for a racer like Dusty. If they couldn't find him a replacement gearbox, it was the end of Dusty's racing career!

"I'm so sorry," Dottie said.

Super Suits

Thanks to Baymax, Hiro and his friends had survived Yokai's microbot attack. But now, they needed to figure out who the masked man really was and how to find him. Then Baymax spoke up. "His blood type is AB-negative. Blood pressure 130 over 90. Cholesterol levels are –"

"Baymax, you scanned him?" Hiro asked.

Baymax nodded. With the robot's scans, Hiro could easily track down Yokai! He could boost Baymax's sensor to search the whole city for a match.

Hiro was ready to face the masked man again. There was only one thing left to do: he had to upgrade everyone's tech. They needed superpowers!

Hiro pointed to a framed picture of some superheroes on Fred's wall and smiled.

Fred grinned. He felt like they were in one of his comic books. "Our origin story begins," he said dramatically, "We're gonna be superheroes!"

Hiro headed home to start work on the team's gadgets in his garage lab. It felt good to be doing what he loved most.

For Baymax, Hiro created a new, tougher suit of armour, this time in glossy red and purple. The suit featured rocket fists, wings, thrusters in the boots, and an improved sensor.

For Fred, Hiro created a super-jumping, fire-breathing monster suit. He built laser gloves for Wasabi, a portable chemistry lab in Honey's handbag and super-fast discs for Go Go that she could skate on and throw as weapons.

Finally, Hiro built his own suit. It had advanced computing capabilities, but its main purpose was to keep Hiro safely attached to Baymax while the robot was flying.

As the team of friends stepped out in their new super suits, Hiro smiled. They all looked terrific!

Wearing the suits and with their gear in hand, the friends decided that they needed somewhere to practise their new superhero skills. They agreed the gardens at Fred's mansion would be the perfect place, with Fred's butler, Heathcliff, playing the part of Yokai.

Things didn't start off well. Wasabi sliced through pillars with his lasers, Go Go was very shaky on her new wheels and Fred set the grass on fire!

"I breathe FIRE!" he said, very excitedly.

Baymax's first attempts at flying weren't great, either. But with practice, the team's skills began to improve, and Baymax's flying became steadier too.

At last, Hiro thought everyone was ready for battle. He looked at Baymax. "Fire up that super-sensor!" he said.

Woody Meets Bonnie

Woody had escaped Sunnyside Daycare and tried to get home to Andy, but a little girl called Bonnie had found him dangling in a tree and taken him home!

Now at Bonnie's house, Woody was part of a lively game of make-believe.

"We need a spaceship," Bonnie said, heading to the wardrobe.

"Look," Woody said once Bonnie couldn't hear, "I need to know how to get out of here."

"But why?" asked the doll. "This is the best place ever."

Bonnie returned and swept the toys up into a game of make-believe that ended with the toys being launched into the air! They landed on the bed, as Bonnie laughed happily. She hugged them all close. Woody hated to admit it, but he was having a great time.

Back at Sunnyside, Andy's toys were unhappy after being played with by some rough toddlers! The children had gone and the toys were putting themselves back together.

"Andy never played with us like that!" cried Rex as he freed his tail from a pegboard.

"We should be in the Butterfly Room with the big kids!" said Mrs. Potato Head.

Buzz offered to sort everything out. "I'll go talk to Lotso about moving us to the other room," he said. But when he tried to leave, they discovered all the doors and windows were locked.

"We're trapped!" said Mrs. Potato Head.

Finally, Buzz spotted an open space above the door. Working together, the toys managed to get Buzz through, and out of the room. From up high, Buzz could hear two toys named Twitch and Chunk in the hallway below. The pair stopped by the Butterfly Room to pick up Ken, then continued to the teachers' lounge. After they disappeared inside, Buzz jumped down and followed the group. He sneaked into the lounge just as they were climbing into a vending machine.

Buzz followed Ken and the others, and discovered a group of Butterfly Room toys sitting at the top of the vending machine! Buzz hung back in the shadows.

"So what do you guys think of the new recruits?" Ken asked the others. "Any keepers?"

"All of them toys are disposable," replied Twitch. "We'll be lucky if they last us a week!"

Buzz was shocked! These toys knew how dangerous the Caterpillar Room was – and they had sent Andy's toys there on purpose! He had to warn his friends!

But when he turned to go, Big Baby was waiting for him…. What was going to happen to Andy's toys now?

Lady *and the* TRAMP
A Tramp Tale

It was a warm evening, just about the time that the first star comes out to shine, and *long* past the time for Lady's and Tramp's puppies to go to sleep.

"Just one more story, Dad," begged Scamp.

Tramp rolled his eyes.

"Well …" he said, "okay, but just one."

Happily, the puppies snuggled down onto their cushion. Tramp stretched out beside them.

"Did I ever tell you kids about the time I stole my very first sausage?" he asked.

"*Tramp*!" Lady warned him from her seat across the parlour. "That hardly sounds like a proper story for the children."

"Oh, tell it, Dad!" Scamp urged him.

"Well, maybe 'stole' isn't exactly the right word," Tramp reassured his wife. "And besides, it's got a great moral!" And with that, he began his tale:

"Now this all happened way back when I was just a little pup, already living on my own in the big city. I hope you puppies know just how good you have it living here in this nice house, with Junior and Jim Dear and Darling. Your old dad, though, was not so lucky. Oh, I had a lot of friends. And I had a lot of fun. But I'd be lying if I said I wasn't hungry – just a little – nearly every day.

"Well, one day I was especially hungry, and my nose was picking up all sorts of savoury scents. If there was bacon frying a mile away, I could have told you how many strips. So you can imagine the interest I developed in a certain, spicy smell coming from the butcher shop. Well, I followed my trusty nose, which has still never let me down and, sure enough, there was a heaping tray of steaming sausages. Can you believe it?"

"So you jumped up and gobbled them all up! Right?" Scamp broke in.

"That's my boy!" Tramp laughed. "But no. Don't forget, I was just a little guy. Couldn't reach the tray. All I could do was think about how to get that sausage … when up walked a lady with a kid in a carriage. Well, at first I was irate. Competition! But then I noticed the crumbs all over the carriage. Hey! I thought to myself. This might be the ticket – this kid obviously can't hang on to anything. Sure enough, when the lady handed the kid a piece of sausage, the kid dropped it, and down it fell into my waiting mouth! Delicious!

"See, Lady," Tramp added with a grin, "no stealing!"

"And what exactly is the moral of that story?" Lady asked.

Tramp laughed. "Why, good things come to those who wait, of course!"

Laughter is the Best Medicine

"I hope Quasi is okay out there!" Laverne said fretfully.

The other two gargoyles in the bell tower, Hugo and Victor, nodded in agreement. Their friend Quasimodo had just left Notre Dame to help the young soldier Phoebus search for the Court of Miracles. It was certain to be a dangerous mission.

"The only thing we can do is stay strong, and be hopeful," Victor said solemnly.

Hugo smirked. "How can we *not* be strong?" he said. "We're made of stone, remember?"

"Good one!" Laverne giggled. "Rock solid."

"You know that's not what I meant." Victor frowned at Hugo. "And both of you — don't you have any sense of the seriousness of this situation? Our dear compatriot is out there somewhere, facing grave peril...."

"*Grave* peril?" Laverne said. "Way to be optimistic, Victor — you've already got poor Quasi in his grave!"

"Hoo-hoo!" Hugo whooped. "You slay me! If I were alive, I'd be dying right now!"

As the two of them rolled around on the tower floor, chortling loudly, Victor glared at them.

"I see," he said sternly. "So you two would rather mock me and crack bad jokes than join me in my concern for poor young Quasimodo."

Laverne stood up and brushed herself off. "Why does it have to be an either-or thing, Victor?" she asked. "Just because we're laughing, it doesn't mean we're not worried too."

"But our friend could be in real danger!" Victor exclaimed.

"That's right," Laverne said. "And standing around here all stone-faced isn't going to help him any."

Hugo nodded. "If we spend all our time thinking about how terrible everything is, we'll go nuts."

Waving his arms to help make his point, he accidentally hit a bird's nest that was tucked into one of the eaves. The occupant of the nest squawked and flew upward. Laverne ducked just in time to avoid having the bird fly straight into her face, but then she tripped and fell and landed on the ground. The bird banked upwards, still squawking as it flew over Hugo.

Hugo leaped backwards — and landed on Laverne's hand. She yelled and yanked her hand out from under him. Hugo lost his footing, and landed in a heap on top of Laverne.

Victor stared at his friends, who were trying to untangle themselves.

Then he started to laugh. He laughed harder and harder, until he could hardly speak.

"You know," he said finally, "I think you just might be right. I feel much better already!"

Disney
Peter Pan
A Feather in His Cap

Peter Pan and Tinker Bell were off on an adventure and the Lost Boys were bored.

"Never Land is a dull place without Peter Pan," Slightly complained.

Then Rabbit spoke up. "We can play Pirates! That's always fun."

"Can't," said Slightly. "I lost the feather off my pirate hat."

"We could find another feather," Tootles suggested.

"An extraordinary feather," Cubby said. "Like Captain Hook's."

"That's it!" Slightly cried. "I'll steal Captain Hook's feather!"

A short time later, the Lost Boys were sneaking aboard Hook's pirate ship. Luckily for them, the pirates were taking a nap!

There, hanging from a peg on the mast, was Captain Hook's hat.

"There it is," whispered Tootles. "Get it!"

"M-m-m-me?" stammered Slightly.

Smee, Hook's first mate, awoke with a start. He thought someone had said his name. "Smee you say! That be me. But who be calling Smee?"

He opened his eyes and spied the Lost Boys. "Ahoy!" he cried, waking up the others. Quick as a flash, the Lost Boys were caught.

Captain Hook burst from his cabin. "Lash them to the mast!" he commanded. "We'll catch Peter Pan when he comes to save his friends."

Floating high on a cloud, Peter Pan and Tinker Bell saw their friends being captured.

They flew down to Pirates' Cove and landed on the ship's mast. Peter cupped his hands around his mouth and made a most peculiar sound.

"Tick tock," Peter went. "Tick tock!"

Down on deck, Captain Hook became very frightened. "It's that crocodile!" he cried. "The one that ate my clock and my hand! Now he's come back to eat me!"

"Tick tock … tick tock," went Peter.

"Man the cannons!" Hook cried. "Shoot that crocodile!"

The Lost Boys, tied to the mast, were forgotten. As the pirates ran in circles, Tinker Bell began to flap her wings. Fairy dust sprinkled down onto the Lost Boys. Soon they floated right out of the ropes and up into the clouds. On the way, Slightly snatched the feather from Hook's hat and stuck it in his own.

Peter Pan, Tinker Bell and the Lost Boys met on a drifting cloud.

"Thanks for saving us!" exclaimed Tootles.

"You helped me scare old Hook!" Peter Pan cried. "That's a feather in all your caps."

"But the best feather of them all is in mine," Slightly said, as he showed off Captain Hook's prized feather!

Disney·PIXAR

MONSTERS, INC.

Back to School for Boo

Mike was sitting in Boo's bedroom, telling jokes and acting silly. He was collecting laughs to help power the city of Monstropolis.

Boo was happy to see Mike, but she wasn't laughing quite as much as usual.

"Is something wrong, Boo?" Mike asked.

"School starts!" Boo said. "No photos!"

Luckily, Mike quickly worked out what Boo meant. School was about to begin again and she wanted to tell her class what she'd done over the holidays – but she needed pictures.

"Why don't you come to Monsters, Inc. with me?" Mike said. "We'll surprise Sulley."

Boo jumped up in excitement. "Yay!"

Boo and Mike went to Monsters, Inc. by stepping through Boo's wardrobe door. Mike found an old camera in the store room and started to take pictures of Boo.

Then Mike led Boo to the Laugh Floor. "Oh, Sulleeey!" he called out to his blue, furry friend. "I have a surprise for you."

"Kitty!" Boo exclaimed.

Sulley was so happy to see Boo! He gave her a big hug.

Then, all night long, they raced from one place to another, all over Monsters, Inc. – and Monstropolis – taking photographs!

By the end of the visit, Boo had taken lots of photos. She and Mike were trying to decide which were the best ones to take to school.

Sulley's eyebrows shot up. "School? What do you mean 'school'?"

Mike explained that Boo needed great pictures to share with her class.

Sulley was not happy.

"You know that's forbidden!" he exclaimed.

"Gee, Sulley, I was just trying to help," Mike said.

Sulley softened. "I know, Mikey, but it's my job to protect Monsters, Inc. We have to keep the monster world a secret from the human world."

"How are we going to tell Boo?" said Mike.

Sulley looked over his shoulder. Boo was already looking sad.

Sulley hated to see Boo so disappointed.

"Please, Kitty?" she said.

"Okay," Sulley finally told her. "I'll let you take back one photo. But I get to pick it."

Mike grinned, and Boo cheered!

At school the next day, Boo told her class all about her special adventure.

Her classmates didn't believe her. Her teacher didn't believe her. So Boo pulled out the picture....

The teacher gasped. "That looks like Bigfoot!" she cried.

Boo giggled. "Not Bigfoot. That's Kitty!"

Disney
PLANES 2

Crash, Bang, Fire!

At Propwash Junction, Dusty Crophopper was determined to prove he could still be a racer. A faulty out-of-production gearbox wasn't going to stop him!

He took off and sped across the treetops. It felt good to fly and to fly fast. Suddenly, the warning light that Dottie had fitted started to flash. Dusty knew what he had to do. He slowed down his speed and the dial hand returned to the green zone and back to safety.

But Dusty had been so busy staring at the warning light that he didn't realize he was too close to a water tower. Before he could take evasive action, he clipped the top of the tower and went into free fall. He landed hard and skidded right into the Fill 'n' Fly petrol station. Barrels went flying.

Dusty scurried out of the way just as the filling station's roof collapsed and its petrol pumps exploded.

KABOOM!

Dusty was horrified. What had he done?! "Fire!" he yelled. "Fire!"

Mayday, the airfield's old fire engine, heard Dusty's cry and appeared on the scene at once. He took aim at the blaze, but his old fire hose was full of holes and water sprayed in every direction other than towards the fire.

Desperate, he called for volunteers to help topple the high water tower that dominated the town's skyline. It even had Dusty's name on it, the town was so proud of him.

Mayday, Skipper, Chug and Dusty tied ropes round the legs of the tower and then, at Mayday's command, they tugged and pulled as hard as they could. The tower creaked and groaned, before falling down with a crash, sending a huge wave of water across the airport tarmac.

The fire quickly fizzled out, much to everyone's relief.

That was a close one, thought Dusty. *Maybe my racing days really are over.*

The next day, Ryker and Kurtz, two of the airport's safety officials, declared that Propwash Junction's airport was unsafe. It would have to be shut down until Mayday and his hoses were upgraded. They also ordered a second certified firefighter must be hired in order for the airport to stay open. In the meantime, they decided no one was allowed to fly in or out.

Everyone in Propwash Junction knew what that meant: the big Corn Festival would have to be cancelled.

"I'm so sorry," Dusty said, feeling terrible. "This is all my fault."

THE INCREDIBLES

A Super Summer Barbecue

One hot summer afternoon, Helen Parr stood in the kitchen frosting a cake. It was almost time to leave for the barbecue.

"Hey, Mum," said Helen's eldest son Dash, running into the room at Super speed. "Why do we have to go to some silly neighbourhood barbecue?"

"Dashiell Robert Parr," said Helen. "We're lucky to have been invited. You know we're doing our best to fit in here. And remember: no Super powers outside the house."

A while later, the Parrs walked around the block to their first neighbourhood party. Helen placed her cake on the dessert table. Her husband Bob headed over to the grill to help out. Her daughter Violet looked around for someone to talk to and Dash watched some children compete in a sack race. He couldn't join in because it might reveal his Super speed.

"Are you too chicken to play?" A boy teased. Dash scowled. When the mean boy hopped by, he mysteriously tripped and fell. Dash smiled to himself and brushed off his sneaker. His speed had come in handy, after all.

Meanwhile, out of the corner of her eye, Helen saw Jack-Jack atop a high brick wall. He was about to topple off! In a flash, she shot her arm all the way across the yard and caught

him. She sighed with relief and cuddled Jack-Jack. The other mother just rubbed her eyes and mumbled something about not sleeping much the night before. Oops, Helen thought to herself.

A while later, Helen saw the neighbours enjoying her cake. She looked around the yard and spotted Dash telling a story. Violet was eating an ice cream cone with a girl her age. Wow, it looks like we really fit in here, Helen thought. But just then, she overheard one of the neighbours.

"There's something strange about those Parrs," he said.

Had someone discovered them? Were their Super powers about to be revealed?

"All that may be true," someone else added, "but that Helen sure makes a terrific cake!" Everyone agreed, and the conversation ended.

The Parrs chuckled to themselves. Their cover wasn't blown after all! Maybe they were a little strange compared to the average family, but they were doing their best to act normal.

Bob and Helen rounded up their children and headed for home, pleased with the way things had gone. As they reached their house, Helen gave Bob a great big kiss, which the kids did their best to ignore.

Moon Mater

Mater and Lightning McQueen were looking up at a large full moon.

"Yep," said Mater, "I've been up there."

"Pffft! You have not," Lightning said. But Mater insisted. He began to tell a story about the time he went to the moon. Mater described driving past NASCA, the National Auto-Spacecraft Administration. Inside, a monitor showed the surface of the moon. On-screen, a moon buggy named Impala Thirteen was stuck on the edge of a crater!

"He needs a tow!" cried one of the forklifts who worked at NASCA. Then Roger the space shuttle saw Mater driving by and Mater agreed to help.

On the day of his flight, he made his way to the shuttle launchpad. He was wearing a space suit and rocket jets. He rolled onto the space shuttle and strapped in.

At the base of the launchpad, smoke spilled out of the booster rockets. Then fire, followed by even more smoke. Finally, blast off! The shuttle launched into the sky.

"We have lift-off!" Mission Control announced.

As Roger rocketed up into space, he whooped with joy. "Wooooooo-hoooooo!"

Inside the shuttle, Mater looked out of the window. "See ya later, Earth."

Soon Roger's rockets had carried them deep into space. They were nearly at the moon!

"Operation Tow Mater is a go!" Mission Control said over the radio. It was time for Mater's moon landing. He floated out of the shuttle and into space.

"Good luck," Roger said. "See you on Earth." The shuttle began the trip home. The rescue mission was up to Mater now. Using his jets, he steered to the surface of the moon. He bounced over to the Impala Thirteen.

"Connect your rescue apparatus to the frontal structural component of the linear axle assembly," Impala Thirteen instructed.

"Uhh," Mater replied. "How 'bout I just give you a tow?" He fastened his tow hook, blasted his jets and pulled the moon buggy free!

"Mission accomplished!" Impala Thirteen said. "Now take us home!" Mater fired his jets and rocketed towards Earth with Impala Thirteen on his towline.

In Radiator Springs, Mater had just finished his story. "Oh, come on," Lightning said. "That did not happen."

Suddenly, Roger the shuttle set down next to them. "Suit yourself," Mater said, and then he drove up a ramp into the shuttle.

Fast Friends

"Here, kitty, kitty," called Penny, peering underneath her bed. "Come on, I won't hurt you." She reached her hand out towards the old orange cat she had seen race into the girls' dormitory room at the Morningside Orphanage and dart under the bed. Now the cat was hiding under there, looking too afraid to move.

Penny had lived at the orphanage for a long time. But, in all her years there, she had never known that a cat lived there too.

"Whatcha doin' under there?" Penny asked.

Surprisingly, the cat answered her. "I'm hiding from the headmistress," he whispered. "Is she coming this way?"

Penny looked up and over towards the door of the dormitory. She saw the headmistress poke her head into the girls' room, glance around hurriedly, then head off down the hallway.

Penny hung down over the side of the bed again. "Nope, she's gone," she said to the cat. "The coast is clear."

Breathing a sigh of relief, the cat ambled towards Penny, came out from under the bed and jumped up onto the windowsill, looking at her. Now Penny could get a better look at him. The cat was wearing a red woollen scarf around his neck and a pair of glasses on his nose, and his long white whiskers looked just

like a moustache. He had a very kind face.

"Thanks," the cat said to Penny. "That was a close one."

"Why was the headmistress after you?" Penny asked him.

"Oh," the cat said with a chuckle, "she got me a while back to keep mice out of the basement." He stretched, yawned and jumped down to lie in a patch of sunlight on the floor. "But I don't mouse too well any more. I'm getting too slow to chase anything. I'm not as young and spry as I used to be. Say, my name's Rufus. What's yours?"

"Penny," she replied with a smile. She reached under her pillow and pulled out her teddy bear. "And this is Teddy."

"Well, hello, Penny," said Rufus. "And hello, Teddy."

Teddy just stared back at Rufus blankly.

"Quiet little guy, huh?" Rufus said to Penny. "What's the matter? Cat got his tongue?"

Penny giggled. "Teddy's very good at keeping secrets. And so am I. You can come hide under our bed whenever you need to. We won't tell."

"You won't?" Rufus replied. "Aw, that's mighty good of you." And so, feeling safe and secure by the side of his new friends, Rufus closed his eyes and settled down for a catnap.

Stuck at Sunnyside Daycare

All of Andy's toys – except Woody, who had tried to go home but had been found by a little girl – were stuck at the Sunnyside Daycare centre. They had thought Andy wanted to throw them away, so they jumped into a box going to the nursery instead.

The trouble was, the toys were trapped in the Caterpillar Room – where young toddlers played very roughly with them! Buzz had just sneaked out of the room and overheard a meeting some of the Sunnyside toys were having – Buzz heard them say they *knew* the toddlers would play rough!

Back in the Caterpillar Room, the other toys gathered around Mrs. Potato Head. She had started to see strange images, coming to her through the eye she'd lost at Andy's house.

"Andy's out in the hall," she said, holding a hand over her remaining eye. "He's looking in the attic. Why is he so upset?" She gasped. "Andy's looking for us! I think he did mean to put us in the attic!"

"Woody was telling the truth!" Slinky cried. Now that the toys realized their mistake, they knew what they had to do.

"Guys, we've got to go home!" cried Jessie.

Down the hall, Big Baby and the others had discovered Buzz. They tied him to a chair inside a cupboard. When Lotso arrived, he released Buzz and acted as if the space ranger's capture had been a mistake. Lotso even said Buzz could be moved to the Butterfly Room – as long as his friends stayed behind.

"I can't accept," said Buzz. "We're a family. We stay together."

Angrily, Lotso called for the Bookworm to bring the Buzz Lightyear Instruction Manual. The gang held Buzz down, and then, using the booklet as a guide, opened up Buzz's back panel. "Stop! Nooooo!" Buzz cried, as they flipped a switch in his back.

Then, Lotso and his henchmen went to the Caterpillar Room. Andy's toys, knowing nothing about what had happened, were relieved to see him. "There's been a mistake," Mrs. Potato Head explained. "We have to go!"

But Lotso didn't care. "Here's the thing, Sweet Potato," he said, grinning nastily. "You ain't leaving Sunnyside." He wanted Andy's toys to stay with the littlest kids, so his gang wouldn't have to!

Then, suddenly, Buzz appeared. But instead of greeting his friends, he began knocking them over with kung-fu kicks!

Jessie and the others stared in shock, wondering what had happened to their friend. Why was Buzz acting so strangely?

Bambi
A Manner of Speaking

Bambi and his mother were out for a summer's walk. As always, they stopped by the rabbit den where Thumper lived.

"And how are you today, Thumper?" asked Bambi's mother.

"I'd be better if my mum didn't just give me a dumb old bath," he said.

"Thumper! Mind your manners!" his mother scolded him.

"I'm sorry, Mama," Thumper said. He looked back at the doe. "I'm fine, thank you," he replied.

Bambi and Thumper were given permission to play, so they headed off into the woods.

"So, what do you want to play?" Bambi asked Thumper.

"How about hide-and-seek?" Thumper suggested. "I'll hide first, okay?"

Bambi turned his back to Thumper, closed his eyes, and started to count. "One … two … three … four … five …"

"Save me! Help! Bambi, save me!" Thumper cried. Bambi whirled around to see Thumper hopping towards him with a terrified look on his face. A moment later, a mother bear emerged from a nearby cave with three small cubs toddling behind her.

Though he was terrified, Thumper *still* managed to make a rude comment. "That's the meanest-looking creature I ever saw!"

"I beg your pardon?" the mother bear said. "First, you come into my home and disturb my children while they're sleeping. And then you have the nerve to call me mean? I think you owe me an apology!"

"Do it!" whispered Bambi. "Apologize."

"I'm s-s-sorry you're mean," Thumper stammered.

"Thumper!" Bambi cried. "That isn't funny."

Thumper looked confused. "I wasn't trying to be funny," he said.

"Try again!" the mother bear boomed.

"Um," Thumper tried again. "I'm, um, sorry I disturbed your cubs … and, um, you look just like a bear mum should look … which is big. And nice. Yup, you sure look nice."

Before the mother bear let Thumper and Bambi go, she said, "Like I always tell my children: manners are important!"

Bambi and Thumper ran home as quickly as they could. When they arrived at Thumper's, his mother said, "Just in time for a nice lunch of greens." Thumper was about to tell his mum how awful he thought the greens tasted, then changed his mind. "Thank you, Mama. That sounds wonderful," he said.

Thumper's mother beamed. "What lovely manners! I guess you have been listening to me, after all!" she said, as pleased as could be.

The Fox and the Hound

The Chase

"Whoopee!" Tod cried as he tumbled head over tail towards the water. He hit the surface with a splash. A second later, his friend Copper landed right next to him.

"It certainly is a beautiful day," Copper said.

"Yeah, it sure is," Tod agreed. The two friends swam to the edge and climbed up on the bank. As they sat in the warm sun, a great big blue butterfly landed on Copper's tail.

"Looks like you've made a friend," said Tod.

But the butterfly was frightened away by a booming voice.

"Copper!" the voice rumbled. It was Amos, Copper's master. Amos was usually grumpy, and right now he sounded angry too. "Where are you, mutt?" he shouted.

Tod silently climbed out of the water. He could tell that Amos was nearby, and that his other dog, Chief, was with him.

Copper creeped up beside Tod. "I'd better go," he said. "Amos sounds awfully mad."

"Why don't you sneak back to your barrel so you're there when he gets back," Tod suggested. "He can't be mad if you're already home when he finds you."

Copper scratched behind his ear. "But he's right in my path, and Chief is with him. Chief will hear me or smell me for sure."

Tod grinned. "You just leave that to me."

He winked at his friend and dashed up the hill, right past Amos and Chief.

"There's that varmint fox!" Amos cried as Chief took off after Tod, barking like mad.

Amos gave chase, running as fast as he could on his long, skinny legs.

Tod leaped over branches and darted around trees. More than once, Chief got close, his hot breath on Tod's tail. But Tod was smart. He led Chief towards a rocky outcrop and dashed into a small cave. Chief stuck his snout into the opening, growling away. But he was too big to fit.

"Never mind, Chief," Amos said when he finally caught up. "We'll get him later."

Chief gave a final growl into the cave, but Tod had already escaped at the other end and was dashing home.

Exhausted, Amos and Chief started home, too. And, by the time they got there, Tod was napping next door in front of the Widow Tweed's fireplace, and Copper was sitting in his barrel. Next to him, his supper bowl was empty.

"There you are," Amos grumbled. He shook his head. "And I suppose you've been sitting here almost the whole time. We could have used your help catching that dang fox – it's almost as if you're trying to avoid hunting him!"

Piston Peak

Dusty Crophopper was feeling guilty. He had let his pride get the better of him and had caused a bad fire at Propwash Junction's airport. It was declared unsafe – nothing was allowed to fly in or out until Mayday the fire engine could be upgraded and another firefighter was hired. This meant the annual Corn Festival would have to be cancelled. Dusty, the town's hero, had upset everyone!

He headed to the fire station to see Mayday and check he was okay after his ordeal.

At the station, he looked at the old photos on the wall and one in particular caught his eye. It was a picture of Mayday, and flying above him was a bi-plane spraying something over the ground.

"Is this you and an old crop duster?" Dusty asked Mayday.

Mayday looked at the photo and smiled. It wasn't a crop duster, he explained. It was a SEAT – a Single Engine Air Tanker. Instead of spraying crops with insect repellent, a SEAT dropped water on to fires.

That's it! Dusty thought. He now knew a way to make up for what he'd done. He'd become Propwash's second firefighter!

Mayday arranged everything. Bright and early the next day, Dusty flew off towards the air-attack base in Piston Peak National Park. Mayday's friend Blade Ranger, the head of the base, had agreed to train Dusty to become a firefighter.

Dusty had never been to the park before, but he'd heard about it. As well as being a huge and beautiful wilderness, it was also the home of the magnificent Fusel Lodge, the largest log building in the world. Its grand reopening celebration was just getting underway as Dusty arrived. The park superintendent, Cad Spinner, welcomed a steady stream of important guests – sports cars, coaches, SUVs and many more vehicles of all shapes and sizes.

Dusty landed at the base and rolled to a stop. No one seemed to notice. They were all far too busy doing other things: Windlifter, a heavy-lift green helicopter, was hoisting logs; Lil' Dipper, a yellow and red super-scooper, was sunning herself and having a snooze; Cabbie, a large transport plane, was listening to the radio; and the smokejumpers, small utility vehicles, were having fun, racing up mud mounds and jumping off them.

Dusty took it all in. With this lot for company, it looked as if he was going to have a very interesting time!

Disney·PIXAR

MONSTERS, INC.

Monster Laughs

Sulley was worried. As the new head of Monsters, Inc. it was his job to make sure the power levels stayed high. But none of the monsters seemed to be getting enough laughs.

"Mikey, we've got a power problem," Sulley said to his friend. "It's been a year since we switched from scare power to laugh power and the monsters aren't funny anymore. All their routines are old and dull."

Mike thought for a moment. "I got it!" he said, snapping his fingers. "I'll write some new jokes for all the monsters!"

Mike spent the next few nights writing jokes and inventing gags. He put on a show for the other monsters....

"Back in the day when I was scary, I gave 'eye-scream' a whole new meaning! But honestly, can you believe kids were afraid of me? I'm just 50% eye. That's not scary – that's just an eye sore!"

He wrapped up the performance with the perfect impression of a bowling ball!

After he finished his act, Mike handed out comedy scripts to each of the monsters and told them to perform the jokes just like he had – those kids would be laughing in no time!

But things didn't go so well. A monster called Pauley tried one of Mike's jokes on a little girl.

"Why did the one-eyed monster have to close his school?" he asked. "Because he only had one pupil!"

The girl just gave Pauley and his *sixteen* eyes a blank stare.

"They're terrible!" said Mike. "I need to round them up for some practice. If they can learn to perform the jokes just like me, our power levels will go through the roof!"

"But Mike, that's the problem," said Sulley. "The other monsters can't perform the jokes like you, because they're not you."

The next day, the monsters were feeling downhearted. Then, suddenly, a very tall monster called Lanky slipped on a banana skin. When he landed, his arms and legs were all tangled up. Lanky started to laugh, and so did all of the other monsters!

Mike thought for a moment. "That's it!" he cried. "Instead of copying me, you just have to be yourselves! That's how to be funny!"

"That's right," said Sulley. "If you've got 16 eyes – use them! If you have really long limbs – use them! Be proud of who you are!"

A few days later, the Laugh Floor buzzed with activity. Behind wardrobe doors, kids roared with laughter.

"Great job, Mikey," said Sulley. "Power levels are going back up!"

THE JUNGLE Book

Monkey Trouble

"Hey, let me go!" Mowgli cried. "Baloo!" But the big bear couldn't help him. Mowgli was being carried off through the treetops by a band of wild monkeys!

The monkeys laughed and chattered as they swung Mowgli from one tree to another. One monkey dropped him, and Mowgli yelled. But another monkey caught him by the ankles just in time. Then a third monkey pulled him away by one arm, swinging over to another tree on a large vine, where more monkeys grabbed at him.

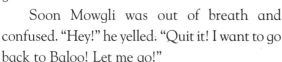

Soon Mowgli was out of breath and confused. "Hey!" he yelled. "Quit it! I want to go back to Baloo! Let me go!"

The monkeys laughed. "Sorry, Man-cub!" one shouted. "We can't let you go. You might as well forget about that bear!"

"Yeah!" another monkey said, catching Mowgli by the arm. "You're with us monkeys now. We're better than any old bear! You'll flip for us monkeys."

He tossed Mowgli straight up. Mowgli felt himself flipping head over heels.

A second later a pair of monkeys caught him by the legs. "See, Man-cub?" one of them said. "Monkeys know how to have fun!"

Mowgli laughed, feeling dizzy. "That was kind of fun!" he cried. "Do it again!"

The monkeys howled with laughter. They tossed Mowgli up, over and over. Mowgli somersaulted through the treetops until he couldn't tell up from down any more. After that, the monkeys taught him how to swing from branch to branch and vine to vine. They even showed him how to shake the trees to make bananas fall into his hands.

"Being a monkey is fun!" Mowgli exclaimed through a mouthful of banana.

Maybe it was good that the monkeys had found him, Mowgli thought. Being a monkey might even be more fun than being a wolf or a bear. And it was definitely more fun than going to the Man-village.

Mowgli swallowed the banana and looked around at his new friends. "What are we going to do next?"

A monkey giggled. "We're going to see King Louie."

"Yeah!" another monkey said gleefully, clapping his hands. "He's the most fun of all!"

"King Louie?" Mowgli said suspiciously. He didn't like the way the monkeys were grinning at him. "Who's that?"

"You'll see, Man-cub!" the monkeys cried, swinging through the treetops.

Mowgli shrugged. How bad could this King Louie be?

A Not-so-relaxing Holiday

No doubt about it: Hercules badly needed a holiday!

"But what about your training!" argued Phil. "You can't stop now! If you're ever gonna be a god, you've got to train like one!"

"If I don't take a break," said Hercules, "I'm never going to become a god, because I'll be so burned out. Sorry, Phil, but I've got to go."

And, with that, he put away his dumbbells and his javelins, cancelled his Herculaid Sports Drink TV advert, and rounded up Pegasus.

"We're off to the Greek Islands, my friend," he told the winged horse. "Sand castles, beach blankets, umbrella drinks … here we come!"

And, before you can say 'Mount Vesuvius', there they were, at the finest resort in the ancient world, soaking up the sun and doing absolutely nothing.

"A hero could get used to this," said Hercules as he bobbed in the water, sipping a smoothie and adjusting his sunglasses.

Suddenly, a cry rang out from the beach. "Shark! Shark!"

"Shark?" said Hercules. "In the Aegean Sea?"

But sure enough, a big, grey dorsal fin was speeding towards the crowded shore!

"Help!" cried the people in the water.

"Help!" cried Hercules … until he realized he was the one who could save them.

He swam up to the shark, grabbed it by the tail and tossed it up into the sky, all the way to the Atlantic.

"Whew," said Hercules, as the people clapped and cheered.

But not five minutes later, another frightened scream rang out – this time from the hills.

"Volcano!"

From the island's mountain centre rose a plume of thick, black smoke and fiery bursts of molten lava.

"Help!" cried the people.

Hercules knew what he had to do. He raced around the island until he found the biggest boulder. He rolled it all the way to the mountain top, then with one great push, he tipped it over the edge and into the bubbling mouth of the volcano. A perfect fit. The volcano was stopped.

"Hooray!" cheered the people.

Before any more natural disasters could occur, Hercules decided it was time to pack up and head back home.

"Back so soon, Herc?" asked Phil, pleasantly surprised.

Hercules shrugged. "Let's just say that for a hero, work can sometimes be easier than holiday!"

DISNEY·PIXAR
FROM THE MOVIE **INSIDE OUT**

A Bad Dream

Inside Riley's mind, two of her Emotions – Joy and Sadness – were trying to make it back to Headquarters with Riley's core memory spheres. These spheres held memories of the things that mattered most to Riley and kept her Islands of Personality running.

Joy, Sadness and Riley's old imaginary friend, Bing Bong, made it on to the Train of Thought, the fastest way to travel through the Mind World to get to Headquarters. But they hadn't been on the train long when it came to an abrupt halt. Riley had gone to sleep, and when Riley was asleep, the train went nowhere.

But Sadness had an idea. She spied Dream Productions off in the distance. All of Riley's dreams were made there, and Sadness thought they could wake Riley up with a dream.

Joy, Sadness and Bing Bong walked on to the set of Riley's dream for the night. It was teeming with actors in costume and staff wheeling set pieces around, and the camera operator was talking with the dream director. A special filter was used on the camera to make everything look completely real to Riley.

Sadness thought that a scary dream would wake Riley up best, but Joy wanted to wake Riley up with a happy dream.

"That's never happened before," said Sadness. But Joy was certain it would work.

She and Sadness put on a cute dog costume and ran on to the stage, while Bing Bong looked after the all-important core memories.

Back at Headquarters, Fear was at the console. He watched on the screen as the dog ran around. Then, suddenly, the dog split in half! Fear's mug flew from his hand, spilling tea everywhere!

At Dream Productions, the dog costume had come apart when Joy had run faster and Sadness hadn't kept up. Now Sadness was chasing Joy around the set. Through the reality filter, it looked pretty scary!

As Riley began to stir in her sleep, the Dream Production guards realized what Joy and Sadness were up to.

"They are not part of this dream!" the director yelled at the security guards. "Get them!"

Joy and Sadness hid offstage, but the guards spotted Bing Bong and he was arrested.

The guards took Bing Bong down into Riley's Subconscious, which contained her deepest fears. Joy and Sadness followed to attempt a rescue. Down there, they met a huge scary clown called Jangles. This gave them an idea. Before long, Jangles was stomping through the set of Dream Productions and Riley sat bolt upright in her bed, wide awake and terrified. Sadness's idea had worked! The Train of Thought would be moving again in no time!

Pinocchio

In a Tangle

One night, while Pinocchio was sleeping, a loud crash woke him. He jumped up and raced downstairs to Geppetto's workshop.

"Is anybody here?" Pinocchio called.

"Meow!" It was Geppetto's kitten, Figaro.

"I hear you, but I can't see you!" called Pinocchio.

Suddenly, the puppets above Geppetto's workbench began to move.

"Yikes!" cried Pinocchio, startled.

Pinocchio looked up to see Figaro tangled in the puppets' strings. Pinocchio began to laugh.

"That's funny!" he said.

"Meow!" cried Figaro. He didn't think it was funny! The kitten struggled to get free, but he only became more tangled in the strings.

Pinocchio just laughed harder.

Jiminy Cricket hopped down from the hearth. He rubbed his tired eyes. "What's going on?" he asked.

Pinocchio pointed to the little kitten.

"Pinocchio, maybe you should help poor Figaro instead of laughing at him," Jiminy said.

"Maybe I should leave him there," replied Pinocchio. "Then Geppetto can see how naughty he's been."

"Meow!" poor Figaro wailed.

"That's not very nice," said Jiminy. "How would you feel if you were all tangled up?"

Pinocchio sighed. "I guess I wouldn't like it very much."

He was about to free the kitten, when he suddenly exclaimed, "Hey, Jiminy, look at that!"

Figaro's paws were now wrapped around the strings in such a way that when his paws moved, the puppets began to dance!

"That's a neat trick," said Pinocchio. "Figaro can work the puppets!"

The kitten moved his paws some more, and all the puppets danced on their strings.

"I have an idea," said Jiminy Cricket. "Do you want to hear it?"

Pinocchio and Figaro both nodded.

The next morning when Geppetto awoke, he got a surprise.

"Look, Father!" Pinocchio said. "Figaro can make the puppets dance!"

Pinocchio winked at Figaro, and the cat leapt onto the puppet strings again.

"Amazing!" Geppetto cried, watching the show. "We can put on a puppet show for all the children of the town!"

Pinocchio was thrilled to see Geppetto so happy.

"But when did you discover Figaro's talent?" asked Geppetto.

"Last night," said Pinocchio, "when I found him in your workshop … uh, hanging around."

Disney
WRECK-IT RALPH

A Team Again!

Wreck-It Ralph, the Bad Guy from the *Fix-It Felix, Jr* computer game, had realized that his friend, Vanellope, from the *Sugar Rush* game, really did belong there! Vanellope had become a glitch in the game and the other racers had tried to tell her it was because she didn't belong.

But Ralph had discovered that the leader of *Sugar Rush*, King Candy, had reprogrammed the game and stolen Vanellope's computer code! That was why she glitched. Ralph found out that if Vanellope ever crossed the finish line, she'd become an official racer again!

Ralph had left his own game because he was fed up of being the Bad Guy. In reality, he wasn't bad. All he wanted to do was prove that he could be the hero.

But by leaving his own game, Ralph had put it in danger. The owner of the arcade would think it was broken and take it away! So Fix-It Felix, the game's Good Guy had been searching for Ralph to bring him back.

Ralph soon learned that Felix and Vanellope were being held prisoner in King Candy's castle dungeon. Ralph wrecked his way into Felix's cell and told him about Vanellope. Felix agreed to fix her broken racing kart right away. Next, Ralph crashed through to Vanellope. They were a team again!

The race had already started, but Ralph pushed Vanellope onto the track anyway. She quickly caught up to the other racers, and glitched and twitched past almost everyone. Finally, she pulled up next to King Candy.

"This is my kingdom!" he snarled.

"Race you for it!" Vanellope replied.

King Candy slammed into Vanellope's kart, to force her to crash. But she concentrated very hard and glitched away just in time!

As Vanellope glitched … so did King Candy! The crowd watched on the screen as the king flickered, and turned into … TURBO!

Turbo had been a very popular racing character long ago, until a newer racing game had arrived. Feeling jealous, Turbo had left his own game and tried to take over the new one. But when Turbo appeared in the wrong game, everyone thought it was broken! In the end, both games were unplugged and taken away.

Everyone gasped.

"You've ruined everything!" Turbo screamed at Vanellope.

But Vanellope zoomed forwards.

"She's going to do it!" Ralph cheered, as his friend raced towards the finish line. Finally, Ralph felt like he was the Good Guy.

Happy Campers

It was a warm, sunny day on Ant Island – the perfect day for Princess Dot and her fellow Blueberries to go on a camping expedition! Flik volunteered to be their leader.

"Single file! Forward march!" called Flik. "Follow me, Blueberries. Watch out for those twigs!"

"This is gonna be so much fun, Flik!" said Dot, marching behind him. "Pitching our tents! Making a campfire! Telling ghost stories all night long!"

"Well, we've got to get to our campsite first," Flik reminded her. "The perfect campsite for the perfect campout!"

"Where's that?" asked Dot.

"I'm not exactly sure," said Flik. "But don't worry! I'll know it when I see it."

So on they hiked, until they came to some soft moss beside a quiet stream.

"Is this it?" asked Daisy excitedly.

Flik shook his head. "Definitely not," he said. "Too out in the open."

"We're getting tired," Dot said.

"Chins up, Blueberries," said Flik. "We'll find the perfect campsite soon. I'll bet it's just across that stream."

Flik guided the Blueberries onto a broad leaf. Together they rowed across the water. But the other side of the stream was not quite perfect enough for Flik either.

"No worries," Flik said. "See that hill over there? I'll betcha the perfect campsite is just beyond it."

The Blueberries followed him up the grassy hill and down the other side.

"We made it!" the Blueberries cheered.

"Not so fast," said Flik, frowning. "The ground is too damp here. We'll have to keep looking."

"But Flik! We can't go any further," they complained.

"Nonsense!" said Flik, tightening his backpack. "You're Blueberries! C'mon!"

And so, with the Blueberries dragging their poor, tired feet, Flik hiked on. He looked behind a big rock, but it was too dusty. He looked near a hollow log, but a troop of boy beetles was already there. He even looked inside an old, discarded shoe, which might have actually worked … if it hadn't been so stinky.

Just when the Blueberries thought they couldn't walk another inch, Flik suddenly froze in his tracks. "The perfect campsite! We've found it! Let's pitch those tents, Blueberries, and get a fire started!"

But instead of cheers, Flik heard only silence. He turned around and saw that those poor Blueberries, still wearing their backpacks, were already fast asleep!

Disney·PIXAR
MONSTERS UNIVERSITY
Young Mike Wazowski

When Mike Wazowski was in his first year of school, he went on a trip with his class to Monsters, Inc. Mike was the smallest monster at Frighton Elementary – and the least popular – so when his teacher told everyone to pair up, nobody wanted to be Mike's partner.

"Well, Michael, looks like it's you and me again," said the teacher, taking Mike's hand.

A tour guide met the class and took them inside.

"We're entering a very dangerous area," he warned. "This is where we collect the scream energy to power our whole world."

The little monsters' eyes widened when a group of Scarers walked into the room. Scarers risked their lives by entering the human world to scare children. This important work provided the power for the whole of Monstropolis.

The guide warned the little monsters to stay in the viewing area and never to cross the red safety line marked on the floor. But that didn't stop Mike. He followed one of the Scarers into the human world!

Mike watched as the Scarer creeped up to the sleeping child and frightened him. It was the most exciting thing Mike had ever seen!

It was then that Mike decided he wanted to be a Scarer when he grew up.

The years passed and Mike never gave up on his dream. He decided to go to Monsters University to study Scaring.

On Mike's first day, a group of monsters called the Smile Squad greeted Mike happily. They helped him to register and told him all about the university. Soon Mike was touring the campus. When he got to the School of Scaring, he stood and stared. He was finally here. He couldn't wait to begin his lessons!

Monsters University wasn't just about studying. There were lots of clubs to join, too. The Greek Council handed Mike a leaflet. "We sponsor the annual Scare Games. It's a super-intense scaring competition where you get a chance to prove you're the best!"

Mike liked the sound of that! Then it was time to meet his roommate, Randy. He was a friendly eight-legged monster who could disappear without warning. It was a great talent, even if his glasses did give him away.

Mike started to unpack. All he needed to do now was graduate with honours and become the greatest Scarer ever.

"Aren't you even a little nervous?" Randy asked.

"No," said Mike. He had been waiting for this moment his whole life.

Peter Pan
Tiger Lily

It was a hot summer night in Never Land – so hot, in fact, that the poor Lost Boys couldn't sleep. And so it was decided that instead of trying to stay in their hideout in Hangman's Tree, Peter Pan and the Lost Boys would camp out for the night in the wild wilderness.

Certainly, they thought, the woods would be cool and shady, and the trees would catch any breeze kind enough to blow through. But little did they know how mysterious – and spooky – a forest could be once the sun went down.

"It's dark out here," said Cubby.

"And awful quiet," said Tootles.

"Won't you tell us a story, please, Peter?" asked Slightly, who was shivering in his fox suit despite the sticky heat.

"Very well," agreed Peter. "If it will make you all be quiet! I will tell you the story of the very first time I ever camped out in the wilderness – which, by the way, was the first time I met Tiger Lily…."

"I had made myself a fire, a great big one, 'cause it was autumn and the nights were getting cool. I'd just laid my head down on a patch of nice, soft moss, when all of a sudden I heard a rustling in the shadows."

"*Indians?*" the Lost Boys gasped.

But Peter shook his head.

"Not Indians," he told them. "That's what I thought at first too. No, this was something bigger. It was a *bear*! It jumped out of the trees, growling and waving its big paws in the air like Captain Hook swattin' blue flies. I've never seen such a mean, angry beast, before or since!"

"So wha-wha-what did you do?" asked the Lost Boys.

"Told him to get lost, of course. To *scram*! Apparently, he didn't understand English, however, 'cause he just kept charging.

"Well, I'm not going to lie to you; I started to get nervous. And then, there she was – Tiger Lily – as quiet as a mouse. Without a 'hi' or 'how do you do', she grabbed a stick from my fire and waved it at the bear. The next thing I knew, the bear had turned around and was running off crying! I suppose Tiger Lily saved my life that night," said Peter. "And it wasn't the last time either. The end."

"Um … Peter," said Cubby, peering out into the darkness, "do you know what ever happened to that bear?"

Peter thought for a moment. "Nope," he said and shrugged. "Probably still out there, wandering around, I guess." He yawned a big, mischievous yawn. "Now stop yer yammerin' and close your eyes and go to sleep!"

Heavy Metal Mater

Everyone was gathered at Flo's V8 Café for karaoke. Lightning McQueen looked over at Mater. "Why don't you get up there and sing?" he asked.

"I don't want to steal the show," Mater replied. "I was a big rock star."

"What?" Lightning couldn't believe it.

"I started out in a garage band … " Mater described how his rock band, Mater and the Gas-Caps, rehearsed in a garage. Soon Mater and the Gas-Caps had a gig at the Top-Down Truck Stop. When the band finished, all the trucks cheered.

"That so rocked!" called a waitress named Mia. "Do you guys have a record?"

The guitar player shook his head, but Mater smiled. He had an idea. Soon, Mater and the Gas-Caps were in a recording studio. Mater sang so loudly that everyone in the recording studio heard him. Doors began to open. Cars peeked out. "What's that sound?" someone asked. A music agent named Dex knew the answer. "Sounds like angels printing money to me!" He liked the song.

Dex rolled into Mater's recording booth. "Say, you boys are good," Dex told the band. Then he noticed their name on the drums. "All you need is a new name."

"'A new name?" repeated Mater. He tried to think of one, but nothing came to mind.

At that moment, a delivery car entered the studio. "Where do you want this heavy metal, Mater?" he asked.

"That's it!"

Heavy Metal Mater was an overnight success. They packed stadiums and had thousands of fans. Their concerts instantly sold out. Word had spread quickly about their amazing performances. A giant Mater balloon with wings lifted up from behind the stage and floated over the audience.

In Radiator Springs, Lightning interrupted the story. "You were Heavy Metal Mater?"

"No," the tow truck replied. "We was Heavy Metal Mater!" Then he continued his tale. Except this time Lightning was in the band, too. Mater described how he was onstage at the concert. Then a platform rose up. Lightning was on it, wearing sunglasses. "Are you ready to rock?!" Lightning yelled. Then he jumped down and joined Mater.

At Flo's V8 Café, Lightning interrupted again. "I'm sorry," he said with a laugh, "that did not happen."

"Well, suit yourself," Mater replied, motioning to the sky. Lightning looked up. The balloon from the concert was flying overhead! Had Mater been telling the truth…?

Woody Discovers the Truth

Buzz, Jessie and most of Andy's other toys were at the Sunnyside Daycare nursery. They now knew Andy hadn't meant to throw them away – and they just wanted to get back home to him. Woody had already escaped, and been taken home by a little girl called Bonnie, but the rest of the toys were being held prisoner by the evil pink teddy bear, Lotso!

Lotso and his helpers had found Buzz's reset button – and now the space ranger was helping to hold his own friends captive!

Lotso's gang put Andy's toys into wire crates. When Mr Potato Head fought back, Big Baby put him in 'the Box' – a covered sandbox in the playground.

Suddenly, Barbie walked in. "Ken? What are you doing to my friends?" she asked in surprise. When she realized what was happening, she insisted on staying with Andy's toys. And so, she became a prisoner, too.

"We've got a way of doing things here at Sunnyside," Lotso explained. "Life here can be a dream come true. But if you break the rules…." He threw Woody's hat, which he had found, onto the floor.

The toys gasped. "What did you do to him?" cried Jessie. Lotso simply chuckled and left, leaving the prisoners under Buzz's guard.

Meanwhile, Woody had discovered that Bonnie lived just blocks from Andy's house.

"If you guys ever get to Sunnyside Daycare," Woody told Bonnie's toys, "tell them Woody made it home."

"Sunnyside?" Bonnie's toys gasped. Quickly, they took Woody to Chuckles, an old clown toy who knew all about Sunnyside – and Lotso. Long ago, Chuckles explained, he, Lotso and Big Baby had belonged to a little girl named Daisy. One day, the toys were accidentally left behind during a trip. Lotso led them on a long journey home, but when they arrived, Daisy had a new pink bear. Heartbroken, Lotso turned to Big Baby and ripped off the pendant with Daisy's name. Eventually, the three ended up at Sunnyside, but Lotso had never stopped being angry. He controlled the nursery with cruelty, and Andy's toys were in danger.

Woody was worried. He wanted to get back to Andy, but he couldn't leave his friends. He had to go back and rescue them!

The next day, Woody hitched a ride back to Sunnyside in Bonnie's bag. He sneaked into the Caterpillar Room and looked for his friends. What he saw was horrid – his friends were getting thrown around by toddlers! He had to save them.

THE ARISTOCATS
The Cosiest Carriage

One day O'Malley took Duchess and her kittens down to the junkyard to visit O'Malley's old and dear friend, Scat Cat.

Scat Cat lived in a broken-down carriage that had once been very grand indeed. But the wheels had fallen apart long ago, and the cushions were shredded.

To top it all off, there was an huge hole right in the middle of the worn, tattered roof.

Still, as far as Scat Cat was concerned, his home was perfect. "I feel free here," he told the kittens. "I can come and go as I please. And when I stretch out on the cushions at night, I look up and there are the stars, a-twinklin' and a-winkin' back at me!"

The kittens had a grand time playing with Scat Cat in the junkyard. But they were glad to return to the soft pillows, cosy blankets and warm milk waiting for them back at Madame Bonfamille's mansion.

But a few days later, who should appear at Madame's doorstep but Scat Cat himself. "You'll never believe it," he said. "I went into town to stretch my legs, and when I got back … poof! The carriage was gone!"

"Well, naturally," said Duchess, "you will have to stay with us! I'm sure Madame would be delighted to have you as our guest."

But after only one night, Scat Cat began to feel sad. Everything at Madame Bonfamille's happened according to a schedule. Scat Cat missed doing as he pleased.

"But you know what I miss most?" Scat Cat told O'Malley and the kittens. "My old carriage. What I wouldn't give to be able to look up at the sky and count the twinklin' stars…."

The kittens decided to help Scat Cat. For a while, Madame had been complaining about her old carriage. So, Berlioz climbed into it and began clawing at the old cushions. Toulouse and Marie joined him, and soon, the cushions looked just like the ones in Scat Cat's old carriage!

Finally, Toulouse came crashing down through the carriage roof, making a huge hole. "Oh, my!" exclaimed a voice. The kittens turned, and there was Madame. She surveyed the damage … and smiled! "At last I have an excuse to buy a new carriage," she said. "Let's take this one out to the junkyard at once."

"I don't believe it!" cried Scat Cat, when the kittens led him to his new home, back in the junkyard. "It's purr-fect! How can I ever thank you?" he asked the kittens.

"It was our pleasure," said Berlioz. He flexed his claws. "It's not every day we're thanked for clawing something to pieces!"

Disney · PIXAR

THE INCREDIBLES

The Parr Family

During the golden age of the Supers, Mr Incredible was the world's greatest hero. With the power of Super strength, he caught criminals, stopped disasters and protected the public from harm.

Mr Incredible's greatest fan was a boy called Buddy. He wanted to be a Super like his hero. Buddy decided to change his name to Incrediboy, and he even invented some rocket boots that allowed him to fly. He asked Mr Incredible if he could be his sidekick, but Mr Incredible told Buddy that fancy boots didn't make someone a Super. Supers were born, not made.

Mr Incredible married another Super, Elastigirl. They loved each other and the future seemed bright … until disaster struck.

People started to sue the Supers and claim they hadn't wanted to be saved! The government told the Supers to stop being heroes. They had to go into hiding and live like normal people.

So Mr Incredible became boring, average Bob Parr, and Elastigirl became Helen. They had a shy daughter, Violet, who could turn invisible and create force fields, a Super-fast son named Dash, and a baby called Jack-Jack who seemed to have no Super powers at all.

With all these Super powers, family meals could get chaotic. Controlling Super kids was tough. Helen adjusted very well to normal life and focused all her efforts on the kids. Bob worked in a boring job at an insurance company and desperately missed being a Super.

Bob couldn't stop dreaming of the past. He would occasionally give himself away by using his powers. Then the whole family had to be relocated!

One night, Bob went out with his friend Lucius. Lucius Best was known as Frozone, literally the coolest Super of all! They were tuned into the police radio, listening to reports of crimes in progress. He was hoping to save someone – just like in the good old days. When he heard about a fire at a nearby block of flats, Bob convinced Lucius they should go and help.

"We're gonna get caught," said Lucius.

The two Supers saved several people – but in order to escape the fire, they had to break into the jeweller's next door. A policeman thought they were thieves! Lucius had to use his Super powers to freeze the policeman, and the two Supers escaped.

Nearby, a mysterious woman watched them from her car … but Bob wouldn't find out who she was just yet.

DUMBO
Lend Me Your Ears

"I think I can, I think I can, I think I can," chugged Casey Jr, the circus train. The train moved slowly around a bend. "I think I can. I think I … *Ah-choo!*" he sneezed.

Suddenly, he came to a halt. "I know I can't," he admitted finally. The animals and the performers poked their heads out, wondering what was wrong.

"Well?" asked the Ringmaster.

"Casey Jr here has a cold," the engineer replied. "He's going to need some rest before he can take us any further."

The Ringmaster frowned. "But we're due at the fairground in a few hours. What will we do? After all, the show must go on!"

The engineer just shrugged and turned his attention back to the sneezing, coughing and spluttering little engine.

The Ringmaster went down the train, swinging open the doors to all the cages and cars. "Come on, everyone," he said. "Might as well stretch your legs."

The animals lumbered, scampered and pranced onto the wide open field. Next, the clowns and acrobats and animal trainers sauntered out. Some set up crates in the grass and played cards, others rehearsed and a few pulled out packed lunches and sprawled on the ground.

Dumbo the elephant and his mother, Mrs Jumbo, took a drink from the bucket of water the Ringmaster had set out.

Mrs Jumbo gazed around. "Looks like we're in the middle of nowhere," she said. "I do hope poor Casey Jr is feeling better soon."

"Me too," Dumbo's friend Timothy Q. Mouse said hopefully.

Just then there was a clap of thunder. Rain began to fall from the sky. The animals and performers ran for the shelter of the circus wagons. Dumbo held on to his mother's tail, but just then, the wind picked up. The gust caught Dumbo's huge ears and sent him flying backwards.

"That's it!" yelled the Ringmaster over the howling wind. "Dumbo, come with me!" He led Dumbo over to the train, climbed onto the front wagon, and motioned for the little elephant to join him.

"Now spread out those great ears of yours!" the Ringmaster said. Dumbo's ears billowed out, catching the wind like giant sails and pushing Casey Jr along the tracks. "The show will go on!" the Ringmaster shouted happily.

"I know I can. I know I can. I know I can," chanted Casey Jr. And then he added, "Thanks to Dumbo!"

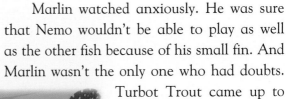

Nemo's Best Shot

"Come on, Dad! We're going to be late!" cried Nemo. Nemo and Marlin were hurrying through the busy swimming lanes of the colourful Great Barrier Reef.

"Are you sure you want to play pearl volleyball?" Marlin asked nervously. "There are lots of other things you can do. Sponge jumping, for example. Or maybe reef dancing."

"Reef dancing!" cried Nemo, horrified. "No way! That's for babies! I want to play pearl volleyball!"

At Sea Urchin Stadium, Mr Ray made the opening announcements. "Hello and welcome, everyone! Before we get started, let's give a big thank you to Ms Esther Clam for donating today's ball."

Everyone applauded as Esther opened her shell and spat out the pearl.

"Let's play pearl volleyball!" cried Mr Ray.

"Good luck, son," said Marlin. "Just remember what I told you – "

"I know! I know!" said Nemo, rolling his eyes. "When you give it your best shot, even if you lose, you win."

The players lined up on either side of the sea fan net. Ray's Raiders were on one side, and Nemo's team, the Fighting Planktons, were on the other.

Marlin watched anxiously. He was sure that Nemo wouldn't be able to play as well as the other fish because of his small fin. And Marlin wasn't the only one who had doubts. Turbot Trout came up to Nemo on the court.

"Coach may be letting you play today," Turbot snapped, "but you better not mess up the Planktons' winning streak."

Turbot didn't know Nemo had spent many hours smacking around pebbles in a dentist's fishtank.

"Just watch and learn," murmured Nemo.

Suddenly, the pearl came right to Nemo. *Smack*! Using his good left fin, Nemo sent the pearl flying right over the net. The pearl flew so fast, the other team couldn't return it. Nemo scored his first point for the Planktons!

Nemo played like a pro. He scored again with his good fin, then with his tail. And, just to show his father and Turbot Trout, he scored the winning point with his little fin.

"Go, short fin!" cried Turbot Trout. "With a player like you, we're going to go all the way to the Lobster Bowl Clam-pionship!"

"Wow, Nemo," said Marlin after the game. "That was amazing."

"Thanks, Dad," said Nemo. "I gave it my best shot, like you said. And we actually won too!"

The Hic-hic-hiccups

"What a day!" Pumbaa said as he led Simba and Timon through the forest.

"What a day, indeed," Timon agreed.

"Hic!" said Simba.

"What was that?" Timon cried.

"Don't be scared. It's just that I have the – *hic!* I have the hiccups," Simba explained.

"I'll tell you what to do," Timon said. "Forget about it! They'll go away – eventually."

"Forget about it? *Hic!* But I can't roar," Simba explained. And to demonstrate, he opened his mouth really wide. But, just as he was about to roar, he hiccupped!

"See?" he said sadly.

"Have you tried licking tree bark?" Pumbaa asked.

"Licking tree bark?" said Simba.

"It always works for me," Pumbaa explained. "That or closing your eyes, holding your nose and jumping on one foot while saying your name five times fast – backwards."

Timon watched Simba hop around on one foot, holding his nose with his eyes closed. "Abmis, Abmis, Abmis – *hic!* It's not working!" Simba cried.

"Maybe there's something caught in his throat," Timon offered.

"There's nothing caught in his throat," Pumbaa said.

"How do you know?" Timon asked.

"I just know about these things," Pumbaa answered.

Suddenly, right on cue, Simba interrupted their argument with the biggest hiccup of all.

"HIC!"

And, wouldn't you know, just then the biggest fly you've ever seen came soaring out of Simba's mouth. It flew right into a tree and crashed to the ground.

The fly stood up groggily and shook itself off.

"It's about time, buddy!" the fly said to Simba.

Simba was about to reply, but he was interrupted by two voices, shouting in unison –

"DINNER!"

The fly gave a frightened squeak and flew off, as Timon and Pumbaa both pounced on the spot where it had been just a moment earlier.

The Great Escape

Buzz, Jessie and most of Andy's other toys were trapped at Sunnyside Daycare. Woody had escaped, but had come back after hearing an evil bear named Lotso controlled the nursery. Woody had creeped inside the room where his friends were trapped and watched as they were played with roughly by toddlers. He was shocked!

RIIING!!! RIIING!!! A toy telephone sidled up to Woody. The cowboy picked up the receiver and heard, "You and your friends aren't ever getting out of here now." Lotso kept tabs on everyone, the phone said. The only time toys left was when they were thrown out. The telephone said there was a toy monkey who, whenever he spotted an escaping toy, screeched until the toy was caught.

After the kids went out to play, Woody came out of hiding. The others told him about Lotso's cruelty and Buzz's strange behaviour – Lotso had reset Buzz, and he didn't recognize his own friends anymore. They also gave Woody back his hat that he had left behind.

"Oh, Woody," said Jessie, "we were wrong to leave Andy."

"It's my fault for leaving you guys," Woody replied. "From now on, we stick together."

But Jessie knew Woody needed to get home before Andy left for college.

Woody nodded. "We're busting out of here tonight." He pointed out of the window. The rubbish chute would be their escape route!

That night, the toys put a complicated escape plan into action. Some of the toys distracted Buzz, which gave Woody and Slinky a chance to surprise the Monkey – and grab the nursery keys.

Barbie forced Ken to confess that Buzz had been reset to 'demo' mode. Then Mr. Potato Head distracted Big Baby, which gave the toys a chance to capture Buzz. Then, Mr. Potato Head's parts escaped and attached themselves to a tortilla! He kept a lookout while Jessie and the others got the keys from Slinky, allowing everyone to slip into the playground!

Barbie found Buzz's instruction manual. Then she, Woody and Slinky held Buzz down while Hamm found the instructions to reset the space ranger. Suddenly, Buzz beeped – and began speaking Spanish! There was no time to figure out what had happened. They hustled Buzz out of the door and into the playground. When Buzz saw Jessie, he dropped to his knees: "Mi florecita del desierto!"

"Did you fix Buzz?" asked Jessie, confused.

"Sort of," Woody replied.

Would Buzz ever get back to normal?

Disney
PLANES
2

Meeting the Air-attack Team

Dusty Crophopper had only just arrived at Piston Peak National Park for his firefighting training when the emergency horn blared. There was a wildfire in the park! The air-attack team sprang into action. Smokejumpers rolled up a ramp into Cabbie, the transport plane. Maru, a mechanic, pumped fire retardant foam into Lil' Dipper, the super-scooper. And Windlifter, the heavy-lift helicopter, thundered into the air.

It was all so exciting! Dusty decided he had to follow to get in on the action, so he took off right behind them.

Rescue helicopter Blade Ranger was already on the scene. Blade Ranger was the one who had agreed to train Dusty, so Dusty watched Blade carefully as he dumped bright red fire retardant on to the blaze.

Blade told Windlifter to drop retardant next and together they worked to snuff out a large part of the wildfire.

Then Cabbie flew over the area and the smokejumpers parachuted to the ground. They got straight to work, clearing an area of logs, branches and anything else that might cause the fire to spread faster.

Dusty watched the team working together to put out the fire. However, he didn't notice Dipper flying in to drop retardant, and Dipper had no idea that Dusty was right below her.

But Blade saw what was happening and ordered Dusty to move. "Get out of this airspace!" he yelled.

"Oh, sorry," said Dusty. "I didn't mean to get in …" But before he could finish – *SPLASH!* – Dusty was covered with the fire retardant!

Back at the base, Maru cleaned Dusty off.

"Once you dry out," Blade grumbled, "you can wing it on back to the lodge with the rest of the tourists."

Feeling embarrassed, Dusty explained he was there for training.

"You're the plane Mayday radioed me about?" asked Blade.

"This isn't just any plane," Dipper said. "It's Dusty Crophopper!" Dusty was famous since he won the Wings Around the Globe Rally. He had become a racing legend.

Blade wasn't impressed. "Maru," he said, "rip off his landing gear."

What?! Dusty thought, suddenly scared. What on earth were they going to do to him? Without landing gear, Dusty would never be able to fly again!

Maru laughed. No, they weren't punishing him. They were going to replace his landing gear with essential firefighting equipment – pontoons to carry water.

The Birthday Surprise

Today was Mickey's birthday! He jumped out of bed and saw Pluto staring out of the window. Mickey looked out of the window, too and saw his friends walking by.

I wonder what they're doing, he thought.

Donald's arms were full of cups and plates. Daisy had lemonade. Goofy was holding balloons. And Minnie was carrying a cake.

"Could they be having a birthday party ... for me?" Mickey said to Pluto.

Mickey and Pluto sat and waited for their friends. When the bell rang, Mickey raced to the door. He threw it open, but it was only Donald – and he looked upset.

"What's wrong?" Mickey asked.

"My favourite hammock is broken," Donald told Mickey. "Can you help me fix it?"

"Sure, Donald," Mickey said.

So Donald, Mickey and Pluto set off. As they walked, an idea popped into Mickey's head. *Maybe there is no broken hammock. Maybe Donald is really taking me to my party!*

Donald led Mickey to his garden. There was the broken hammock. Mickey looked around. There were no balloons and no cake. So Mickey helped Donald fix his hammock.

"That should do it," Mickey said, as he finished tying the hammock's rope round a tree.

"Thanks, Mickey!" Donald said.

I guess there wasn't a party after all, Mickey thought, sadly. Just then, he heard Minnie and Daisy calling him.

The girls led Mickey to their garden. Mickey looked around. The garden was full of pretty flowers, but no party. Mickey was disappointed.

Suddenly, Goofy ran up. "Mickey!" he shouted. "You've got to see this!"

Goofy seems very excited, Mickey thought. He guessed Goofy must be taking him to his party!

"Look, Mickey," Goofy said, pointing to a large rock. Mickey looked, but there was no sign of a party. Then he saw two snails racing on the rock. Mickey and Pluto watched the snails for a while. Then they headed home.

"Oh, well, Pluto," Mickey said, sadly. "I guess there won't be a party after all."

Mickey opened the door to his house....

"Surprise!"

Mickey's friends jumped out at him. They had planned a party after all!

"I don't understand," he said, almost speechless. "How did you ... at my house ... without me finding out?"

Minnie giggled. "We took turns keeping you busy," she explained.

Mickey smiled. He loved surprise parties!

"Happy birthday, Mickey!"

The Sword in the Stone

In the depths of the woods, somewhere in England, Merlin the Magician was waiting for a very special visitor. His name was Wart, a clever but reckless young boy....

"Watch out, Wart! You're climbing too high." And sure enough – *CRASH!* Wart tumbled and landed on a chair in front of Merlin, just in time for tea!

"A great destiny awaits you my boy," Merlin said to Wart. "But first you need to learn a few things....

"There's no great destiny without a great teacher – and I will be that person! Just let me pack my case and then we'll be off."

First lesson: the world of water. Merlin touched his wand to Wart's head and the boy transformed into a fish! Merlin transformed himself too, and they swam in deep water. Wart waved his fins and made bubbles.

Then suddenly, they saw a monstrous fish coming straight for them! Quickly, Merlin changed back into human form and saved Wart from the jaws of the pike.

Second lesson: exploring the forest in the form of a squirrel! Wart immediately made a friend – a charming female squirrel who really liked him.

But, just when a wolf was about to attack him, Wart changed back into a child.

"I'm sorry Miss, I'm a boy, not a squirrel," Wart said to the disappointed girl squirrel.

"What's the third lesson?" Wart then asked his teacher.

"Flying through the air!" answered Merlin, transforming him into a baby bird.

In the company of Archimedes, a grumpy old owl, Wart launched himself into the air. What fun it was to fly!

But in the air, too, danger lurked: suddenly an eagle appeared and threatened the two friends!

Panic-stricken, Wart dove into a chimney. But he fell into the clutches of Madam Mim – a wicked sorceress who lived in the forest!

Luckily, Merlin appeared in the cottage. To overpower the sorceress, he changed himself into a germ and gave her the measles! Well done Merlin!

Later on, Wart came across a mysterious sword thrust into an anvil. Engraved on the sword were the words:

"Who so pulleth me out will be King of England."

To everyone's astonishment, the boy effortlessly pulled the stone out!

Wart, or rather Arthur, was to be King of England. Long Live King Arthur!

Patch's Plan

"Whoa!" Patch said, "Look at all these other puppies!"

His brothers and sisters were still whimpering with fear. They had just been dognapped, and after a long, bumpy ride in a car, they had arrived at a big, draughty house. But Patch was already trying to work out a way to get back home. He looked around the large, shabby room. "Hey," he asked the closest stranger. "Where are we?"

The spotted puppy smiled at him. "Oh, you must be new!" he said. "Which pet shop did you come from?"

Patch scowled at the strange new puppy. "We're not from a pet shop – we were stolen from our house."

Several other puppies heard him and moved closer. "Stolen? Really?" they exclaimed.

The first puppy shrugged. "Well, bought or stolen, we're all stuck here now."

"Maybe *you're* stuck here," Patch said boldly. "Our parents and their human pets will be here soon to rescue us, just see if they don't!"

"I hope so," Patch's sister, Pepper, said. "I wonder why someone would want to steal us, anyway?"

Patch didn't know. But he was sure that their parents would find them soon. In the meantime, he wanted to make sure he and his siblings stayed well away from all the pet-shop puppies, so there wasn't any confusion.

"We don't know why there are so many of us," the strange puppy told Pepper. "I guess Cruella just really likes puppies."

Patch gasped aloud. "Cruella?" he cried. "Do you mean Cruella De Vil?"

His brothers and sisters shuddered. Their parents had told them scary stories about that nasty woman. Could it be true?

"Yes, she's the one who bought us," several of the other puppies spoke up, while others nodded their heads.

This changed everything! "We have to get away," Patch declared.

Rolly sighed. "We know," he said. "Mum and Dad will be here soon. I just hope we get home in time for breakfast...."

"No, you don't understand!" Patch shook his head. "Cruella is bad news – that's what Dad always says. We have to get away from her now – all of us!" He gestured to the entire group of puppies, bought and stolen. It didn't matter where they'd come from. What mattered was they were in this mess together. "We have to work as a team."

The first puppy smiled at him. "I'm with you!" he exclaimed. "When we're done with her, Cruella will be seeing spots!"

Akuma Island

Hiro had finished building new supersuits for Baymax, Wasabi, Go Go, Honey, Fred and himself. Now it was time to use them to defeat the masked man, Yokai, who had stolen Hiro's microbots and set the fire that had killed his brother, Tadashi. Their only hope of finding him was the medical information Baymax had stored after scanning Yokai during a previous attack. Now, they just had to find the match!

The group returned to the dock where they had battled Yokai. "Fire up that super-sensor!" Hiro ordered Baymax.

Baymax scanned all of San Fransokyo, then reported, "I have found a match on that island." Baymax pointed to a small dot of land in the bay.

They flew to Akuma Island where they came across an old laboratory. Inside, they found a video. They activated it and were not surprised when Alistair Krei – owner of the technology company, Krei Tech – appeared on the screen.

"I present Project Silent Sparrow!" Krei announced to an audience, as he revealed two round portals. "Teleportation," he said proudly. "The transport of matter through space is not science fiction anymore. Ladies and gentlemen, you're here to witness history!"

A female pilot sat in a nearby space pod.

"Ready for a ride, Abigail?" Krei asked her.

At Abigail's nod, the pod shot into a portal. But moments later, disaster struck. The portal exploded and the pilot was lost!

Stunned at what they'd seen, the friends agreed Krei must be the masked man. The large device they'd seen the microbots moving must have been the remaining portal.

"Oh, no," Baymax said. The friends turned. The masked man was outside! He commanded his army of microbots to attack.

"Go for the transmitter, behind his mask!" Hiro shouted.

The friends worked together to battle Yokai and, finally, Hiro managed to remove the mask....

Yokai was Professor Callaghan! He had been Tadashi's teacher at school and Hiro thought Callaghan had died in the fire, too!

Hiro couldn't believe what he was seeing. "The explosion ... you died," Hiro sputtered.

Callaghan's face was cold and stern. "No, I had your microbots," he said.

"Tadashi went in there to save you!" Hiro shouted, anger rising inside him.

"That was his mistake!" Callaghan spat back, harshly.

Callaghan's words filled Hiro with shock and rage. "Baymax, destroy!" Hiro shouted.

Disney
Lady and the **TRAMP**

Trusting Trusty

"Tramp!" cried Lady one morning. "One of our puppies is missing!"

"Don't worry," said Tramp with a yawn. "Scamp is always getting into mischief."

"It's not Scamp," said Lady. "It's little Fluffy! She never gets into trouble. Tramp, what should we do?"

"You look inside. I'll look outside," said Tramp worriedly. He searched their back garden. Then he went to the next garden, and the next.

From a neighbour's porch, Trusty the bloodhound called, "Howdy! Whatcha looking for?"

"My daughter, Fluffy! She's missing," said Tramp.

Trusty's long floppy ears pricked up. "A missing puppy – now that's serious! And I should know. I used to help my grandpa track down missing persons through the swamps!"

"I know," said Tramp. He'd heard Trusty tell that story 100 times.

"Have you found a trail yet?" asked Trusty.

Tramp shook his head.

"Well, let me at it!" Trusty loped back to Tramp's garden. He put his big nose to the ground. *Sniff, sniff, sniff....*

"Tramp, have you found Fluffy?" Lady called from the dog door.

Tramp ran over. "No," he replied. "But Trusty offered his ... uh ... services."

"He can't smell any more," Lady whispered. "I know he tracked that dogcatcher's wagon and saved you – but he hasn't tracked anything since."

"He helped us once," said Tramp. "I think we should trust him again."

Just then, Trusty shouted, "Look at this!"

He had spotted a bluebird's feather below a window. "That's the window the puppies look out of," said Lady.

"Look! A bit of puppy fur," said Trusty. "And footprints!" Trusty followed the trail of footprints to the back of a shed.

And that's where Trusty found the missing puppy! Fluffy was fast asleep under a big tree.

"Fluffy! What happened?" Lady cried.

"I woke up and saw a bluebird," said Fluffy with a yawn. "And I didn't want Scamp to bark and scare it away, like he always does. So I didn't wake anyone. I followed the bird all the way to this tree. Then I guess I got sleepy."

Lady walked over and gave Trusty a kiss.

"Thank you," she told the bloodhound.

"Aw, shucks," said Trusty, blushing. "It weren't nothin'."

As the bloodhound trotted home, Tramp turned to Lady. "See that," he said with a grin, "I told you we should trust Trusty!"

Disney · PIXAR

MONSTERS UNIVERSITY

Mike Meets Sulley

Mike Wazowski had been the smallest monster at Frighton Elementary School, and the least popular. When he grew up, Mike was still small, still unpopular – but Mike didn't care. He had made it to Monsters University and was about to begin the best Scaring Programme in the world! It was his lifelong dream to become a Scarer. It was a dangerous but important job. Scarers entered the human world to scare children – who were deadly to monsters – and collect their screams. Monsters, Inc. turned those screams into energy to power Monstropolis!

On the first day of classes, Mike and his roommate Randy entered the Scare School lecture hall. As their teacher, Professor Knight, was greeting them, the head, Dean Hardscrabble, swooped in. Everything about Hardscrabble was terrifying. Her wings were huge, her legs numerous and she was monstrously ugly! As a professional Scarer, she had broken the all-time Scare record.

"At the end of the semester, there will be an exam," said Hardscrabble. "Fail that and you are out of the programme."

After Dean Hardscrabble left, Professor Knight asked, "Who can tell me the properties of an effective roar?"

Mike's hand shot up. He was giving his answer when an enormous "ROAR!" erupted from the back of the classroom. It was James P. Sullivan, or Sulley for short – a huge blue monster, and the son of a legendary Scarer.

"I expect big things from you," Professor Knight told Sulley.

Mike was annoyed. Sulley had come to class late and hadn't even brought a pencil and notebook!

After class, Mike went back to his room, but his peace was disturbed by a creature flying through his window. It was Archie the Scare Pig, mascot of rival university Fear Tech. Sulley had stolen him!

Mike chased Archie through the university, followed by Sulley. Finally, he caught Archie but Sulley scooped them both up and held them triumphantly above his head. Everyone thought Sulley was a hero!

The top club on campus, Roar Omega Roar, wanted Sulley to join them. Mike tried to explain what had really happened, but the RORs wouldn't listen. Their president told Mike to go and hang out with the losers' club, the Oozma Kappas. Sulley laughed. ROR was for Scare students who had chances, he said.

"My chances are as good as yours!" Mike said angrily, and he promised Sulley he would out-scare him in every way in the coming year. The challenge was on!

Disney · PIXAR
BRAVE
Together Again

Merida was a free-spirited princess who lived in the ancient Scottish Highlands. Merida's mother, Queen Elinor, had wanted Merida to be a 'proper' princess and marry in order to keep peace in the kingdom. The clans had come to compete for Merida's hand, but Merida had refused to choose a suitor. She had argued with her mother and slashed the family tapestry.

Soon after, a witch gave Merida a spell, which turned Queen Elinor into a bear! Now, Merida just wanted her mother back. A riddle from the witch had told her to "mend the bond torn by pride". So, Merida had sewn the tapestry back together.

But her father, King Fergus, and the other clansmen had chased Elinor-Bear into the forest, not realizing it was really the queen.

The men were about to hurt Elinor-Bear when, suddenly, another bear appeared.

"Mor'du!" Merida said with a gasp. It was the bear that had taken her father's leg.

The lords ran forward to attack the giant bear, but Mor'du swatted them away easily. Then he grabbed Fergus and tossed him aside.

Mor'du closed in on Merida. Bravely, Merida raised her bow and arrow. Then, with a deafening roar, Elinor-Bear charged at Mor'du and shoved the demon bear away from Merida.

After a vicious battle, Elinor-Bear pushed Mor'du against a huge stone. The stone fell, crushing Mor'du beneath it.

In the silence that followed, Merida draped the mended tapestry over her mother. But nothing happened. Merida watched as Elinor-Bear's eyes turned cold and more bear-like.

"I want you back! I just want you back, Mum," Merida said. "I love you!"

Then, Merida felt a hand brush her hair. She looked up and saw her mother smiling down at her. When their bond was repaired, the spell had been broken. Elinor had changed back into the queen!

The triplets, too, had turned back into boys. The whole family was together again.

Back at the castle, Merida and Elinor began a new tapestry, one that would forever record the story of the challenge they had faced – and conquered – together.

Later, they watched as the clans sailed for home. Queen Elinor would never again doubt that Merida's strong, free spirit was that of a proper princess, and the future Queen of DunBroch.

As for Merida, she had finally come to appreciate her mother's strength and courage. She knew now that she wouldn't change a thing about her.

DISNEP
MICKEY
& FRIENDS

A Prize-winning Pair

Max and his dad, Goofy, were sitting at the breakfast table. Max looked at the funny pages, while Goofy leafed through the rest of the paper. "Listen to this!" said Goofy. "Channel 10 sponsors the Father & Son of the Year Contest. The father and son who can prove that they have achieved something truly incredible together will appear on national TV on Father's Day to accept their award."

"Too bad Bigfoot ruined that video we took of him last summer," said Max. "Finding him and living to tell about it — now that was incredible!"

Max paused for a moment. "Hey, I know! Why can't we go back and find him again? And this time we'll make sure we have proof."

"Okay, Maxie. Count me in!" said Goofy. "And we can even get a little fishing in too."

Goofy and Max reached the campsite that night, pitched their tent, and went to sleep. Soon they were awakened by a loud crash.

"It's him!" cried Max. "Get the camera!" But, when they poked their heads out, they saw it wasn't Bigfoot at all, but Pete and P.J.

"I'm sorry," said P.J. "I told my dad about your trip, and now he wants *us* to win that prize. We're out here looking for Bigfoot too."

The next day, Pete set up a barbecue with several juicy steaks. "This will lure him out

for sure," he told P.J. The trick worked. In a matter of minutes, Bigfoot crashed through the trees and made a beeline for the meat. "Tackle him, P.J.!" yelled Pete.

Though he was scared, P.J. did as he was told. Bigfoot threw him around like a rag doll while Pete turned on the camera. "The judges are going to love this!" cried Pete.

"Help!" P.J. begged.

Goofy and Max heard P.J.'s cries and came running from the lake. Without saying a word, Goofy jabbed the monster in the backside with a fishing lure while Max threw a fishing net over the monster's head. Howling, the monster dropped P.J. to the ground.

"You were awesome," Max told Goofy.

"Right back at you, son," Goofy replied.

"Got it!" Pete said triumphantly. "Here, P.J., take some footage of me." He struck a hero's pose in front of the captive monster.

Back at home, Pete sent the video to Channel 10. But, after viewing the tape, the judges decided it was Goofy and Max who deserved the award instead.

But on Father's Day – the day they were to appear on TV – Goofy and Max decided to go to the beach together instead. They realized they didn't need anybody to tell them what an incredible father-and-son team they were. They knew it already!

TOY STORY 3

My Heart Belongs to Daisy

Andy's toys were escaping from Sunnyside Daycare, and from the evil bear, Lotso. They wanted to get back home to Andy before he left for college.

Together, the friends creeped past Big Baby and across the playground. Quickly, the group headed over to the tool shed ... and the rubbish chute.

Woody climbed into the chute and slid down into the dark. When he stopped, he was outside – the sky above and a huge bin full of rubbish below. "Come on down!" he called.

Once all the toys had arrived, Slinky formed a bridge between the chute and the lid of the huge bin. But suddenly, Lotso appeared! He kicked Slinky's paws off the bin's lid.

The toy telephone wheeled into view and joined Lotso and his gang. The bear had forced him to reveal Woody's escape plan! "I'm sorry, Cowboy," the phone said. He looked bruised and battered. "They broke me!"

As the groups stood and looked at each other, a rubbish truck turned into the alley. The toys could hear it rumbling towards them.

"Why don't you come back and join our family again?" Lotso asked the toys.

"You're a liar and a bully and I'd rather rot in this dumpster than join any family of yours!" Jessie replied.

Lotso scowled. "I didn't throw you away," he replied. "Your kid did. There isn't one kid who ever loved a toy, really."

"What about Daisy?" Woody asked. "She lost you. By accident."

Woody had found out that Lotso had once belonged to a little girl called Daisy, but he'd been replaced when he'd got lost. Woody held up the old pendant a clown called Chuckles – who had also belonged to Daisy – had given him. It read: "My heart belongs to DAISY."

Lotso was stunned. "Where did you get that?" he demanded.

"She loved you Lotso," declared Woody. "As much as any kid ever loved a toy!" He threw the pendant across the huge bin, where it landed at Lotso's feet.

"She never loved me!" Lotso exploded. "She left me! Love means being together forever or it isn't love!"

Lotso's gang stared at him in disbelief. They had never seen Lotso so angry and upset. Big Baby stepped towards the pendant and picked it up. His eyes filled with tears and his lip trembled. "Mama!" he cried – Big Baby had also once belonged to Daisy. She had loved her toys as much as Andy loved Woody, Buzz and the rest of his toys. Would Lotso let Andy's toys go home now?

DISNEY · PIXAR
FROM THE MOVIE **INSIDE OUT**

Running Away

After Joy and Sadness had created a scary dream to wake Riley up, the Train of Thought started moving again, and the two Emotions were finally on their way back to Headquarters with Riley's core memory spheres.

But things weren't going so well for the Emotions in Headquarters. Anger, Fear and Disgust were finding it hard to keep Riley happy without Joy around. Riley had already cried in front of her new classmates, and had argued with her parents and best friend. Three Islands of Personality had collapsed into the Memory Dump and Riley was starting to forget who she was. After everything that had happened, Anger decided the best thing for Riley to do was run away – back to Minnesota. After all, Riley's happy core memories were made in Minnesota. If she went back, she could just make more.

"Who's with me?" Anger asked.

Fear and Disgust agreed, so Anger plugged an idea bulb in the console.

The idea entered Riley's head just as she awoke from her scary dream. She climbed out of bed and fetched her computer.

"She took it," said Anger, after Riley accepted the idea. "There's no turning back."

Clicking through to a bus website, Riley looked at a map and selected her route.

At that moment, Joy and Sadness were on the Train of Thought moving towards Headquarters.

Joy turned to Sadness. "Hey, that was a good idea. About scaring Riley awake," she said.

"Really?" said Sadness. She was glad to know she'd been helpful. Then the pair found a memory on the train and discovered that it was both of their favourites. Sadness remembered it as the day that Riley's hockey team had lost the play-offs when she missed the winning shot. But Joy loved the memory because the whole team had come to cheer Riley up.

Meanwhile, Riley had secretly taken her mum's credit card to buy a one-way bus ticket. Usually, Riley would never lie to her parents – in fact she would normally tell them everything.

Back in the Mind World, the tracks beneath the Train of Thought suddenly began to crumble. Some Mind Workers helped Joy, Sadness and Bing Bong, escape before the train plummeted over the cliff edge. Joy looked up to see a huge space where Honesty Island used to be – it was gone!

"That was our way home!" Joy cried. "We lost another island ... what is happening?"

"Haven't you heard?" replied a Mind Worker. "Riley is running away!"

Disney · PIXAR

MONSTERS UNIVERSITY

Thrown Out

Mike Wazowski was determined to do well at Monsters University. He had always wanted to become a Scarer and he was going to work hard. But he was up against Sulley, son of a famous Scarer and a very popular monster at the university.

Mike worked harder than anybody else. He read every book he could find on Scaring. He practised making frightening faces in the mirror.

Sulley, meanwhile, was having fun, and his grades showed it. Johnny, the president of Roar Omega Roar, the coolest club on campus, said they wouldn't let Sulley stay in ROR unless he did better.

On the day of the Scare final exam, Johnny took Sulley's fraternity jacket. "It's just a precaution," he said. "RORs are the best Scarers on campus." Suddenly, Sulley didn't feel all that confident.

At the lecture hall, Professor Knight explained that each student would enter the scare simulator and perform a Scare on a robot child. Dean Hardscrabble would then decide who would move on in the Scaring Programme.

While they were waiting, Mike and Sulley got on each other's nerves. Before they knew it, they were in a scaring face-off. Everyone noticed Mike and Sulley roaring at each other – including Dean Hardscrabble. She was looking right at Sulley when he stumbled back and knocked her record-breaking scream can to the floor! The can flew around the room, releasing the scream as it went.

"It was an accident!" insisted Sulley.

Dean Hardscrabble seemed calm, but after the exam she said that neither would be continuing in the Scaring Programme. Mike begged for another chance, but Hardscrabble's decision was final. So Mike and Sulley were put in the Scream Can Design Programme.

"Some say that a career as a Scream Can Designer is boring, unchallenging and a waste of a monster's potential," droned Professor Brandywine. After a few minutes in his class, Mike and Sulley agreed!

Back in his room, Mike threw a book against the wall in frustration. His calendar fell down, revealing a leaflet about the Scare Games. He remembered about the annual Games from his first day at university.

"It's a super-intense scaring competition where you get a chance to prove you're the best!" a monster had told him.

Mike smiled and grabbed the leaflet. The Scare Games were the answer to his problems!

Flower's Power

It was a warm summer afternoon in the forest, and a shy little skunk named Flower was playing a game of hide-and-seek, searching for his friend Thumper. He had been looking for quite a while.

"Come out, come out, wherever you are!" Flower called. "I give up."

"*Surprise!*" shouted Thumper, bursting out of a thicket. "Here I am! *Ugh!*" Thumper wrinkled his nose. "What's that *smell?*"

Flower blushed bright pink. "Sorry," he said miserably. "I sprayed. It happens when I get scared."

"*Whew!*" Thumper waved his paw in front of his face. "You should warn us before you let out that kind of stink!"

"Well *you* should warn *me* before you jump out like that," Flower said. "Anyway, it'll go away … in a day or two."

But a day or two was too long for his friends to wait. The smell was just too strong!

"Sorry," Bambi told Flower. "I, uh, think my mother's calling me," he said.

"Me, uh, too," Faline gasped. "See you later, Flower … in a day or two."

"Or three!" Thumper added, giggling.

And the next thing he knew, Flower was all alone.

Poor Flower. If only he weren't a skunk, he thought. If only he didn't *stink* so much

whenever he got scared. What was the point? It only drove his friends away. But now it seemed he couldn't even play hide-and-seek!

No matter what his mother and father said, being a skunk stunk!

And that's why Flower wouldn't have been very surprised if, two days later, his friends had still stayed away. But, to his bashful pleasure, there, bright and early, were Bambi and Faline – with Thumper hopping close behind.

"Want to play?" Bambi asked Flower cheerfully.

"Anything but hide-and-seek!" said Flower.

"How about tag?" said Thumper. "Ready or not, you're It!"

But before the game could begin, a soft *crunch, crunch* of leaves made the friends turn.

"Wha-wha-what's that?" Bambi said, staring straight into a hungry-looking, red face.

"That's a fox!" said Thumper.

"A fox?" shrieked Flower. "Oh no!" He spun around and lifted his tail and buried his head in fear … and the next thing the friends knew, the hungry fox was running away, whimpering and rubbing his nose.

"Sorry," Flower sighed, blushing.

"Don't be!" said Bambi and Thumper.

And do you know what? Flower wasn't!

Cruella Sees Spots

Cruella looked around the living room of the old De Vil mansion and rubbed her hands together. The room was full of Dalmatian puppies. Everywhere Cruella looked she saw spots, spots, spots! At last, her dream was coming true! Cackling with glee, Cruella thought back to the day this had all started....

It had begun as a perfectly miserable day. Cruella had been shopping for fur coats all morning and she hadn't found a single thing she liked.

"Too long! Too short! Too black! Too white!" she screeched, knocking an armload of coats out of the shop assistant's hands. "I want something unusual! I want a coat that has never been seen before!"

Cruella stormed out of the shop, slamming the door so hard that the glass cracked. She needed something to cheer her up. Just then she remembered that her old school friend, Anita, lived nearby.

Soon Cruella stood at the door, ringing the buzzer impatiently. She could hear cheerful piano music coming from an open window.

Just then, a pretty brown-haired woman answered the door. Her eyes opened wide when she saw the skinny woman, covered in fur, standing on her doorstep. "Oh, Cruella!" she cried. "What a surprise!"

"Hello, Anita, darling," Cruella said, walking into the sitting room. At that moment, a tall, thin man strolled down the stairs, smoking a pipe. But, when he caught sight of Cruella, he leaped back in fright!

"Ah, prince charming," Cruella said, smirking at Anita's new husband. Roger scowled. Suddenly something else caught Cruella's eye. Two black-and-white spotted dogs were sitting in the corner of the room.

"And what have we here?" Cruella asked.

"Oh, that's Pongo and Perdita," Anita explained. "They're wonderful pets." But Cruella wasn't looking at the dogs. She was looking at their coats. Their glossy fur wasn't too long or too short. It wasn't too black or too white. Cruella had never seen anything like it before. It was perfect.

"And soon we'll be even happier," Anita went on. "Perdita is going to have puppies!"

"Puppies!" Cruella shrieked. Suddenly she had an idea that made her smile an evil smile.

"Oh, Anita, you have positively made my day. Now, you must call me just as soon as the puppies arrive. I think they are *just* what I have been looking for."

Pongo snarled, but Cruella didn't notice.

"What a perfectly *marvellous* day," Cruella said to herself as she strode out of the door.

... And *that* was how it all started.

First Day of School

It was the first day of a brand-new school year for Nemo and his friends.

"Hey, Tad! Hey, Pearl!" called Nemo as he swam into the playground. "Isn't it great to be back at school?"

"Well," said Tad, "I wouldn't go *that* far."

"What do you mean?" asked Nemo. "It's gonna be awesome! I heard this year we get to learn how to subtract and speak Prawn."

"Sure," said Tad, "but did you hear who's gonna be teaching us all that?"

"Who?" asked Nemo.

Just then, up swam Sheldon, Jimmy and Jib.

"Hey, Sheldon," Tad called out. "Why don't you tell Nemo here about our new teacher, Mrs Lobster?"

"Mrs Lobster?" said Nemo.

"Yeah," said Sheldon. "Ooooh, they say she's the worst!"

"Who says she's the worst?" asked Nemo.

"Well, Sandy Plankton, for one. He says his cousin, Krill, had her last year – and that she was so mean, he'll never go to school again!"

"And you know what I heard from Sandy," said Tad. "I heard she has these great big claws, and that she uses them to grab students real hard when they give the wrong answer!"

"Oh!" said Pearl. "Don't say that. You're going to make me ink!"

"Yeah," said Nemo. "That sounds awful!"

"I know," said Jimmy. "Sandy says Mrs Lobster never goes on field trips like Mr Ray did. And she sends you home with tons of homework, and makes you stay after school if you forget to bring it in the next day!"

Oh, no! Nemo shuddered. All summer long he'd been looking forward to this day. And now school hadn't even started yet and already he wished it would end!

"Don't look now," Sheldon whispered, "but I think she's coming!"

"I'm gonna ink!" whimpered Pearl.

Nemo shut his eyes and wished with all his might for his dad to come and take him back home….

"Hello there," said a warm voice. "You must be my new pupils! I'm Mrs Lobster."

Huh? thought Nemo. Surely this wasn't the Mrs Lobster the kids had been talking about. And yet, when he opened his eyes, there she was, taking the register.

"Jib, Jimmy, Nemo, Pearl, Sheldon, Tad … my, what a smart-looking class. I do hope you kids are ready to have fun."

Nemo sighed. That silly Sandy Plankton – they should know by now not to believe everything he said. Because Nemo was pretty sure: this was going to be a great year, after all!

HERCULES

Family Reunion

Meg paced up and down the room. "What's wrong?" Hercules asked his girlfriend.

"We're going to visit your parents," Meg told him. "I want to make a good first impression."

"You're smart and kind and intelligent," Hercules said, smiling. "How could you make anything other than a great impression?"

"All right, all right!" Phil cried. "Enough with the sweet talk. I have a cavity already. Can we get out of here?"

"Absolutely!" Hercules exclaimed. Pegasus galloped over and whisked them away.

Meanwhile, Hercules' parents, Amphitryon and Alcmene, were getting ready for their son's visit. Amphitryon was pacing too.

"Is everything all right?" Alcmene asked.

"Yes, of course," Amphitryon answered. "Why wouldn't it be?"

"Maybe you're nervous because your son is coming home and you haven't seen him in quite a while," Alcmene said.

Before Amphitryon could answer, they heard a sound.

"Look!" Amphitryon cried. "It's Hercules!"

And, sure enough, Hercules came charging up to the door. He leaped off Pegasus and gave a hearty hug to each of his parents. Then he introduced Phil.

"Mighty fine to meet you," Phil said as he slipped them his business card. "Fine boy you raised! Feel free to contact me if you find any more like him."

"And who's this?" Amphitryon asked.

"This is my friend Meg," Hercules said, blushing.

Just then, Pegasus snorted. "Oh, and how could I forget my pal Pegasus?" Hercules cried.

"All right, all right, enough with the niceties," Phil interrupted. "It's been a long trip. I'm hungry. Where's the grub?"

"Wait!" Hercules said. "I know you have prepared a wonderful meal, but first, I want to tell you what has happened since I left." He took a deep breath. "I've learned that I'm the son of Zeus and Hera. That's where I've got all my physical strength. But, without everything I learned from you, my adoptive parents," Hercules continued, "all that would mean nothing."

Amphitryon and Alcmene beamed with pride.

Then they all sat down for a feast worthy of the gods. Amphitryon and Alcmene were glad to have Hercules home; Hercules was happy to be home; Meg was honoured to be their guest; and Phil was thrilled to finally get to eat some home-cooked food!

Training Begins

Inside the hangar at the air-attack base in Piston Peak National Park, Maru the mechanic was working hard to replace Dusty's landing gear with pontoons so Dusty would be able to land on water.

"I rebuilt these," Maru said, proudly. "They're better than new."

But Dusty found it impossible to move while wearing the pontoons.

"You have to pop the wheels, genius," Maru instructed.

Dusty was relieved to find the pontoons had little wheels. He popped them out and ... Phew! That was better! He could move again.

He moved slowly around the hangar, trying to get used to the pontoons. He rolled up to Maru's bulletin board on the wall. It was covered with photos of what appeared to be fearless daredevil planes. He thought it might be similar to the Jolly Wrenches Wall of Fame.

"What do you have to do to get your picture up here?" he asked.

Maru shrugged. "Crash," he said.

Dusty had been doing quite a bit of that lately! He had a faulty gearbox and it was leading him into all sorts of trouble. Dusty quickly decided he didn't want a place on *that* Wall of Fame.

Dusty's training started at Anchor Lake

with Blade Ranger, the head of the base and his new firefighting coach. Blade started with lessons on how Dusty should fill his pontoons with water. But it wasn't easy. It was more like ice skating than flying! Dusty skipped across the surface of the lake and nearly slammed into the trees.

Back at the base, Dusty was taught about different fires and how to fight them. And he learned that flying after sunset was the quickest way to get your picture on the Crash Wall of Fame – a lot of the planes on the wall had crashed in the dark.

Blade tested Dusty's low-altitude flying at Augerin Canyon. This was something Dusty could do – and do well. He aced the course.

At the end of the canyon, Dusty had to fly under a bridge then pull straight up in front of Whitewall Falls. But his warning light started to flash and he had to back off.

"If you don't push it," Blade warned, "you won't be certified."

How can I push it with a faulty gearbox? thought Dusty. Tomorrow, he was going to be putting out real fires in a training exercise with flaming barrels. He had to prove to Blade he could do it. He needed to go back to Propwash Junction with that certificate. Only then could the airport open again and the Corn Festival go ahead.

Big Baby Gets Revenge

Andy's toys were escaping from the Sunnyside Daycare nursery – they wanted to get back home to Andy, before the teenager left home for college. But an evil pink bear, Lotso, had stopped them. Lotso didn't want Andy's toys to leave.

Standing on the edge of a huge rubbish bin, Woody mentioned a girl called Daisy. He had found out that Lotso and his sidekick Big Baby's old owner, Daisy, had loved them very much, but had lost them.

Big Baby was upset hearing Woody talk about his 'Mama'. Furious, Lotso shoved Big Baby. "What? You want your mummy back? She never loved you!"

The bear turned to Stretch, the octopus, who was standing behind Woody and the others. "Push them all in!" he commanded. "All of them, or you're next!"

But Big Baby was upset. Suddenly, he hoisted Lotso into the air – and threw him into the huge bin! Then Big Baby slammed the lid … and smiled. He'd had enough of Lotso's cruelty. He was ready for a better life.

"Come on! Hurry!" cried Woody, starting to run across the closed lid towards safety. A rubbish truck was on its way to collect the rubbish – including them!

The toys followed Woody and climbed to safety on a wall. But suddenly, Woody heard a squeak. He turned and saw an Alien caught between the bin lids!

"No one gets left behind!" Woody cried, going back to free his little friend.

Just then, Lotso's paw reached up from the bin and grabbed Woody's leg! Horrified, the toys watched as Woody was yanked down – just as the rubbish truck arrived!

Jessie, Buzz and the rest of Andy's toys fearlessly jumped onto the huge lid and tried to force it open. But the rubbish truck was lifting the entire container and tilting it towards the back of the truck.

The lid swung open, with Woody desperately clinging on.

"Jess!" cried Woody.

"Woody!" Jessie shouted, grabbing the cowboy doll's hand just as Lotso went tumbling past.

But as the huge bin tilted upside down and rubbish rained down on them, Woody and Jessie couldn't hold on any longer.

First Woody, then all the rest of the toys, fell into the back of the rubbish truck, heading for the landfill site!

How were they going to get home to Andy now?

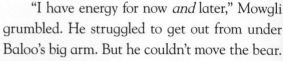

Mowgli's Nap

When Baloo yawned, you could almost see his tonsils. Mowgli leaned forward for a better look. The big bear blinked sleepily.

"Am I ever sleepy." Baloo stretched, leaned against a tree trunk and scratched his back as he slid to the ground. "I think it must be time for an afternoon snooze."

"Good thinking, my friend." High above them, stretched out on a branch, Bagheera the panther dangled a limp paw. His golden eyes were half closed in the heat of the day.

"A nap? Not for me!" Mowgli shook his mop of dark hair. "I'm not tired."

"Now, hold on a second there," Baloo said. "Don't you want to go hunting with us after it cools off? You're going to need energy."

"I have plenty of energy," Mowgli insisted. "I have energy right now!" He started to walk away from the bear, but Baloo stretched out a paw and grabbed the boy's ankle.

"Not so fast," Baloo said.

"You may have energy, but if you use it now, you will not have it to use later," Bagheera said wisely.

"Listen to the cat." Baloo yawned. "He knows what he's talking about." And with that, Baloo pulled Mowgli onto a pile of leaves and held him down with one great paw.

"I have energy for now *and* later," Mowgli grumbled. He struggled to get out from under Baloo's big arm. But he couldn't move the bear.

"Good nap, Man-cub," Bagheera purred at the scowling Mowgli.

A moment later, the panther and the bear were sleeping soundly. As soon as Mowgli heard their snores, he hoisted up the arm that was pinning him down.

"Good nap, yourself," Mowgli whispered. And he tiptoed off to swing in the trees and drop sticks on the animals below.

Baloo's snores shook the jungle for an hour, perhaps two, before Mowgli returned to the shady napping spot again. He'd had a grand time in the treetops, but the sun and the swinging had tired him. The great grey bear looked so soft and peaceful lying against the tree, that Mowgli could not help himself. He curled up against his friend and closed his eyes.

Not two minutes later, Bagheera awoke and stretched his inky paws. The panther flicked his tail under Baloo's nose.

"I'm up. I'm up and ready to go!" Baloo sat upright. Then, spying Mowgli, the bear gave the boy a good shake. "How about you, Man-cub? You awake?"

But the only sound that came from Mowgli's mouth was a loud snore.

How Bad Could He Be?

Wreck-It Ralph was the Bad Guy from the *Fix-It Felix, Jr* computer game. But he was fed up of playing the Bad Guy. He wanted to be a hero! So, he left his game and found the Medal of Heroes in the *Hero's Duty* game. But Ralph accidentally released a dangerous cy-bug, which had multiplied.

The cy-bugs were now attacking the *Sugar Rush* game, where Ralph's new friend Vanellope was trapped! She couldn't leave because she was a 'glitch' – an old game character called Turbo had stolen her computer code. The only way Vanellope could be an offical *Sugar Rush* character again was to cross the game's finish line. But the cy-bugs had attacked just before she reached it!

In *Sugar Rush*, everything was made from sweets. Ralph knew that he needed a bright light to defeat the cy-bugs – that was what killed them in their own game. Ralph had an idea! He headed straight for Diet Cola Mountain. On the way, though, a cy-bug attacked him….

Ralph fell and smashed into the mountain. Under him, a Mentos stalactite broke loose and fell towards the hot diet cola below … along with Ralph. But just in time, someone appeared and grabbed him. It was Vanellope!

The sweets from the mountain hit the cola and … *KABOOM!*

A glowing tower of cola spewed out of the mountain. The cy-bugs turned and flew into the light! Not even the Turbo-bug could resist. *ZAP! ZAP!* All of the bugs were destroyed.

Once the cy-bugs were gone, Fix-It Felix – the Good Guy from Ralph's game – repaired the broken *Sugar Rush* racetrack. Ralph pushed Vanellope gently across the finish. The whole game glitched then returned to normal. But one thing had changed – Vanellope had transformed into a princess!

At last, everyone knew the truth. Turbo had stolen Vanellope's royal identity, and now she had it back.

It was almost morning, and the arcade was due to open. Everyone needed to return to their games. Vanellope gave Ralph a hug.

"You could just stay here and live in the castle," she said.

"I'm already happy," replied Ralph, "because I have the coolest friend in the world."

Back in the arcade, Mr Litwak was just about to unplug *Fix-it Felix, Jr* when a little girl shouted that the game was working. The kids lined up to play. Ralph was back and the *Fix-It Felix* game was saved! Ralph still worked as a Bad Guy, but now he knew he didn't need a medal to be a Good Guy. A little girl like Vanellope liked him … how bad could he be?

Peter Pan

We're Going on a Picnic

"Cap'n?" Mr Smee knocked softly on Captain Hook's door. There was no answer. The chubby first mate pushed his way inside, carrying a breakfast tray. "I've got breakfast, Cap'n."

"I'm not hungry!" Captain Hook replied. "Go away!"

"But, Cap'n. You have to eat." Smee was getting worried. The Captain hadn't eaten in days. In fact, he hadn't even got out of bed! "I know you feel bad about Pe –" Smee stopped himself from saying the dreaded name just in time, "– that flying boy. And the croc – I mean – that ticking reptile, too." Captain Hook was really angry about being beaten by Peter again. Even worse, Peter had set the crocodile right back on Captain Hook's trail. "But we haven't seen hide nor scale of either of them for a week. I think the coast is clear."

There was no reply from Captain Hook.

Smee thought for a minute. "I know how to cheer you up!" he cried. "We'll have a nice old-fashioned picnic! Won't that be lovely!"

Again, silence from Captain Hook.

"Ah-ah-ah! No arguments!" Smee left the breakfast tray and hurried down to the galley. A picnic on Mermaid Island was just what the doctor ordered!

Smee whistled merrily as he made herring-and-pickle sandwiches (Captain Hook's favourite)

and packed them in a wicker basket. This was Hook's day! Smee carefully folded a gingham tablecloth and placed it in the basket, along with his tin whistle. He was going to make sure that Hook had a good time, whether he wanted to or not!

Once the picnic basket was packed, Smee called down to Hook, "It's time to go, Cap'n!"

After a while, Captain Hook finally appeared on deck, blinking in the sunlight. "Fine," he said grumpily. "But I know I'm not going to have fun!"

Smee let the rowing boat down into the water and Hook began to climb down the rope ladder. Once he was safely in the boat, Smee picked up the picnic basket.

TICK TOCK TICK TOCK TICK TOCK.

"Smee!" cried Hook. "Help me!"

Smee peeked over the side of the ship. The crocodile was about to take a bite out of the boat!

In a panic, he threw the only thing he had on hand – the picnic basket. It landed right in the crocodile's open mouth. The crocodile stared at Smee in surprise. Then, without a sound, it slipped back under the water.

"My picnic!" cried Smee. "My tin whistle!"

"Next time you have any smart ideas about cheering me up," said the Captain, glaring at his first mate, "keep them to yourself!"

Mater the Greater

Lightning McQueen and his friends were enjoying a few oil cans at Flo's V8 Café when … "Whoa!" Mater sped backwards over a ramp. He crashed into a pile of cans. "I used to be a daredevil," he explained. Mater began to tell the story of his days as a daredevil. One of the events was at a sports arena. The announcer called: "Ladies and gentlecars, Mater the Greater!"

In the stands, fans waved signs and cheered. It was nearly time for Mater's big stunt. He would try to jump over a long line of cars!

"And he's off!" the announcer called out. Mater's wheels burned rubber as he drove towards the ramp.

THUD! Mater the Greater landed on the first two cars past the ramp. Each car in the line-up groaned as Mater the Greater tiptoed all the way down the row.

"'Scuse me!" he said. "Pardon me! Comin' through!" At last, Mater the Greater rolled over the last car.

"He did it!" the announcer cried. The crowd went wild! Mater the Greater had made his way over all the cars. It didn't matter to them how he had done it.

"I did all kinds of stunts," Mater told Lightning as he continued. He described being shot from a cannon through a ring of flames.

In another stunt, Mater the Greater dived from a high platform into a tiny pool of water.

"The biggest stunt Mater the Greater ever did was jumping Carburetor Canyon," Mater said. He said even with a rocket strapped to his hood, the jump seemed impossible.

Lightning was starting to doubt the story.

"Jumping Carburetor Canyon? No way!"

"Yes, way," Mater replied. "You remember. You was there, too."

Mater continued his story, except now Lightning was with him.

Lightning had a fancy new paint job, and three huge rockets were strapped to his roof. He even had on Mater the Greater souvenir false teeth!

"Ready, buddy?" Mater the Greater asked.

But Lightning didn't really have a chance to answer. Someone lit his rockets and pushed him down the ramp!

Lightning shot down the ramp and launched into the air. He was about halfway across the canyon when his rockets sputtered … and went out. By this time, everyone at Flo's V8 Café was listening. They were all waiting to hear the end of Mater's story.

"Well, what happened?" Lightning asked.

"You didn't make it," Mater replied. "Well, see ya later!"

Disney
Pinocchio

Boy's Best Friend

Like all little boys, Pinocchio wanted a puppy. And, like all little boys, he promised to feed it and walk it and do everything and anything required to care for it.

"Puppies are a lot of work," Geppetto told his son. "And puppies like to chew things, like slippers – and wood." The toy maker glanced over at the rows and rows of wooden toys on his workbench. "No, I don't think a dog is a good idea," he said finally.

That afternoon, when Pinocchio returned from school, Geppetto had a present waiting. The boy wasted no time in opening the box. "It's a dog," Pinocchio said, trying to hide his disappointment. "A wooden dog." Not wanting to hurt Geppetto's feelings, Pinocchio thanked his father and placed the toy on his bed.

A few days later, as Pinocchio was walking home from school, he heard a puppy whimpering in an alleyway. With a little coaxing, the puppy emerged. "Why, you look just like the wooden dog my father carved for me," Pinocchio said.

Pinocchio wondered what to do. "Well, I can't leave you here all by yourself," he decided. The boy went home and tied the dog to a tree a few doors up the street. Then he sneaked the puppy a bowl of food and went back inside.

After Geppetto had fallen asleep,

Pinocchio slipped outside and scooped up the dog. "Now, you're going to have to be very quiet," he warned.

Once inside, the puppy sprang from Pinocchio's arms and made a dash for Figaro. As the dog bounded after the fleeing cat, they upset chairs and knocked over crockery. "Look out!" cried Pinocchio. Geppetto soon appeared in his night clothes. "What's going on here?" he asked.

"Well …" Pinocchio began. Suddenly, the puppy sprang onto Pinocchio's bed, knocking the wooden dog beneath it. Geppetto blinked. The puppy looked just like the toy he had made for his son!

"Could it be?" the toy maker asked. "Pinocchio! You wanted a puppy so much that the Blue Fairy must have turned your toy dog into a real one!"

Pinocchio just picked up the pup and brought it over to meet Geppetto. A day later, when Pinocchio finally found the courage to tell Geppetto the truth, the little puppy was in no danger of becoming an orphan again.

"Well," Geppetto said affectionately when he found the pup carrying the wooden dog around the house, "I suppose we have room for two dogs here – especially if one of them walks the other!"

Disney·PIXAR

THE INCREDIBLES

A Mission for Bob

Bob Parr had a boring job. Nobody knew that he was actually Mr Incredible – a Super who used to save people from disaster. Being a Super had been banned many years ago, and Bob was trying to live a normal life with his wife, Helen – or Elastigirl, as she was once known!

One day at work, Bob wanted to help someone who was being mugged outside, but his boss wouldn't let him go. Bob was so frustrated at not being allowed to help that he gave his boss a tiny push, but it carried all of Bob's Super strength.

WHAM! Bob's boss crashed through five walls, and Bob lost his job. Bob was worried. He didn't want to tell Helen he was fired, but what could he do without a job?

At home, Bob was clearing out his briefcase. Suddenly, a computer fell out! On the screen was a woman who had secretly watched Bob save people from a fire the night before. Helen didn't know, but Bob had started using his Super powers again.

"My name is Mirage. I represent a top-secret division of the government," she said. "A highly experimental robot has escaped our control…." She had a very special top-secret mission for Mr Incredible!

Mirage told Bob that if he could stop the malfunctioning Omnidroid battle robot before it caused any damage, he'd be paid three times his yearly salary! Bob accepted. He needed the money – but more importantly he needed the adventure.

Bob knew Helen wouldn't approve, so he told her he was going on a business trip. He was taken to the island of Nomanisan, where Mirage told him to shut the robot down, and do it quickly. "And don't die," she added.

Mr Incredible soon met the robot, and the fight began. The Omnidroid was a fast learner when it came to defending itself, but in the end Mr Incredible tricked it into destroying itself.

Mirage and her boss watched the robot's defeat. "Surprising," said her boss.

After a celebration dinner with Mirage, Bob flew home. He was excited about getting back into Super work. He began to lose weight, bought a new car and even played with the kids more! Things were looking up. But he'd ripped his suit, so he decided to visit Edna Mode – the former fashion designer for the Supers. She agreed to mend the old suit for sentimental reasons, but insisted on making him a new bold, dramatic outfit!

Bob was excited about what the future might hold….

Flik's Big Date

Flik loved Queen Atta very, very much. So, he decided to plan the most romantic evening for the two of them an ant could possibly imagine.

"I'll pick you up at eight tonight," Flik told Atta when he met her in the anthill early in the morning. Then off he hurried to get ready for their big date.

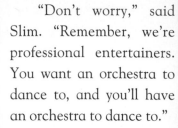

First, there was the dinner to prepare: sprouted wheat with sunflower seeds and wild truffles; free-range millet on a bed of dandelion greens; and Queen Atta's favourite dessert: gooseberry mousse.

The perfect menu! Flik thought. It was sure to impress Atta.

Then Flik went down to the stream to find the perfect leaf for a romantic moonlit cruise. "This elm leaf should do," Flik said as he tied the leaf to a root near the shore. "And I'll use this twig for my oar. Yes, Atta's going to love this."

But that wasn't all that Flik had planned.

"How's it going?" he asked the circus bugs, who were back for a visit and busy practising their instruments just up the hill from the stream.

"Brilliant!" Slim replied. "Just brilliant. Don't worry about a thing. It's all under control. We'll have Atta's favourite song memorized by tomorrow night, no problem!"

"But our date is tonight," said Flik.

"Oh," said Slim sheepishly.

"Told you so," said Francis.

"Don't worry," said Slim. "Remember, we're professional entertainers. You want an orchestra to dance to, and you'll have an orchestra to dance to."

"Are you sure you wouldn't like some magic instead?" Manny the Magician asked. "I have found that nothing inspires romance in a lady quite like cutting her in half."

"Um, I think I'll stick with the dancing," said Flik. But, speaking of inspiring romance, he'd almost forgotten all about the fireflies!

"Come on, guys!" he called to the dozen or so he'd hired for that evening. "I want some of you in the trees, some of you along the water, and the rest of you over there by the picnic blanket … perfect!" he said as their thoraxes lit up the quickly falling night. "Dinner is ready. Boat is ready. Music is … almost ready. Everything is set to go!"

Suddenly, Flik looked down at his watch, and his heart skipped a beat. "Oh, no! It's eight o'clock!" he yelled. "I've really got to go!"

Can you believe it? Flik was so busy getting everything ready, he'd almost forgotten to pick Atta up for their date!

A Major Mess

High in the bell tower of Notre Dame cathedral, the gargoyles, Victor, Hugo and Laverne, began their 45th game of hide-and-seek that day.

"Ready or not, here I come!" called Victor. "And no one better be hiding in Quasimodo's underwear drawer! It's neither funny nor proper." And with that, he leaped over a pile of rumpled clothes and began searching among stacks of books and games and other scattered objects.

The tower, you see, was a mess! Quasimodo had only been away for a few days and still the tower looked like a hurricane had hit it. And why was that? Simply because the gargoyles were slobs!

Quasi had asked them to look after his things – particularly his carvings and precious bells – while he was away. "And of course," Quasi told them, "feel free to make yourselves at home." And, well, they had!

They had tried on his clothes and left them scattered all over the floor. They had leafed through his books and played all his games, without ever putting a single thing back. And they had even used his pillows for pillow fights!

And so it was with some shock and horror that Victor suddenly stopped their game and shrieked, "Do you know what day it is?"

"Excuse me?" said Hugo, peeking out from behind a pillar.

"It's Friday!" said Victor. "The day that Quasi returns home!"

"Oh!" Hugo gulped, gazing at the mess. "He's not going to be happy with us, is he?"

"Oh, but he *is*," said Victor, "because we're going to clean all this up. If we don't, he'll never trust us again."

"Maybe he shouldn't," muttered Hugo.

"Where is Laverne? Laverne!" Victor called. "Come out, come out, wherever you are. We have work to do!"

And work they did. They folded the clothes. They made the bed. They put the books back on the shelf. They washed the dishes and scrubbed the floor. They dusted Quasi's hand-carved models and carefully put them back. And they polished every one of Quasi's bells.

"You missed a spot on Big Marie!" Victor called to Hugo … just as Quasimodo arrived.

"Guys! I'm home!" he shouted.

"Quasi! We missed you! How was your holiday?" the gargoyles asked.

"Great!" said Quasimodo. "You should try it sometime!"

And, after all the work the gargoyles had just done, a holiday is exactly what they needed!

September 14

101 DALMATIANS

A Helping Paw

The dairy barn was warm and cosy, and 99 exhausted, hungry pups were taking turns to drink warm milk from the motherly cows.

"We'd nearly given up hope that you would get here," the kindly collie said to Pongo and Perdita, who had just arrived with the puppies.

"We're so very grateful to you for your hospitality," Perdita murmured wearily.

"Just look at the little dears," said one of the cows. "I've never seen so many puppies in one place before!"

Pongo, Perdita and the puppies had just come in from a long and weary march in the cold. It was very late, and the pups waiting for a drink of milk could barely keep their eyes open. The puppies had recently managed to escape from the dreadful old house owned by Cruella De Vil. They had been held prisoner there, guarded by two villains named Horace and Jasper. Cruella was planning to make a fur coat out of their lovely spotted fur. Luckily Pongo and Perdita had rescued them all just in the nick of time.

The pups had their dinners and gathered around the collie, thanking him for his hospitality.

"Not at all, not at all," the collie replied.

"Do you have warm milk for supper every night out here in the country?" asked Rolly.

The collie chuckled. "No, but we do eat very simple country fare. I'm sure it's plainer than the food you eat in the city, but we eat big meals because of all the chores we do."

"And is it always this cold in the country?" asked Patch.

"Well, now," replied the collie. "I suppose most of you come from the city. No, it isn't always this cold, but there are plenty of differences between living in the country and living in the city. Take leashes, for instance. We don't keep our pets on leashes here, the way you do in the city, since our pets have a lot of wide-open space to roam around in. There aren't as many dogs nearby, but there are certainly other sorts of animals that one doesn't see in the city. Take cows, for instance. And then there are sheep and horses and geese, and …"

Suddenly, the collie stopped talking. A tiny snore escaped one of the pups he had just been talking to. He looked around and realized that every one of the pups, as well as Pongo and Perdita, had fallen into a deep sleep.

"Poor little things," he said quietly, as he trotted outside to stand guard. "They've been through so much. I do hope they get home safely soon."

The Monster of Paradise Falls

Carl Fredrickson had dreamed of becoming an explorer since he was a boy. He had met a girl called Ellie who shared his dream, and they grew up and got married.

Carl had promised Ellie he'd take her to Paradise Falls one day. But they never managed to save enough money to go. When Ellie passed away, Carl missed her very much. One day, when he was being forced to move out of their home, he tied thousands of balloons to the house and flew to South America – to Paradise Falls. And he accidentally took a young boy called Russell along with him.

Carl and Russell had met a large, strange bird – Russell had named it Kevin, but then discovered it was a girl! They also met a talking dog called Dug. He had been sent by his pack to capture Kevin. More dogs had appeared and taken Carl and Russell to their leader. Much to Carl's surprise, their leader was Charles Muntz – a famous explorer who had been his and Ellie's childhood hero!

Muntz invited Carl and Russell into his giant airship – the *Spirit of Adventure*! When Dug tried to follow, the other dogs blocked his way. "He has lost the bird," declared Alpha, the leader of the pack. Dug was left outside.

Onboard the airship, the dogs served dinner while Muntz told Carl and Russell about the Monster of Paradise Falls.

"I've spent a lifetime tracking this creature," Muntz said.

"Hey, that looks like Kevin!" said Russell, noticing a bird skeleton.

"Kevin?" Muntz asked.

"That's my new giant bird pet," Russell explained. "I trained it to follow us."

Muntz became very angry. He thought Carl and Russell were trying to steal the bird from him.

At that moment, they heard a wail outside. Kevin had followed Carl and Russell into the cave! All the dogs began to bark. In the confusion, Carl and Russell slipped away.

"Get them!" Muntz roared at his dogs.

Carl and Russell untied the house and started to run. The snarling dog pack came racing after them. Kevin scooped Russell and Carl onto her back and raced for the cave opening, with the house still floating behind.

But Kevin wasn't fast enough to stay ahead of the pack. The dogs were closing in. Suddenly, an avalanche of rocks tumbled down and blocked the dog pack. "Go on, Master. I will stop the dogs!" someone cried.

It was Dug! He had come to rescue Carl and Russell. But would Carl, Russell and Kevin be able to escape…?

DUMBO
Dumbo's Parade Pals

When Dumbo's circus came to town, the animals and circus folk marched in a big parade. The crowd loved seeing all the circus animals marching down the street.

Well, it may have been fun for the crowd, but it was no fun for Dumbo. His feet hurt, and he was *hungry*.

Then Dumbo noticed a peanut on the ground. He picked up the peanut with his trunk and ate it. Then Dumbo saw another peanut, and another. Leaving the parade, Dumbo followed the trail of peanuts all the way to a playground.

"See, the peanuts worked!" exclaimed a little girl with pigtails. "Now we have our own elephant to play with."

The girl and her friends surrounded Dumbo, patting his head. They marvelled at his long trunk and big ears. "What a wonderful little elephant!" they cried.

"Let's have our own circus," said a boy.

"I'll be the ringmaster!" cried the little girl. She led Dumbo to the middle of the playground. "Ladies and gentlemen! Presenting our star attraction – The Little Elephant!"

Dumbo knew just what to do. He stood up on his two back legs. Then he juggled some balls with his trunk. The children cheered.

Suddenly, Timothy Q. Mouse appeared. "Here you are!" he said to Dumbo. "We have to get back and get ready for the show!"

Dumbo nodded, and waved goodbye to his new friends. The children watched him go, looking disappointed.

"I wish I could see him in the circus tonight," one of them said. "But I don't have enough money for a ticket."

"Me neither," said the other children.

Dumbo was sorry that the nice children he had met would not be able to go to the circus. That night, he felt very blue as he put on his stage make-up and warmed up his ears. Finally, he tucked Timothy into the brim of his hat and climbed onto a tall platform.

"Ladies and gentlemen!" the ringmaster cried. "I give you *Dumbo, the Flying Elephant!*"

Dumbo leaped off the platform, and his giant ears unfurled. The crowd cheered as Dumbo flew around the tent.

Suddenly, Dumbo spotted his playground friends. They were sitting in the first row! He swept by them, patting each child on the head with his trunk. The girl with pigtails waved at Dumbo. "Your mouse friend gave us free tickets!" she cried.

Dumbo smiled and reached his trunk up to the brim of his hat, where Timothy was riding. He gave Timothy a pat on the head too. He was the luckiest elephant in the world to have such wonderful friends!

Disney · PIXAR
FINDING NEMO

What a Crab!

Nemo was having trouble at school – and its name was Ruddy. The big crab was mean to Nemo and the other kids whenever he got the chance. The trouble was, he was crafty and he never did it when the teachers were looking.

One day, he shoved Nemo into a tide pool and made him late for their coral lesson. Another time, he taunted Nemo by saying, "My dad's bigger and stronger than your dad!"

"Ignore him," Marlin told his son. "And just so you know, his dad *may* be bigger and stronger than I am, but he's certainly not as smart or good-looking."

"My friends and I have tried everything," Nemo complained to his shark friends, Bruce, Chum and Anchor. "But he won't leave us alone. What do *you* think we should do?"

"Just leave it to us!" said Bruce. "We're experts in behaviour modification."

The next day, three huge shadows fell over Nemo's classmates as they played in the school playground.

"Hello," Bruce said, putting a fin around the crab. "You must be Nemo's new little friend."

While Ruddy trembled, Bruce snarled, "We just wanted you to know that any friend of Nemo's is a friend of ours. You are a *friend* of Nemo's, aren't you?"

Everyone looked at Ruddy. "Oh, yeah!"

he managed to splutter, throwing a claw around Nemo. "You bet! Nemo and I are buddies. Yessiree!"

"Good!" Anchor said. "Because you don't want to know what happens to anyone who's not nice to our little pal here."

Chum cleaned a piece of seaweed from between his razor-sharp teeth with a spiny urchin. "You should stop by for lunch sometime," he said to Ruddy with a wink.

When Mrs Lobster arrived to pick up the class, the sharks said goodbye and swam away.

Ruddy sidled up to Nemo. "You're friends with three sharks?" he said. "Wow! That's pretty cool! I wish I had friends like that. In fact, I wish I had any friends at all."

"How do you expect to have friends when you're so, well, *crabby* all the time?" Nemo said.

Ruddy admitted that he hated being the new kid. He had decided to pick on everyone else before they had a chance to pick on him.

"If you promise to stop acting mean, I promise to be your friend," Nemo said.

"Deal," Ruddy agreed. "Besides, I guess I'd better be your friend if I don't want your shark pals to eat me."

Nemo didn't say a word. Bruce, Chum and Anchor were vegetarians, but Ruddy didn't need to know that – at least not today!

DISNEY·PIXAR
MONSTERS
UNIVERSITY
The Scare Games

At Monsters University, Mike Wazowski was signing up for the Scare Games. Having failed his final exam for the Scare Programme, this was his only chance to prove that he had what it took to be a top-class Scarer. That's all he'd ever wanted to be and it seemed that only two people stood in his way. The first was Dean Hardscrabble, head of the Scare Programme. The second was James P. Sullivan, better known as Sulley, son of a famous Scarer and now fellow failure of Scare School.

He had caused nothing but trouble for Mike throughout the year.

After signing up, Mike proposed a deal to Dean Hardscrabble: if his team won the Scare Games, she would have to let them all into the Scaring Programme. Dean Hardscrabble agreed – but on the condition that if they lost, Mike would leave MU for good.

Mike needed to join a club to participate in the games. Only the Oozma Kappas – the losers' club – would have him. But they needed one more member to make a team.

"The star player has just arrived," said Sulley, joining the rest of the Oozma Kappas.

Mike was furious. Sulley was so full of himself! But without Sulley they wouldn't be allowed to compete, so Mike had to agree.

Later Mike and Sulley moved in to their new house with the other OKs – Don, Squishy, Terri and Terry, and Art. Mike and Sulley discovered that not one of the OKs had any Scaring experience. And worse still, the Oozma Kappas' house was Squishy's mum's house!

The next morning, Mike woke up annoyed. Sulley was an awful roommate. His paw hung down into Mike's bunk and he shed his fur!

Just then, an invitation arrived to the first Scare Games event. It was called the Toxicity Challenge and it was to take place that night in the sewers.

When the OKs arrived, they found out there were six teams. The object of the challenge was to get through a pitch-black tunnel filled with stinging glow urchins as quickly as possible. The last team through would be eliminated.

The teams took off! Mike and Sulley charged ahead while the other OKs struggled through the urchins. The Roar Omega Roar team stormed through to win, with Mike and Sulley finishing close behind them, but the rest of the OKs finished last. It was a disaster! But then the Jaws Theta Chis were disqualified for cheating. Mike sighed with relief. The OKs were back in the Games!

All in this Together

While escaping the Sunnyside Daycare centre, Andy's toys had been foiled by Lotso – the evil pink bear that ran the nursery. Now they were stuck inside a rubbish truck! They wanted to get home to Andy, before he left home for college.

Inside the truck, the toys found themselves in darkness. "We all here?" Woody asked as they gathered together.

The truck rumbled forwards, then lurched to a stop. Woody could hear its forklift picking up another huge bin. "Against the wall! Quick!" he yelled.

But Jessie was stuck. Buzz raced over and freed her just as the bin began emptying above them. He threw her out of the path of falling rubbish – as a TV crashed down on him!

Desperately, his friends dug him out … and were thrilled to discover that Buzz was back to his old self! He had been reset to 'demo' mode by Lotso, and had ended up speaking Spanish when the others had tried to fix him.

Soon the truck arrived at the Tri-County Landfill, and dumped its whole load out onto the ground. The dirty, frightened toys struggled out from under the debris and saw a giant rubbish heap. In the distance, they could see a huge crane.

"The claaaaw!" shouted the Aliens excitedly, as they toddled off towards the crane.

Woody tried to go after them, but a huge bulldozer roared across his path. The Aliens were gone. Then the bulldozer turned towards Woody and his friends. Soon, the toys were trapped in a tide of rubbish … heading towards a pit!

The toys fell and fell until they landed on a conveyor belt. Buzz got his head stuck in a can which suddenly flew up and stuck to another conveyor belt above them. It was magnetic! Slinky got pulled up, too – and saw that the lower belt led right into a shredder! The rest of the toys tried to save themselves by grabbing onto any metal they could find.

Suddenly, a pink paw reached out from underneath a bag. "Help!" begged Lotso.

Woody and Buzz dropped down and used a golf club to pry the bag off the trapped bear. The shredder was just inches away!

As Lotso scrambled free, Woody grabbed his paw. They pointed the golf club towards the magnet and all three were lifted to safety.

"We're all in this together," Woody told the grateful bear as they joined their friends.

Even though Lotso had been cruel to Woody and the other toys, the sheriff knew, in times of trouble, they should all stick together.

Timon and Pumbaa Tell It All

It was a very hot day on the savannah. Simba, Timon and Pumbaa were lying in the shade, barely moving. It was too hot for the three friends to do anything except talk. Pumbaa had just finished telling a story about the biggest insect he had ever eaten (to hear him tell it, it was the size of an ostrich) and a silence fell over the little group.

"I know," said Simba. "Hey, Timon, why don't you tell me the story of how you and Pumbaa met each other?"

Timon looked at Pumbaa. "Do you think he's ready for it?" he asked.

"Knock him dead," said Pumbaa.

"It all started in a little meerkat village far, far away," began Timon.

"No," interrupted Pumbaa. "You've got it all wrong. It all started near a little warthog watering hole far, far away."

"If I recall correctly, Simba asked *me* to tell the story," said Timon. "And this is the story as told from *my* point of view."

"All right," said Pumbaa sulkily.

"And in that little meerkat village there was one meerkat who didn't fit in with the rest. All the others were content to dig, dig, dig all day long," said Timon. "*I* was that isolated meerkat. How I hated to dig! I knew I needed to go elsewhere, to find a home of my own, a place

where I fitted in. So I left. Along the way I ran into a wise old baboon who told me what I was seeking – *hakuna matata* – and pointed me in the direction of Pride Rock. So I boldly set off towards this rock of which he spoke. And on my way there, I …"

"Met me!" Pumbaa interrupted.

Timon gave him a dirty look and continued. "I heard a strange rustling in the bushes. I was scared. What could it be? A hyena? A lion? And then I found myself face to face with a big, ugly warthog!"

"Hey!" said Pumbaa, looking insulted.

"We soon realized we had a lot in common – our love for bugs, our search for a home to call our own. So we set out for Pride Rock together. A lot of bad things happened along the way – hyenas, stampedes, you name it. But before long we managed to find the perfect place to live. And then we met you, Simba!"

"That's a nice story," Simba said with a yawn. "Now I think I'm going to take a nap…."

Pumbaa cleared his throat. "It all started near a little warthog watering hole far, far away," he began.

"You always have to get the last word, don't you?" said Timon.

"Not always," said Pumbaa. And then he continued with *his* side of the story.

Peter Pan
Return to Never Land

It had been a long time since Wendy's adventures in Never Land. But she never stopped believing. Years later, Wendy still loved to tell stories of Peter Pan, Tinker Bell and the Lost Boys to her own children. Her son, Danny, never tired of hearing his mother's stories. But her daughter, Jane, didn't have time for childish stories of pirates and pixie dust.

One night, Jane was fast asleep when a noise woke her. She gasped. Standing over her was Captain Hook!

"Hello, Wendy," Hook said, mistaking Jane for her mother.

Before Jane could say a word, the pirates stuffed her into a sack and jumped aboard Hook's flying pirate ship!

They set sail for the second star to the right and straight on till morning. When they arrived in Never Land, Hook tried to use Jane as bait to trap Peter Pan. He threw the sack with Jane inside into the sea!

Suddenly, something dived into the water, catching the sack just in time. It was Peter Pan!

Peter flew to a nearby rock and freed Jane. "You're not Wendy," he said, confused.

Jane gasped. Peter Pan and Tinker Bell were right before her eyes! It seemed her mother's stories had been true after all!

When Jane explained she was Wendy's daughter, Peter took her to meet the Lost Boys. "Boys, this is Jane!" he said. "She's going to stay here and be our new mother and tell us stories."

Jane shook her head. "I'm not very good at telling stories," she said. "I have to go home."

The Lost Boys didn't understand why Jane wanted to leave. "What's the matter with her?" they asked Peter.

"I don't know," said Peter. "She acts like … a grown-up!"

Later that day, Peter found Jane building a raft. She wanted to sail home!

"The only way out of here is to fly," he told her. "All it takes is faith, trust …"

"And pixie dust?" finished Jane, sounding thoroughly unimpressed.

Peter took Jane back to the woods to see the Lost Boys and Tinker Bell. "Anyone can do it," said Peter excitedly. "Show her, Tink!"

Tinker Bell sprinkled pixie dust on the Lost Boys and they began to fly! She then scattered lots of pixie dust on Jane, too. But Jane still couldn't fly.

Jane became frustrated. She would never get home at this rate! "I don't believe in any of this!" she cried. "And I especially don't believe in fairies!"

Peter, Tink and the Lost Boys watched in shock as Jane stomped off to be alone.

Disney · PIXAR

THE INCREDIBLES

I'm Syndrome!

Bob and Helen Parr were Supers, but they had to stop using their powers when people started complaining about them – some people didn't want to be saved! But Bob had missed his life as a Super and had started Super work again. A woman called Mirage had seen him doing this, and brought him to the island of Nomanisan and given him a mission to defeat an evil robot called an Omnidroid. He had succeeded.

Bob's wife, Helen, didn't know about any of this – Bob knew she'd be upset, so didn't tell her.

Bob was feeling good. He started exercising more and even had a new Super suit made by fashion designer Edna Mode. The new suit arrived just in time. Mirage had a new assignment for Bob.

Bob told Helen it was a business conference and flew back to the island. But Helen had discovered a blonde hair on his jacket. She wondered where he was really going….

Mr Incredible got quite a shock when he arrived for his briefing. A new and improved Omnidroid attacked him! This time the robot was unbeatable. As it defeated the hero, a stranger in a black costume appeared.

"It's too much for Mr Incredible," the stranger gloated. "I went through quite a few Supers to make it worthy to fight you. But you're worth it. After all, I'm your biggest fan."

"Buddy?" Mr Incredible said. Buddy was once Mr Incredible's number-one fan. As a boy, Buddy had asked to be the Super's sidekick. But Mr Incredible had explained to him that Supers were born, not made.

"My name's not Buddy, I'm Syndrome!" Buddy cried. "And now I have a weapon that only I can defeat!"

As Mr Incredible tried to escape, Syndrome froze him in his immobi-ray. "Who's Super now?" he yelled. But then he lost control and accidentally flung Mr Incredible off a waterfall.

Syndrome threw a bomb after him but Mr Incredible found safety in an underwater cave. Syndrome sent a probe to find him. But the hero hid behind the remains of Gazerbeam – a Super who had died battling the Omnidroid.

Just before he died, Gazerbeam had used his laser vision to etch the word KRONOS on the cave wall. What could it mean? Bob wondered.

Meanwhile, Helen had found Bob's newly mended suit. She knew that Edna must have fixed it, so she went straight to her to find out what Bob was up to – and where he was! It was up to Helen to help her husband now.

Tokyo Mater

One afternoon at Flo's V8 Café, three flashy modified cars roared past. "I used to be an import," Mater said. Mater described how he was driving through Carburetor County and saw an older car....

Mater pulled up. "Looks like you could use a tow somewhere," he said.

"It is very far," replied the older car. His name was Ito-san.

"Well, no tow is too far for Tow Mater!" exclaimed Mater. Mater towed Ito-san all the way to Tokyo! Mater had never seen so many tall buildings. Then Mater accidentally bumped into Kabuto, the leader of a gang of ninja cars.

"You scratched my paint," Kabuto snarled. He circled around Mater. "Dorifuto de shoubu da!" he said in Japanese.

"He challenges you to a drift race." Ito-san said that in a drift race, a car drives fast and steers hard into turns. That type of driving makes the car slide on the road. "We will race at midnight," Kabuto said, then sped away.

"You need modification," Ito-san said. With help from some other cars, Mater soon got a slick blue paint job and a large rear spoiler. At midnight, he pulled up to the starting line.

"Race to the top of Tokyo Tower. First one to seize the flag will become King of All Drifters," Ito-san explained.

Kabuto and Mater zipped through the streets. Mater was driving so fast that he missed a turn. "You can't drift! Ha!" Kabuto laughed.

But then Mater went the wrong direction on a one-way street, and sped down an alley. He saw Kabuto up ahead, and drove up next to him.

"Good," said Kabuto. "But not good enough. Ninjas, attack!" A group of ninjas suddenly appeared. Mater was forced to slow down while Kabuto sped off laughing.

Back in Radiator Springs, Lightning asked, "What did you do?"

"Well, shoot. You oughta know," Mater replied. "You was there, too!"

Mater described how he was surrounded by ninjas. Suddenly, Dragon Lightning McQueen was there. "I'll take care of this – dragon style!" he said. With a kick of his rear tyre, Lightning sent each ninja flying.

Meanwhile, Kabuto was nearly at Tokyo Tower. But just then, Mater landed in front of him. "Well, hey!" Mater shouted. He took off down the highway, driving backwards. Kabuto chased after him. Then Kabuto pushed Mater over the railings. Mater quickly threw his tow hook onto the tower and pulled himself up to the top. He had finished the race first! "I win!" Mater said proudly.

THE EMPEROR'S
NEW GROOVE

Leaping Llamas!

"**S**o Yzma and Kronk were out to get me the whole time! Some friends *they* were," Kuzco muttered as he trotted through the forest. Things had not been going very well for the Emperor-turned-llama. First, well, he had been turned into a llama. Then, while trying to get back to his palace, he had learned that his trusted adviser, Yzma, had actually been trying to kill him!

No, Yzma was no friend of his. Kuzco paused to scratch his ear with a hind hoof. And now he was all alone, without a friend in the world – not even that grubby peasant, Pacha. Actually, Pacha had probably been the closest thing Kuzco *had* to a friend. But now he was gone too.

Kuzco sighed. His best bet was still to get back to the palace. The problem was, Kuzco had spent his whole life having things done for him. Now that it was time to actually do things for himself, he wasn't sure if he could.

"Why me?" the llama whined to himself, as he wove in and out of vines and bushes. He was pretty sure he was headed in the right direction, but the forest was so dense and dark. Why, there could be *anything* hiding in that tree … under that fern … behind that rock….

Behind that rock! Kuzco quickly leaped back as a panther lunged at him from behind a large rock. The panther's hungry jaws clicked shut just inches from Kuzco's snout.

"Heeeelp!" the llama bleated. Kuzco ran as fast as he could, but the panther was still gaining on him. This is it, thought Kuzco. I'm doomed!

Up ahead of him, Kuzco spotted a deep ravine. It was only about ten feet wide. "Okay," Kuzco said to himself. "Here's your chance. Llamas are nimble. Llamas are quick. Llamas can jump … really …

"Faaaaaar!"

Thump.

Kuzco shook his head and looked around him. He had leaped across the ravine! And, back on the other side, snarling and pacing back and forth, was the angry panther.

Kuzco stuck his tongue out at the panther and trotted on his way. He had done it! He had escaped a panther, all by himself! "But I know," he said thoughtfully, "that I could do even better with a friend at my side. I wonder where Pacha went, anyway."

Just then, the forest opened up into a broad, sunny field. Kuzco heard a faint bleat. Llamas! There were llamas here, and Pacha was a llama herder. A broad smile appeared on Kuzco's furry face. He headed towards the herd, and, sure enough, there was Pacha. For the first time since the day he had woken up as a llama, far from home, Kuzco began to feel like he might really stand a chance. It was good to have friends.

The Secret of Blazin' Blade

Blade Ranger, Dusty's firefighting coach at Piston Peak National Park, had set up a training exercise for Dusty. Dusty had to put out lots of flaming barrels by dropping fire retardant from his pontoons at exactly the right moment, from exactly the right height.

The first time he tried, Dusty dropped his retardant too late, putting out only the last barrel in a long line. Then he came in too low and knocked two flaming barrels over! After many tries, hitting just one target was the best he could do. Blade was beginning to wonder if Dusty was cut out for firefighting.

Eager to prove himself, Dusty stayed on his guard, scanning the horizon for fires. So when he saw smoke rising from the forest, he sprang into action. He rushed in and made a perfect drop. Blade grimaced above him. Dusty had doused a family campfire!

"Good job," Blade said. "You just saved those folks from a nice holiday!"

That evening, Dusty talked to his friends back home in Propwash Junction over the radio. Chug told him they'd found a new gearbox for him!

"Are you kidding me?" exclaimed Dusty. He was so relieved. His own gearbox was faulty and, as they were no longer being made, finding a new one to fit had been a real challenge.

"We'll have it in a couple days," said Chug, sounding cheerful.

"Wow! Thanks, that's the best news!" replied Dusty. He couldn't have been happier. Maybe he would be able to race again after all!

Out on the runway, Dusty met Cad Spinner, the park superintendent. Cad was delighted to meet the famous Dusty Crophopper, winner of the Wings Around the Globe Rally. He invited Dusty to the big reopening party at Fusel Lodge.

Cad turned to Blade. "He's more famous than you, Blazin' Blade!"

Dusty was puzzled. "Blazin' Blade?" he repeated. Why had he called Blade that? Dusty found out why later that evening. Outside the main hangar, Dusty whispered a password to Maru, who opened the door. This secret meeting involved everyone but Blade. They all settled down in front of a large TV screen to watch an episode of an old TV show called *CHoPS*, which stood for California Helicopter Patrol. And the show's star was none other than Blazin' Blade!

"If Blade was such a big TV star," asked Dusty, "what's he doing here?"

"Whatever the reason is," replied Dynamite, one of the smokejumpers, "it's his business. And we're not asking."

But Dusty was desperate to know.

Disney·PIXAR

FROM THE MOVIE **INSIDE OUT**

Down in the Dump

Since leaving Minnesota, nothing had gone right for Riley. She hadn't made any friends and she had failed to get on the ice hockey team. Worse still, she'd argued with her parents and best friend back in Minnesota. So Anger had decided the best thing Riley could do was run away.

Riley had taken her mum's credit card, without permission, to buy a bus ticket but because of this, Honesty Island had crashed into the Memory Dump inside Riley's mind!

When Honesty Island crumbled, the Train of Thought had fallen with it. Joy and Sadness had been riding the train, trying to get back to Headquarters with Riley's core memories before everything that made Riley who she was was lost forever. Joy, Sadness and Riley's old imaginary friend, Bing Bong, had managed to leap from the train just before it fell.

After the crash, Joy and Sadness realized they could get back to Headquarters through one of the Recall tubes used to bring memory spheres back from Long Term Memory. Joy and Sadness stepped into the tube, but the tube was narrow and Sadness accidentally touched the core memory spheres. The spheres started to turn blue!

"Sadness, stop!" Joy cried, pushing Sadness out of the tube. "I'm sorry, but Riley needs to be happy." Joy began travelling up the tube alone, but the ground underneath was breaking apart. Riley was running away and Family Island was crumbling! Bing Bong stepped forward to help, but the tube broke, and Bing Bong and Joy fell into the Memory Dump.

"Joy!" Sadness cried. She was left all alone on a cliff overlooking the Dump.

At that moment, Riley was walking to the bus station and she felt nothing.

In the Dump, Joy felt hopeless for the first time ever. She checked the bag for the core memories – they were all still there. Then Joy took out her and Sadness' favourite memory of Riley's afternoon by the twisty tree. One of Joy's tears fell on to the sphere and the memory rewound and turned blue. Joy saw that Riley had been sitting, sad and alone, before the happy part of the memory. She suddenly realized that Sadness was important.

"The team …" she mumbled, "… they came to help because of Sadness!"

Joy slid the memory sphere back into the bag and began to scrabble up the nearest hill of memory spheres. The forgotten memories slid beneath her feet, making it impossible to grip.

Bing Bong saw what Joy was doing, but he knew it was no good trying to climb out of the Dump and told Joy to stop.

"Don't you get it, Joy?" he said. "We're stuck down here!"

Disney

Lady and the TRAMP

A Rainy Night Out

"Yip!" Scamp barked at the squirrel nibbling on an acorn in the grass. His brother and sisters were taking a nap under the big oak tree, and there was nobody else around to have fun with.

"Yip!" Scamp barked again, and the squirrel darted across the lawn. Scamp gave chase. The squirrel zipped up a lamp post and leaped onto a nearby tree branch. With a whimper, Scamp sat down and thumped his tail on the pavement. That was the problem with squirrels. They always got away too easily.

Disappointed, Scamp trotted along the pavement, stopping when he got to an open space. The grass here was tall, and butterflies flitted from wild flower to wild flower.

"Yip! Yip!" Scamp raced through the tall grass. He chased the butterflies to the end of the open space and back again.

It was getting dark. Scamp decided it was time to head home. He hadn't caught a single butterfly, but he'd had fun trying. He couldn't wait to get home and tell his brother and sisters about the new game he'd invented. They'd be so impressed!

Scamp trotted up to the front porch and tried to get through the doggie door. *Thunk!* His nose hit the wood, but it didn't move. The door was locked!

"Yip! Yip! I'm home!" he barked. "Let me in!"

Scamp sat there for several minutes, barking. Nobody came to the door. Suddenly – *boom!* – thunder echoed overhead. Lightning flashed and rain began to fall.

Scamp bolted over to the big oak tree, sat down and covered his eyes with his paws. Thunderstorms were scary!

"I'm not going to cry," he told himself as his eyes started to mist over. He shivered in the dark. He'd probably catch a cold by morning!

Scamp let out a little whimper and moved even closer to the tree trunk. He buried his wet nose in his wet paws and closed his eyes.

Scamp was just falling asleep when a sound made him start. Somebody was coming up the drive!

By the time Jim Dear and Darling were out of the taxi, Scamp was dashing across the lawn as fast as he could go. He bolted through the door just as it opened.

"Scamp, you're soaking wet!" Darling declared as the puppy found his brother and sisters napping in front of the fire. And, as he lay down among them, Jim Dear came over with a warm towel to dry him off.

Home, sweet home, Scamp thought happily, as he drifted off to sleep.

Neon Racers

Lightning McQueen was in Japan for a race hosted by Shu Todoroki.

"*Buona sera!*" Francesco said. "Francesco is looking forward to beating you in Tokyo again."

"Then I'm afraid you will be very disappointed," Lightning taunted.

"You boys are so wrapped up in your rivalry, you won't even notice when I speed right past you," said Carla Veloso with a wink.

Before Lightning or Francesco could respond, a white car cruised up. "Welcome to Japan, everyone. Shu is waiting for you."

At his headquarters, Shu explained the race. "We'll be racing at night – an 85-mile trip from Mount Fuji to Ginza."

Shu motioned for several of his pit-crew members to darken his race shop. "Since we'll be racing in the dark, we'll all need special competition lighting." The other racers gasped. Shu was glowing!

The next evening, the racers – all lit up in bright neon – met halfway up Mount Fuji.

"When the flag drops, you may head straight down the mountain," Shu explained. "Or you may head up … and sign the legendary climbers' book at the top!"

The racers gazed up at the summit.

"That climb looks intense," said Rip. "You can count me out."

"Francesco agrees with Rip," said the Formula car.

"The choice is yours," said Shu. "Good luck, everyone!"

The flag dropped and the race began! Francesco and most of the other racers headed down the mountain. But Lightning, Shu, Carla, Lewis and Vitaly Petrov, the Russian racer, drove up, their neon lighting the way.

When they reached the summit, Shu called out: "There's the climbers' book!"

"Ka-chow!" Lightning said, signing the book. The other racers followed.

As they turned to head back down the mountain, Shu stopped them. "I forgot! There's another reward for reaching the peak: another road that leads straight down! Follow me!"

The five racers flew down the mountain. Suddenly, their road merged with another and they spotted the other racers just ahead of them. They had caught up!

"Where did you come from?" asked Francesco, when Lightning appeared beside him.

"You didn't think I'd make this easy on you, did you, Francesco?" asked Lightning. Smiling and revving his engine, he took the lead!

The two racers were so focused on passing each other, they didn't notice a car behind them. It was Carla Veloso! As promised, she slipped by the two competitors and won the race!

Disney · PIXAR

TOY STORY 3

A Circle of Friends

After escaping the Sunnyside Daycare nursery, Andy's toys had ended up at a rubbish tip! They were on a conveyor belt, but had managed to save themselves from being shredded into tiny bits. Woody had even saved the evil Lotso, even though the pink bear had been horrid to Andy's toys.

All that Andy's toys wanted was to get home. Andy was soon leaving for college, and the teenager wanted to take Woody with him. The rest of the toys were meant to be stored safely in the attic.

The conveyor belt they were all now standing on was angled upwards towards a bright light. At first, they thought they were heading for daylight. But then they realized it was an incinerator! Everyone started running as fast as they could! Lotso managed to reach an Emergency Stop Button.

"Push it!" yelled Woody and Buzz. Lotso was about to push it, to save everyone ... then he stopped. He looked back at the other toys, then, with a cruel smirk, he ran off.

"NOOOOO!!!" yelled Woody.

The toys tumbled downwards towards the fiery blaze. A terrifying roar filled the air. They struggled to climb and claw their way back out, but the rubbish that poured off the belt kept pushing them closer to their doom.

Finally, each toy grabbed on to another until the circle of friends was complete. They were determined to face their fate the best way they knew how – together.

Then, suddenly, a large shadow passed over them. A giant crane was lowering down, down, down over them. Then the jaws opened, scooping up Woody and all the others, too! The toys soared up and away from the fire. As they soared through the air, the toys saw into the cab of the crane – the Aliens were controlling it!

"The clawwww!" The Aliens steered their friends over the pile of rubbish and dropped them gently to the ground. But there was no time to celebrate. "Come on, Woody," said Jessie. "We've got to get you home."

"What about you guys?" Woody asked. "Maybe the attic's not such a great idea."

"We'll be there for Andy," Buzz declared.

Still, the toys wondered if they could make it before Andy left. Luckily, they spotted their neighbourhood rubbish collector nearby, just climbing into his truck! The toys hurried forwards, ready to hitch a ride home.

Lotso found his way onto a truck, too. But he wouldn't be hopping off anytime soon! He was strapped to the front of a huge lorry.

Now Andy's toys just had to get home.

A Lesson in Confidence

"Oh dear!" Olivia, a very worried little mouse, sat with Dr Dawson next to the fireplace in Basil of Baker Street's home.

"What's the matter?" Dr Dawson asked.

"What's the matter?" Olivia repeated indignantly. "My father's been stolen by a peg-leg bat! Have you forgotten already?"

"No, no, dear," Dawson reassured her. "Of course not. I know you must be quite upset."

"Quite upset!" Olivia cried angrily. "I couldn't possibly be more upset!"

"But we're at Basil's now, and he's the best. You even said so yourself," Dawson said.

"But what if he doesn't want to help me?" Olivia asked.

"Why wouldn't he want to help you?" Dawson asked.

"You heard him," Olivia answered. "'I simply have no time for lost fathers,'" she said, quoting the detective.

"He didn't mean it," Dawson said reassuringly. "He's just in the middle of something. Perhaps we caught him at a bad time. But, whatever the circumstances, my dear, you must try not to fret."

"I know you're trying to help me, Dr Dawson," Olivia said, as politely as she could manage. "But I don't know if I can really avoid fretting. My father is out there somewhere, and I just *have* to find him!"

"You're right!" Dawson said. "You do have to find him. You have to help Basil track down your father and, in order to do that, you are going to need a clear mind. Now, can you have a clear mind while you're fretting?"

"Well, it probably doesn't help," said Olivia reluctantly.

"Can you think logically while you're upset?" Dawson asked.

"... Probably not," Olivia said.

"Can you work side-by-side with Basil of Baker Street, the great mouse detective, to save your beloved father while you are *worried*?" Dawson asked.

"No!" Olivia paused as the truth sank in. "No, I can't. I owe it to my father to be level-headed. I can be sad and scared later – right now I have to be a detective, like Basil!" she finished triumphantly.

"That, my young lady, is the smartest thing you could have said. And, if you can hold on to that attitude, your father will be found in no time." Dawson smiled at Olivia.

Just then, Basil came swooping back into the room. "Of course he will. I never miss my mark. Your father is as good as found, because I am just that good!"

Olivia smiled secretly. She knew *she* was just that good too.

THE LION KING

Hot on the Trail

"**O**ver here!" Simba said, sniffing the trail. "It's going this way!"

"Yup, this way," Nala said with a nod, sniffing a stick. "And not long ago."

"I saw that stick first," Simba said. Nala was a good tracker, but Simba had learned from an expert – his mum. She was one of the best hunters in the pride.

"Hmm," Nala said with a sniff. "So what are we following then, master tracker? Can you tell me that?"

Simba was silent. They had seen some footprints, but they weren't clear enough to read. They'd also seen some dark wiry hair on a log, but that could belong to lots of animals.

"Something that isn't very graceful," Simba said. They had seen lots of crushed grass and broken sticks.

"Mmm-hmm." Nala nodded impatiently.

"A rhino!" Simba said confidently.

"A rhino?" Nala rolled onto her back, laughing. "Simba, you crack me up!"

"What?" Simba couldn't hide the hurt in his voice. It *might* be a rhino!

"The footprints aren't big enough," Nala said. "It's Rafiki, the baboon."

Now, it was Simba's turn to laugh. "Rafiki likes the trees, he doesn't use trails like a hyena!" The giggle died in Simba's throat and he felt the

fur on the back of his neck stand up. Hyenas were clumsy and had dark wiry hair....

Nala didn't say anything, but her fur was standing up a little too.

The two lions walked in silence. Ahead of them they heard noises – thrashing and grunting.

"Simba," Nala whispered, "maybe we should turn back."

"Just a little further," Simba whispered.

The young lions creeped through the grass on their bellies as quietly as they could. The grunting and thrashing grew louder. They could see a dust cloud rising. Simba stifled a growl. Something about the smell and the sound was familiar, but Simba could not put his paw on it.

As they creeped closer, two bodies came into view by the side of a termite mound. Simba pounced!

"Pumbaa! Timon!" he shouted, landing between his friends.

"Simba!" the warthog said, grinning. Termites dripped out of his muddy mouth. "Want some?"

Timon held a handful of wriggling insects towards Nala. "There are plenty to go around."

"Uh, no thanks," Nala said as she came out of the grass, giggling. She shot a look at Simba. "I think I'll wait for the master tracker to hunt me up some lunch!"

Disney·PIXAR
FROM THE MOVIE **INSIDE OUT**

Finding Sadness

Two of Riley's Emotions – Joy and Sadness – were lost in the Mind World and now, they had even lost each other! While trying to get Riley's core memories back to Headquarters, Joy had fallen into the Memory Dump, leaving Sadness all alone.

Down in the Dump, Joy and Bing Bong were surrounded by Riley's old memories. The spheres were fading, and disappearing into thin wisps of mist.

Suddenly, Joy had an idea – if they could find Bing Bong's lost rocket wagon in the dump, they could use it to escape!

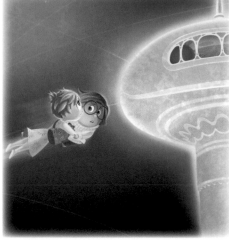

Joy started singing Bing Bong's special song, which powered the rocket wagon. They heard the sound of an engine and followed it until it got louder. They had found it!

The pair sang loudly to make the wagon fly, but each time they took off, they couldn't quite reach the clifftop above. It just didn't have enough power. Joy was ready to give up, but Bing Bong noticed his own hand was starting to fade and urged Joy to have one more go.

On the final try, Bing Bong jumped out of the rocket before it left the ground. Now that it was lighter, the rocket soared up and delivered Joy safely to the top of the cliff.

When Joy realized what Bing Bong had done, she looked over the edge of the cliff and saw him far below, dancing with happiness.

"Take Riley to the moon for me," he called. "I'll try, Bing Bong," Joy replied. "I promise."

Then Bing Bong took a final bow and disappeared. Riley didn't need him anymore. Joy felt sad, but Bing Bong had done a brave and heroic thing. She knew that her next task was to find Sadness before heading back to Headquarters. After all, Riley needed both of them.

Joy walked across the Mind World until she eventually spotted Sadness in Long Term Memory. "Sadness!" Joy called.

"I only make everything worse!" Sadness cried, running towards Cloud Town. She hopped on to a cloud and flew away. Joy tried to chase her but the cloud was moving too fast.

Then Joy spotted the Imaginary Boyfriend Generator nearby and had an idea. Joy turned on the generator and hundreds of Imaginary Boyfriends came out on the conveyor belt. Joy piled the Boyfriends up, making a huge tower. She grabbed on to a Boyfriend and made the tower swing towards Sadness's cloud.

"Joy?" Sadness said in disbelief.

"Gotcha!" Joy cried as she grabbed Sadness in mid-air. "Hang on!"

With one last swing of the tower, Joy let go of the Boyfriend. She and Sadness flew through the air towards Headquarters. *SPLAT!* They hit the back window and slid down the glass.

Bambi

Winter Nap

Bambi nosed under the crunchy leaves, looking for fresh grass. There was none. He looked up at the trees, but there were no green leaves there either. Food was getting scarce in the forest.

"Don't worry, Bambi," Thumper said when he saw the confused look in Bambi's eyes. "We'll get through the autumn and winter. Dad says we always do. We find what we can when we can, and we always make it until spring."

Bambi sighed and nodded. Thumper's dad was smart. He knew lots of things about the forest.

"Besides, it's better to be awake than napping all winter. Yech!" Thumper hated to go to bed, even at bedtime.

"Napping?" Bambi didn't know that some animals slept through the winter months.

"Sure. You know, like Flower, and the squirrels, and the bears. They hole up for months. Haven't you noticed the chipmunks putting their acorns away the past couple of months?" Thumper pointed towards an oak tree.

Bambi nodded.

"That's their food for the winter. As soon as it gets cold enough, they'll just stay inside and sleep," Thumper explained.

"But how will they know when it's time to wake up?" Bambi couldn't imagine life in the forest without all the other animals.

Thumper tapped his foot to think. It was a good question. And, since he had never slept through the winter, he wasn't sure of the answer. "Let's go ask Flower." They headed for the young skunk's den.

"Hello," Flower said.

"Flower, you sleep all winter, right?" Thumper asked.

"It's called hibernation." Flower yawned a big yawn. "Excuse me," he said, blushing.

"So, Bambi wants to know who wakes you up in the spring," Thumper said.

"You'll be back, won't you, Flower?" Bambi asked worriedly.

The little skunk giggled. "Oh, we always come back. Just like the grass and the flowers and the leaves," Flower explained. "I never thought about what wakes us up before. It must be the sun, I guess."

Bambi smiled. He didn't know the grass and leaves would come back in the spring too! He was feeling much better about the forest's winter nap.

Suddenly, Thumper started laughing. He rolled on his back and pumped his large hind feet in the air.

"What is it?" Bambi and Flower asked together.

"You really are a flower, Flower!" Thumper giggled. "You even bloom in the spring!"

Much to Learn

It had been a very bad night in Piston Peak National Park. A storm had raged all night, and lightning and thunder had rattled the hangar walls of the air-attack base. The firefighters woke to find several fires had broken out around the park.

"This is a big one," Blade Ranger said, and at his command everyone jumped into action.

Dusty started to get ready, but Blade told him to stay behind. Dusty was too inexperienced to be flying with them.

"We need every plane we've got," Windlifter pointed out. Blade realized he was right. They needed Dusty; maybe he could help.

Maru snapped Dusty's picture.

"What was that for?" Dusty asked.

"The wall," replied Maru, the mechanic.

Dusty's heart sank. Maru had a Crash Wall – photos of planes that had crashed and burned while on duty.

Up in the air, Blade directed the attack on the fires. Everyone played their part and soon the situation was under control. But then the wind suddenly changed and flames surrounded the smokejumpers!

Dipper was about to release her fire retardant to put out the fire, but Dusty had been watching how it was done. He zoomed past her and made the drop himself –

right on target! The smokejumpers were safe.

Dusty was very pleased with himself, until he got back to base and saw Blade's face. He didn't look happy.

"You broke out of formation," Blade said. "Don't go planning your party yet, champ."

As night fell, Dusty, Dipper, Windlifter and Maru – still covered in soot and fire retardant – arrived at the Fusel Lodge for the grand reopening party.

"Whoa," said Dusty. "Look at this place!"

The lodge was huge and lit up like a Christmas tree. Laser lights were sweeping the sky and flags from all over the world were flying on the roof. Cars, planes, coaches and trains were arriving from everywhere.

"It's so beautiful," sighed Dipper.

As they entered the lodge, robotic housekeepers cleaned up after the friends.

"Dusty!" cried Cad the superintendent, who came over to stand with Dusty. He wanted to be seen with Dusty Crophopper, the famous racing champ. "I'm up for a promotion," Cad explained quietly to Dusty. He wanted to impress his boss, who was watching them.

Maru couldn't hide how cross he was with Cad. Maru knew that Cad had remodelled the lodge with money meant for the air-attack team and it made him really angry!

THE INCREDIBLES

Elastigirl Returns

Mr Incredible and Elastigirl – now known as Bob and Helen Parr – had to give up using their powers when people started suing them. It turned out some people didn't want to be saved by the heroes. They had been trying to live a normal life and had three children. But Bob was bored of the day-to-day grind of an ordinary life.

A woman called Mirage had brought him to an island, where he'd been asked to fight an Omnidroid robot. The robot had defeated him, and the owner of the island turned out to be Buddy – a man who was once Mr Incredible's biggest fan. When Buddy was a boy, he'd wanted to be Mr Incredible's sidekick. Mr Incredible had told him Supers were born, not made – but Buddy hadn't listened. He now called himself Syndrome and he had built a weapon that only he could defeat.

Bob's wife, Helen, was trying to find out where her husband was. She had found Bob's newly mended suit and knew that fashion designer Edna Mode must have fixed it. She went straight to Edna to find out what Bob was up to.

Edna was thrilled to see Helen. She'd so enjoyed making and testing Bob's new suit that she'd made one for Helen too – and one each for their children, Violet, Dash and Jack-Jack! Each new suit came with a homing device for handy tracking.

But Helen was very upset. "You helped my husband resume secret hero work behind my back?"

"I assumed you knew, darling," Edna protested.

Helen phoned Bob's work – and learned he'd been fired almost two months ago. Where was he? Edna passed Helen the homing device that would locate him.

Meanwhile, back on the island, Bob sneaked into Syndrome's base. Using the password KRONOS he hacked into the computer and discovered Syndrome's plan.

Syndrome had killed many Supers perfecting his Omnidroid. Now, he planned to set the robot loose in the city. No one would be able to stop it. Suddenly – *BLEEP, BLEEP* – Mr Incredible's homing device went off!

Now Helen knew where he was – but so did the island's security. They shot out great sticky globules to catch him. Mr Incredible was trapped!

Back on the mainland Helen knew she must find her husband. She realized she would only be able to do it if she became Elastigirl!

It was time for the Parrs to become super heroes once more....

A New Home

Andy's toys were on a rubbish truck, heading for Andy's house. It had been an adventurous few days – after being mistakenly thrown away by Andy's mum, they had ended up at a nursery and held prisoner by an evil bear called Lotso. They escaped, and were nearly destroyed at a landfill site, but the Aliens saved them.

Andy would soon be leaving for college, and he wanted to take Woody with him. The rest of the toys would be stored in the attic. The toys arrived home just as Andy was loading up the car. They snuck into Andy's room and into the box labelled 'Attic' – Woody headed for the box marked 'College'.

"This isn't goodbye," said Woody.

"You know where to find us, Cowboy," Buzz said, then climbed into the box.

Woody waited in the box as Andy and his mum entered the bedroom. "I wish I could always be with you," Andy's mum said sadly.

"You will be, Mum," Andy reassured her.

Woody looked over at a photo of Andy surrounded by his toys. He knew they would remember their special time together, forever. Suddenly, he knew what to do. He sneaked across the room, wrote a note and stuck it on the attic box. When Andy returned, he opened the box and got a wonderful surprise – there were the toys he thought had been thrown away! Then he looked at the note. "Hey, Mum," he called. "Do you really think I should donate these?"

"It's up to you, honey," she called back.

A little later, Andy pulled up in front of a house. A little girl was playing on the front lawn. The note had directed Andy to a girl called Bonnie's house!

"Someone told me you're really good with toys," Andy told Bonnie. "These are mine, but I'm going away now, so I need someone really special to look after them."

Andy took each toy from the box, introducing it to Bonnie. When he got to the bottom, there was Woody. Andy was surprised – Woody didn't belong there! But Bonnie recognized Woody because she'd played with him before. Though it was hard for him, Andy decided to let Woody stay with Bonnie, too. He could see that she already loved him.

Back in the car, Andy took one last look back at his toys. "Bye, guys," he said before pulling away. Bonnie went inside, and the toys watched Andy disappear down the street.

"So long, partner," said Woody.

The others gathered around him. Their life with Andy was ending, but their adventures with Bonnie had just begun.

Disney·PIXAR
MONSTERS UNIVERSITY
Avoid the Parent

It was the day after the first event of the Scare Games at Monsters University. Mike Wazowski was in despair. His future at the university was dependent on his team – and his teammates were useless! The only one who was any good at scaring was Sulley, and he was the one who got Mike into this mess in the first place!

Dean Hardscrabble, the head of the Scaring Programme, had thrown Mike and Sulley out for failing their final exam. The Scare Games were their only way back in. If the Oozma Kappas didn't win, Mike would have to leave the university! His dream of becoming a world-class Scarer would be over.

Mike gathered his teammates for a meeting. The OKs wanted to prove to Mike that they had talent. Don showed Mike how stealthy he could be by lifting his very noisy tentacles off the ground. Terri and Terry claimed they were masters of close-up magic, but their card trick didn't work.

Sulley wanted to ditch the OKs and find another team, but the game rules didn't allow it. So Mike insisted that they do things his way from now on.

The next event was 'Avoid the Parent'. The competitors had to make their way through the library and capture their team's flag without getting caught by the librarian. If the librarian caught them, she would grab them with her giant tentacles and launch them out of the library. Mike told his team to move slowly and quietly.

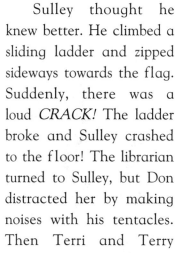

Sulley thought he knew better. He climbed a sliding ladder and zipped sideways towards the flag. Suddenly, there was a loud *CRACK!* The ladder broke and Sulley crashed to the floor! The librarian turned to Sulley, but Don distracted her by making noises with his tentacles. Then Terri and Terry created a distraction to save Don – and Art created a distraction to save Terri and Terry. Mike didn't know what was going on! The librarian gave chase but the OKs made it out through the back door of the library.

"Woo-hoo! We did it!" yelled Art.

"No, we didn't. We forgot the flag!" said Mike, just before Squishy surprised them all by appearing with it in his hand! The OKs took fourth place.

As the triumphant team walked back home, another team drove up in their car. They asked if the OKs were going to the party with the other teams that night.

The OKs were thrilled. They'd never been invited to a party before! Had their luck finally changed?

A Revenge Story

After battling with Yokai, Hiro had managed to remove the villain's mask and reveal who had stolen his microbots and started the fire that killed his brother, Tadashi. Hiro and his friends were all shocked to find that it was Professor Callaghan behind the mask. Callaghan admitted to abandoning Tadashi in the fire and Hiro was furious. He removed Baymax's green nurse chip, leaving the red fighting chip in place, and ordered the robot to destroy Callaghan.

"No!" cried Go Go, as Baymax raised his rocket fist. "Get that chip back into Baymax!"

LAB CAMERA 05

The rest of the team agreed with Go Go. However much they detested Callaghan for what he'd done, they couldn't let Baymax destroy him. Tadashi wouldn't want that – he hadn't invented the robot to be destructive.

Hiro's friends tried to put the nurse chip back and return Baymax to his caregiving mode. While they were struggling, Callaghan escaped. And because Baymax's scanner had been broken in the battle with Yokai, they couldn't even track where he had gone.

"I never should've have let you help me!" Hiro shouted at his friends. Then he jumped on to Baymax's back and flew off in a rage.

At home in his garage, Hiro tried to fix Baymax's scanner. Baymax showed Hiro a video of Tadashi. Hiro's brother had documented each stage of Baymax's construction and how he had made the robot.

"You're going to help so many people." Hiro heard Tadashi say.

Hiro reached out to touch the screen. Tears spilled down his face. He missed his brother so much. But hearing his voice helped Hiro to understand Tadashi had programmed Baymax to help people, not hurt them.

Suddenly, Hiro noticed his friends standing in the doorway. He felt bad for shouting at them. They had only been trying to do the right thing.

"We found something you should see," said Honey. She handed Hiro a hard drive.

Hiro plugged it into his computer and loaded the video. It showed the same lab where the teleportation experiment had taken place. This time though, Callaghan was there, talking kindly to the test pilot, Abigail, his hands resting gently on her shoulders. A close-up revealed that the name printed on her helmet was 'Callaghan'. Abigail was Callaghan's daughter! And she had been lost when the portal exploded!

All of a sudden, everything made sense.

Fred nodded. "This," he declared solemnly, "is a revenge story."

A Purr-fect Night for a Stroll

Bernard was sweeping the floor of the Rescue Aid Society when Miss Bianca appeared.

"I'm going for a stroll," she said. "Would you like to join me?"

"Gosh, I don't know," Bernard said. "It's dark out. And it's raining too!"

"Yes," Miss Bianca said, smiling. "It's the *perfect* night for a stroll!"

Outside, Miss Bianca pulled her collar tight. Bernard opened a big umbrella.

"Let's walk to Central Park," said Miss Bianca.

Bernard choked. "But that's *13* blocks away. Thirteen is unlucky!"

"Don't be silly," Miss Bianca said.

As they walked, it rained harder.

Suddenly, Bernard stopped. "Listen!" he cried.

"Meow!"

"It's a kitten," said Miss Bianca. "He's in trouble."

"Stay back!" Bernard warned. "Cats are dangerous. They eat mice like us!"

"Over there!" cried Miss Bianca, pointing.

Under a postbox, a little orange kitten cowered from the rain. His fur was wet and he looked very sad.

"We've got to help!" Miss Bianca said.

"Let me go first!" Bernard insisted.

He creeped up to the kitten. "Er … hello," he stammered. "Are you lost?"

"I'm lost and very hungry!" the cat cried.

"I was afraid of that," said Bernard, eyeing the kitten's sharp teeth and claws nervously.

"Where are your parents?" Miss Bianca asked.

"I'm an orphan," the kitten replied.

"We must help him!" said Miss Bianca.

"I have an idea," said Bernard. "Follow us!" Bernard took Miss Bianca's arm and they walked to Morningside Orphanage. They knocked, and old Rufus the cat answered.

"Nice to see you two again," Rufus said. "Who's your friend?" he asked.

"He's Young Mister Kitten, and he's an orphan," Miss Bianca replied.

"He's hungry," said Bernard nervously.

"Here's a nice bowl of milk," said Rufus. The kitten lapped it up.

"You know," Rufus said. "I could use a helper around here. Would you like to be adopted?"

The kitten threw his paws around Rufus's neck and purred with joy.

It was late, so Miss Bianca and Bernard said good night. Out on the street, Bianca took Bernard's arm.

"See," she said. "I told you it was the purr-fect night for a stroll!"

Manners, Mowgli!

A strange but delicious smell drifted past Mowgli's nose. Turning around, he spied several platters of food. A moment later, people filed in and sat in a circle around the food. Mowgli was excited. He had just come to live in the Man-village, and he was about to have his first meal!

Mowgli lunged forward and grabbed a piece of meat. He shoved it in his mouth and chewed. He had never tasted cooked meat before, and it was delicious! As the juice dribbled down his chin, he grinned at the humans surrounding him.

They did not grin back. In fact, they were looking at him in disgust. Surprised, Mowgli's mouth dropped open. A piece of half-chewed meat fell out. Why was everyone staring?

"Disgusting," said an elderly woman.

"Why, he eats like an animal!" said a girl.

Mowgli didn't understand a single word they said. But it suddenly dawned on him that he didn't live in the jungle any more. Humans did things differently from the jungle creatures. Mowgli sighed. Would he ever fit in here?

Smiling sheepishly, Mowgli finished chewing and wiped his mouth with his arm. Then he sat back and watched the others eat.

They used strange, sharp sticks to cut with and flattened, paddle-like ones to scoop the food into their mouths. They took small bites and chewed with their mouths closed. Why, they didn't even seem to enjoy the meal at all! How odd!

Mowgli tried to copy them, with little success. The sharpened stick didn't cut nearly as well as his teeth, and half the food fell off the paddle.

"He's as clumsy as a baby," someone said.

"Maybe he really is an animal," said a girl.

At the next meal, Mowgli watched for a long time before he began to eat. The food was strange to him – warm liquid with soft vegetables. Holding his bowl in one hand, he tried to scoop the soup into his mouth with the paddle. But it kept slipping off, leaving him with almost nothing.

Mowgli put his bowl and paddle down with a frustrated sigh. Then, ever so slowly, he picked up the bowl a second time and lifted it right to his lips. Then he took a big gulp of soup, swallowing and smacking his lips.

The others stopped and stared yet again. Then the village elder nodded and lifted his bowl to his mouth and took a long sip, finishing with a lip smack of his own. He smiled at Mowgli. Soon everyone was gulping the soup, slurping and smacking away.

Mowgli grinned. It looked as though he might fit in after all!

HERCULES

The New Neigh-bour

Pegasus grazed peacefully outside the house where Hercules and Meg lived. Now that Hercules was a mortal and not a god, life was a little quieter than it used to be. This morning, however, there was some excitement in the village. Some new neighbours were moving in.

"Let's go over and make them feel at home," Hercules told Meg. They gathered some flowers and headed over to meet them.

A little while later, Pegasus heard a soft whinnying. He turned to discover a beautiful mare approaching him. His heart soared. But then Pegasus remembered the time that Pain and Panic had disguised themselves as a filly and captured him. He was determined not to fall for their trick a second time. He spread his wings and charged, shooing the horse down the hill.

The mare raced past Meg and Herc as they returned home. "Pegasus, what are you doing?" asked Meg. "That's no way to make our neighbours' horse feel welcome." Pegasus gulped. The beautiful horse who had tried to meet him really *was* a beautiful horse!

"If I were you, I'd get over there and try and make it up to her," suggested Hercules.

Within minutes, Pegasus pranced across the neighbours' field, stopped in front of the mare and struck a noble pose. He doubted any filly would be able to resist a stallion as handsome as himself. The lovely horse was unimpressed. She turned so that her tail swished right in Pegasus's face! Herc's horse knew he would have to do something amazing to impress this beauty. He flapped his wings and rose into the air. Then he dipped and swooped and somersaulted across the sky. When the filly started to walk away, he flew alongside her – and crashed right into a tree!

Hercules was watching from the hillside. Pegasus certainly does need some help, he thought.

Meg had an idea. "The right gift might convince that mare to forgive him," she said. She piled a basket high with apples and oats and tied a huge red ribbon around it.

But, when Pegasus went over to deliver the gift, holding the basket handle in his teeth, the female horse kicked it over. Then the mare whinnied and stomped, letting Pegasus know exactly what she thought of him.

Finally, Pegasus realized what he had to do. He sheepishly walked over to the filly with his head bowed. Then he gently nudged her with his muzzle. She neighed and nuzzled him back. All she had wanted was for Pegasus to say he was sorry. Now she understood that even though he was a bit of a birdbrain, her new friend had a good heart.

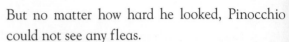

Pinocchio

Imagine That!

The carnival was in town. Pinocchio grabbed his friend Jiminy Cricket and off they went. Pinocchio was amazed at the marvellous sights. There were jugglers to see and games to play. He even saw an elephant doing tricks!

"That elephant is amazing!" Pinocchio cried.

"I suppose," said Jiminy politely.

Next they came to a lion's cage. The big cat opened his mouth and roared.

"Look at those teeth!" Pinocchio marvelled.

Jiminy Cricket nodded. "They're pretty big, it's true."

Then they saw a giraffe.

"What a long neck!" Pinocchio exclaimed.

"Giraffes are all right, I guess," said Jiminy with a shrug. Pinocchio was confused.

"If you don't like elephants, lions or giraffes, what kind of carnival animals do you like?" Pinocchio asked.

"Fleas," said Jiminy.

"Fleas?" Pinocchio said, even more confused.

"Come on! I'll show you," said Jiminy.

Jiminy led Pinocchio to a tent with a sign that read 'Flea Circus'.

Inside, Pinocchio saw a tiny merry-go-round and little swings. There were small animal cages and a little trapeze. There was even a tiny Big Top with three miniature rings.

But no matter how hard he looked, Pinocchio could not see any fleas.

"That's because there *aren't* any fleas," Jiminy explained.

"What's the point, then?" Pinocchio asked.

"The point is imagination," said Jiminy. "Why, you can do anything with your imagination," he continued. "You can even see the fleas at the flea circus."

"But I don't see them," said Pinocchio, confused.

"You have to pretend to see the fleas, and pretty soon you can," said Jiminy. "Like that juggling flea over there. Oops, he dropped his juggling pins."

Pinocchio laughed and joined in the game.

"That flea is going to jump through a ring of fire," Pinocchio said. "I hope he makes it!"

"Now the fleas are doing acrobatics," Jiminy declared.

"They've made a flea pyramid," said Pinocchio. "And the flea on top is standing on his hands."

Finally, it was time to go home.

"What did you think of the Flea Circus?" asked Jiminy Cricket.

"It was the most amazing circus I ever saw, and I didn't really see it at all," Pinocchio replied.

"Yes, indeed. You imagined it," said Jiminy Cricket. "Imagine that!"

Disney · PIXAR

TOY STORY

Buzz Off!

The toys were excited. Bonnie was going to the park with Woody, Jessie and Dolly. The others were looking forward to a day of fun, too. But Jessie was worried. "Keep an eye on Buzz," she told her friends. "I think he may have a loose wire."

Bonnie rushed in and grabbed her bag. "Buzz, you're in charge now," she said as she left.

The peas started bouncing excitedly on their shelf. "Wait! This looks dangerous," said Buzz.

Just then, Slinky slipped from the shelf, causing the Aliens and peas to fall too! They tumbled down on top of Buzz. Buzz stood up and looked around. "Donde esta mi nave?"

"Oh great," Hamm sighed. "He's switched into Spanish mode again."

Rex tried to look in Buzz's back panel, but the space ranger dodged him! The toys tried to catch him, but Buzz grabbed a curtain from the doll's house and held it up like a bullfighter's cape. Hamm ran to tackle his friend, but he skidded and … *CRASH!* Hamm slid right into the bookshelf and a book fell onto Buzz's head! After a moment, Buzz pushed the book away.

"Buzz, are you okay?" Rex cried.

"Buzz, are you okay?" Buzz repeated.

Hamm whispered to Buttercup, "He must have gotten knocked into Repeat Mode!"

The toys were worried. Jessie had asked them to take care of Buzz! They had to fix Buzz before Jessie and Bonnie returned.

"We're gonna have to jiggle his wires," Hamm sighed.

The toys pulled Buzz onto the bed, then Rex jumped. *Boing!* Buzz flew right off the bed and landed on the floor! Then the toys heard the car pull into the driveway.

"Hurry!" Hamm cried.

Rex undid Buzz's back panel and stared at the wires. He didn't know which one to fix!

There was a noise outside and the toys went limp just as Bonnie's mother walked in, put down Bonnie's bag and left again. Jessie climbed out. "Buzz, are you okay?" she asked.

"Oh, he's fine," Trixie propped Buzz into a sitting position. But he fell over with a thunk.

"It's not my fault!" Rex wailed. "There are too many wires!"

Jessie laughed, then she whacked Buzz on the back. Buzz blinked and looked at his friends. "Do I have something on my face?" he asked. The other toys sighed with relief – Buzz was back to normal!

Minutes later, Bonnie arrived. Everything was the way she had left it. "Thanks for looking after everyone, Buzz. I knew this place would be okay with you in charge!"

A Difficult Decision

Carl Fredricksen and Russell had flown to South America in Carl's house. Carl was an old man who had dreamed of being an explorer since he was just a boy. His best childhood friend, Ellie, had shared this same dream. They grew up and got married, and Carl promised Ellie he would take her to see Paradise Falls. But they never managed to save enough money to go, and sadly Ellie passed away.

Carl was being forced to move out of their home, so he decided to take the trip that he and Ellie had always dreamed about. But he accidentally took Russell along for the ride. While walking towards Paradise Falls with the floating house in tow, they had met a strange female bird called Kevin, and a talking dog called Dug. Dug was part of a pack of dogs who wanted to capture Kevin for their leader – the great explorer, Charles Muntz!

But Charles thought Carl and Russell were trying to steal the bird from him, and he sent his pack of dogs after them. Luckily Dug blocked the other dogs' path with some rocks. But he couldn't stop the pack for long.

One dog – Alpha – shoved him roughly aside and jumped over the rocks. Up ahead, Carl, Russell and Kevin had come to the edge of a cliff. They were trapped!

Luckily, Carl and Russell were holding onto the house by the garden hose. Just then, the wind lifted the house into the air – taking Carl and his friends with it! Alpha grabbed Kevin's leg, but he lost his grip.

Carl and his friends had escaped, but Kevin's leg was badly hurt. Russell realized that the bird needed help to get back to her babies.

Out of nowhere, a spotlight appeared and shone down on the bird. Muntz had followed them in the *Spirit of Adventure*! Before Kevin could escape, a net shot out from the airship and trapped her. Carl tried to set her free.

"Get away from my bird!" Muntz snarled. Then he set Carl's house on fire!

Carl couldn't let his house go up in smoke – it held all his memories of Ellie. So he quickly made the decision to give up Kevin instead. The dogs dragged the wounded bird onto the airship. As Muntz lifted off with his prize bird, Carl ran to his house and beat back the flames.

"You gave away Kevin," Russell said.

Carl felt terrible, but what could he do? "I didn't ask for any of this!" he snapped. "Now, whether you assist me or not, I am going to Paradise Falls if it kills me."

Russell watched sadly as Carl walked away, pulling the house behind him.

MICKEY
& FRIENDS

An Uncle Mickey Day

Morty and Ferdie Mouse were oh-so-very excited. Today was their number one favourite kind of day. An Uncle Mickey day! That meant their Uncle Mickey was going to take them out to do all kinds of special, surprising things.

"Uncle Mickey!" the twins shouted when he came to pick them up. "What are we doing today?"

"What *aren't* we doing today, you mean," said Mickey. "I thought we'd start with bowling."

"Hooray!" cheered Morty and Ferdie.

At the bowling alley, Morty and Ferdie discovered that if they rolled the bowling ball together, they could knock at least four or five pins down every time.

Then it was off to the park for some hide-and-seek and a game of catch. Uncle Mickey didn't mind being the finder in hide-and-seek every time. And he didn't mind chasing the balls that Ferdie sometimes threw way, way over his head.

"I'm hungry," said Morty when at last they stopped to rest.

"Me, too," said Ferdie.

"How about some pizza?" suggested Mickey.

"Okay!" the twins shouted together.

At the pizza parlour, Mickey let Morty and Ferdie choose their favourite toppings. Morty picked pepperoni. Ferdie picked black olives. Mickey, meanwhile, had his usual: extra cheese!

"All finished?" asked Mickey. "We'll have to hurry if we're going to go to the carnival."

"All right!" the boys shouted.

After the carnival, where they each won a prize, the boys told Mickey what a great day it had been.

"Well, it's not over yet," Mickey told them.

"Really?" said Morty.

"What's next?" asked Ferdie.

That's when Mickey held up three tickets — and a mitt. A baseball game! Oh, wow!

There was nothing in the whole, wide world that Mickey's nephews liked better than baseball games ... and popcorn ... and peanuts ... and ice cream. And to make things even better, Uncle Mickey caught a foul ball, and their favourite team won. They even watched fireworks at the end of the game.

"Wow, Uncle Mickey! Thank you so much!" said the twins when they finally returned home, tired and full and very, very happy. "This has been one of the best Uncle Mickey days ever!"

"Oh, this was nothing," said Uncle Mickey. "Just wait until next time!"

Late for Supper

Widow Tweed filled the large baking pan with meat and vegetables, then rolled out a flaky crust and set it on top. After crimping the pie's edges, she slipped the pan into the oven. "Chicken pie," she said. "Tod's favourite!"

Humming to herself, she washed the dishes in the sink and tidied up the cottage. Then, she set the table with her best tablecloth and dishes. She added a special milk saucer for Tod.

Widow Tweed looked out of the window and noticed that the sun was setting. "I wonder where that clever little devil has got to," she said.

She watched the sun sink behind the rolling forest hills, then sat down and picked up her knitting. She had a project to finish. Besides, the pie should be ready soon, and Tod was never late for supper.

"Knit one, purl two, knit one, purl two," the Widow said quietly as she put the finishing touches on a soft blanket she was knitting for Tod's bed. She knew the little fox had a fur coat of his own, but everybody liked something cosy to lie on when they curled up to go to sleep.

The smell of chicken pie drifted past her nose, and the Widow got up to take it out of the oven. The crust was golden brown, and the creamy sauce was bubbling around the edges.

She set it on the counter just as she heard a scratching at the door.

"Right on time, as usual," she said as she opened the door. "Dinner's ready, Tod."

But Tod wasn't there. The scratching had just been a small twig blown against the door by the wind. "Tod?" the Widow called, peering into the darkness. "No playing tricks now." But the little red fox did not appear.

The sky was dark now. A few clouds drifted across the moon. The Widow shivered. "Oh, Tod," she said. "Where are you?"

Stepping back into the house, she pulled on her shoes and a sweater. She'd just have to go out to look for him. After lighting an old kerosene lantern, she opened the door for a second time – and nearly tripped over the red fox on her front porch. He sat there quietly, a colourful bouquet of wildflowers at his feet.

"Oh, Tod!" she cried. She picked up the bouquet and scooped him into her arms. "You sweetie pie."

Tod nuzzled the Widow's neck as she carried him into the house and deposited him on his chair at the kitchen table. Soon, the two were sharing a delicious feast of chicken pie. And, after supper, the Widow admired her bouquet above the mantel while Tod curled up in his bed with his cosy new blanket.

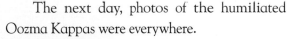

All Shapes and Sizes

It was a great day for the Oozma Kappas at Monsters University. Mike, Sulley and the rest of the team had taken fourth place in the second event of the Scare Games. It was the first time anything had gone right for Mike since arriving at university. It meant that Dean Hardscrabble could not kick Mike out – yet! The deal Mike had struck with the Dean was that she would let Mike back in the Scaring Programme if his team, Oozma Kappa, won the Games. Only then could Mike pursue his dream of becoming a top Scarer.

Something else extraordinary had happened. The OKs had been invited to a party at the house of the Roar Omega Roar club. The OKs were nervous because they had never been to a party before, but everyone gave them a warm welcome. It felt great – and a little strange. Their classmates weren't usually this nice to them.

The OKs started to relax and have fun. They even busted out their best dance moves. Then Johnny, the President of ROR, introduced the OKs. "The surprise team of the Scare Games!" he said.

Suddenly paint showered down on the OKs, followed by confetti, flowers and stuffed animals. The entire room burst into laughter. The OKs looked ridiculous.

The next day, photos of the humiliated Oozma Kappas were everywhere.

"Real Scarers look like us, not like you," Johnny told Mike. "But if you really want to work at Monsters, Inc., they're always hiring in the mailroom."

Sulley stormed off, followed by the other OKs.

Suddenly, Mike had an idea and ran after them. "Guys, I've been doing this all wrong. We're going on a field trip!"

Squishy's mum drove them all to Monsters, Inc., where Mike led the others onto the roof so they had a perfect view of a scare floor. "Take a good look, fellas," said Mike. "See what they all have in common?"

"No, not really," Squishy replied.

"Exactly," said Mike. "The best Scarers use their differences to their advantage."

While all the OKs marvelled at the action on the Scare Floor, Mike and Sulley agreed to start working together.

Just then the security guards spotted them. The OKs started to run, but soon they were struggling. Sulley picked them all up and carried them back to the car!

The OKs drove home feeling inspired. They knew now that monsters of all shapes and sizes could be Scarers. It was their differences that made them great!

101
DALMATIANS

Special Delivery

Now that their family had grown so large, Roger, Anita, Nanny and the Dalmatians had moved to the country, or to the "Dalmatian Plantation", as Roger liked to call it. A weekly delivery of dog food came from the city. It arrived every Thursday at 3pm, and Rolly looked forward to it with eager anticipation.

One Thursday, Rolly and Pepper noticed that the back of the van had been left open. "Are you thinking what I'm thinking?" Pepper asked Rolly.

Rolly nodded. "Snack time!" Rolly and Pepper made a dash for the van and leaped into the back. Pepper clambered up onto the pile of bags and sniffed around. There had to be some loose food somewhere....

"Bingo!" Pepper cried. "Rolly, up here!"

Rolly was there in an instant.

Slurp, slurp, crunch! The two puppies were so busy eating that they didn't see the van driver come out of the house.

Slam! He closed up the back of the van. A second later it was rumbling down the drive.

"Uh-oh," Rolly whispered.

Finally, after what seemed like a very long time, the vehicle lurched to a halt. The back door opened, and the driver began unloading bags of food.

Pepper and Rolly jumped off the van while he wasn't looking. They ran and hid behind the house.

"What do you two think you're doing?" a gruff voice asked.

The puppies spun around. A big bulldog was looking down at them. "This is my property," the dog said. "It is time for you to scram."

The two puppies stared at him.

"Now!" he barked.

"You don't scare me," Pepper said boldly. "You're not half as bad as Cruella."

The bulldog's mouth fell open. "Do you mean Cruella De Vil?" he asked. "You must be Pongo and Perdita's puppies! I heard about your adventures over the Twilight Bark! You live on the Dalmatian Plantation, right?"

"Yes!" cried Rolly. "Can you take us there?"

"You bet!" the bulldog said. "Let's go!"

Luckily, Pongo and Perdita were out that day and didn't realize what a pickle Rolly and Pepper had got themselves into. But there were 97 puppies waiting in the garden as Rolly and Pepper arrived with their escort.

"Wow," said Lucky, after he had heard their tale. "Were you scared of that big mean bulldog?"

"No way!" Pepper spoke up. "That bulldog was all bark and no bite!"

Easy Come, Easy Go

One day, Robin Hood was boasting to his friends in Sherwood Forest about his skills with a bow and arrow.

"I can take from the rich and give to the poor using only a single arrow," said Robin. "And I'll defeat the greedy Sheriff with that same arrow too."

"With one arrow?" asked Little John. He knew his friend was talented, but that seemed impossible.

"One arrow is all I need," said Robin. "And it won't even *touch* the Sheriff."

"Now, that really *is* impossible!" Little John laughed. He was sure Robin was teasing.

But Robin wasn't joking. "Look," he said, "here comes the Sheriff to collect taxes from the poor villagers. I'll show you how easy it is."

Little John and Robin followed the Sheriff to the village. They watched him knock on the door of the first house.

"I am here to collect the King's taxes!" the Sheriff roared. "Give me the money or you'll be thrown in jail!"

The frightened man opened his door and gave the Sheriff a handful of coins. "It's all we have," said the man.

The Sheriff wrote the man's name in a book. "You still owe more," he said. "I'll be back next month for the rest!"

The Sheriff stuffed the coins into a leather bag hanging on his belt. Then he went to all the other houses and collected more taxes. Soon, the Sheriff's leather bag was bulging with the poor villagers' savings.

As the Sheriff prepared to leave, Little John whispered, "Robin, the Sheriff is taking everything they have. We can't let him get away with this."

"No, we can't," agreed Robin.

Drawing back his bow, Robin took aim.

"You're going to shoot him?" asked Little John.

"No need," said Robin.

Instead, Robin shot the arrow at the bag of coins, putting a hole in it. The Sheriff didn't even notice.

"Why did you do that?" asked Little John.

"Just watch," Robin said with a smile.

As the Sheriff mounted his horse, the coins began to drop out of the hole in the bag. By the time he'd trotted out of the village, all the tax money he'd collected had spilled back out. Robin and Little John collected the money and returned it to the delighted villagers. Little John slapped Robin on the back. "You did it, Robin! You robbed from the rich and gave to the poor – and with only one arrow, just like you said."

"Sure," Robin grinned. "And, as the Sheriff is about to learn, easy come, easy go!"

Piston Peak Party Time

The party for the reopening of the Fusel Lodge in Piston Peak National Park was in full swing. Dusty Crophopper and Lil' Dipper, the super-scooper, were called over by two elderly campervans who were guests at the lodge. They introduced themselves as Harvey and Winnie, and they said they needed a little help.

"We honeymooned here 50 years ago," Winnie told them. "And Harvey is trying to find the spot where we had our first kiss."

Harvey looked at a map of the park. "I'm telling you, there was a bridge and a magnificent waterfall," he said.

"That sounds like Augerin Canyon...." Dusty said. He'd been there training a few days before.

"That's right! Anger Canyon!" said Harvey, excitedly.

"By Upper Whitewall Falls," Dusty continued.

"By Whitewash Falls!" Harvey exclaimed. "See? I told you I knew where it was!" His memory was clearly every bit as good as his hearing.

Later in the evening, Dusty and his new friends sat round a firepit outside, talking about their jobs.

"Maybe this firefighting thing will be a second career for you," Harvey said.

"Oh yeah," said Dipper, "this is a second career for all of us. Windlifter was a lumberjack, Cabbie was in the military and I hauled cargo."

When Dusty thought about it, he didn't think it was such a bad idea, but he wasn't ready yet to give up on his racing career.

The next morning, Dusty's old friend Skipper called him on the radio, waking him up. His friends back home in Propwash Junction had some disappointing news. The new gearbox they had found had arrived – but it was the wrong one.

"We've called every parts supplier, repair shop and junkyard in the country," said Chug sadly. "Nobody has your gearbox."

Dusty was overwhelmed with sadness. Maybe his racing career really was over.

But Dusty didn't have time to be disappointed for long. Moments later, Maru, the mechanic, burst into Dusty's hangar. There were two new wildfires burning in the park.

Blade gave the order to scramble the vehicles and, within minutes, Dusty and the rest of the air-attack firefighting team were airborne. Blade directed Windlifter and Dipper to the blaze to the west, while he and Dusty went east. That's when they saw that the fires were moving towards the Fusel Lodge!

DUMBO

Dumbo's Daring Rescue

Dumbo stood on his platform high above the floor of the circus Big Top. Below him, the clowns looked the same size as peanuts. He could hear them calling for him to jump.

"Alright kid. You're on," Timothy said, from the brim of Dumbo's hat.

Dumbo was ready. He knew what he had to do because he did the same thing every night. When the firefighter clowns called, Dumbo would leap from the platform and plummet towards the ground. Then, at the last possible moment, Dumbo would spread his tremendous ears and fly. The audience would cheer. And the show would be over.

"Hey, kid, that's your cue!" Timothy squeaked in Dumbo's ear.

Taking a step forward, Dumbo began to fall. He sped faster and faster towards the floor of the tent. The audience swam into view. They were screaming and laughing. Then, all of a sudden, Dumbo saw something else.

There, in the first row, was a little girl sitting all by herself. She was crying and holding on to a stick of candyfloss.

In an instant, the little elephant forgot all about the act. Spreading his ears, he swooped away from the shouting clowns. He scanned the seats intently. Why was the girl all alone? Where were her parents?

"Dumbo! What are you doing?" Timothy clung to Dumbo's hat as he soared towards the peanut and popcorn sellers. "We don't have time for a snack now!"

Dumbo ignored his friend. The little girl needed help!

At last, Dumbo saw what he was looking for. There, next to the candyfloss stand, were two very worried-looking parents.

"Clara, where are you?" the father called. His voice was lost in the hollering crowd – his daughter would never hear him calling!

Dumbo circled the tent again, turning back towards the bench where the little girl sat sobbing. How could he tell her that her parents were looking for her? He had to bring them together. Swooping low, Dumbo stretched out his trunk and scooped up the little girl.

"Dumbo, what are you doing!" Timothy cried again.

Dumbo sailed back and placed the girl gently beside her parents.

Immediately, the little girl's tears were dried. She was safe in her parents' arms!

The crowd went wild as Dumbo soared high over the arena. Even the clowns were smiling.

"Nice work, kid," Timothy said. "Good show."

Disney · PIXAR
FINDING
NEMO

A Whale of a Tale

"Hop aboard, explorers!" called Mr Ray. Nemo, Tad and the rest of the class jumped on the back of the big manta ray. It was 'special guest' week and they were going to the Drop-off.

When they reached the reef's edge, a royal blue tang fish swam up to meet them.

"And here is today's special guest," Mr Ray announced.

"Hello, everyone," said the blue tang. "I'm Dory … um … am I? Yes! Just kidding! I'm Dory, and I'm very happy to be here!"

"Dory, can you teach us something about whales today?" asked Mr Ray.

"Well, let's see … whales are very big, but they eat little creatures called krill. And I should know. One whale I met *almost* ate me – "

"So it's not true!" blurted Tad.

"What's not true?" Dory asked.

"Sandy Plankton said Nemo made up that story about how you and Nemo's dad got eaten by a whale!" said Tad.

"I did not make it up!" cried Nemo.

"Well," said Dory, "technically, Sandy Plankton is right. We weren't actually *eaten* by the whale – "

Tad smirked, until Dory added, "We were just in the whale's mouth for a mighty long time!"

"Whoa!" said the class. They were quite impressed. Tad frowned.

"You see, the whale was just giving us a ride to Sydney. I find if you talk to a whale beforehand, it clears up most ingestion issues," Dory explained.

"Excellent lesson!" said Mr Ray. "Now teach us a few words in whale."

"Oh, okay," said Dory. "Now repeat after me. Haaaaavvve aaaaaaaaaa nnnniiiiiice daaaaayyyy!"

"Haaaaavvve aaaaaa nnnniiiiice daaaayy!" the class repeated.

"Very good!" said Dory.

"This is stupid," said Tad. "You didn't …"

Suddenly, Tad stopped talking. Everyone just stared at Dory in horror.

Slowly, Dory turned around. A blue whale was right behind her!

Dory simply shrugged and told the whale, "Weeeee weerrrrre juuuuuuuuussst praaaaactisinnnng!"

With a loud bellow, the whale wished her a nice day anyway, then swam off.

"So, Tad, do you believe Dory now?" asked Nemo.

"Wow, that was *so* cool!" cried Tad. "I can't wait to tell Sandy Plankton how I was almost eaten by a whale!"

Nemo and Dory just sighed.

A Silo Scare

Flik took a step back and gazed up at the giant silo he and a troop of ants had just finished building. Now that the colony was using his harvester, they had a surplus of wheat. The silo would store the wheat safely.

"Nice job, Flik," Queen Atta said.

Flik blushed. A compliment from Atta always made his face feel warm. Atta was the smartest and prettiest ant in the colony. She was also its new Queen.

"Thanks, Atta," Flik said, trying to sound casual. "It should keep our wheat dry all winter."

Suddenly, a voice called down from the top of the silo. "Hellooooo," it said.

Flik and Atta looked up. It was Dot, Atta's little sister. She and her Blueberry friends were sitting on top of the silo.

"The view up here is amazing!" Dot called.

"Dot! Be careful!" Atta said worriedly.

Dot grinned down at her sister. "We will!"

"Don't worry," said Flik. "I built in several safety – "

Atta interrupted him. "I have a meeting," she told Flik. "Stay out of trouble," she added in a louder voice. For a second Flik thought Atta was talking to him. Then he realized that she was talking to the Blueberries.

"I'll keep an eye on them," Flik said.

"Come on up, Flik," Dot called as Atta hurried away. "You just have to see the view!"

"Coming!" Flik replied. He did want to see the view, and he also wanted to keep a close eye on the Blueberries.

But, just as Flik got to the top, one of the Blueberries leaped into the silo.

"Wheeeeee!" she cried as she zoomed down towards the pile of wheat.

"The silo is not a playground," Flik told the other girls. "It's for storing wheat, and I built in all these extra safety devices – "

"Come on, Flik," Dot interrupted. "We don't need any safety devices!"

Grinning, she jumped into the silo and slid to the pile of wheat at the bottom. Two other Blueberries followed. But then – *whoops*! – another Blueberry accidentally pushed down a lever. A big pile of wheat tumbled into the silo, heading straight for the Blueberries below!

Panicked, Flik hit a switch. The falling wheat was caught halfway down by a handy-dandy wheat stopper – one of the safety devices he'd built into the silo.

The Blueberries stared at Flik. Just then, Atta walked by. "Dot, what are you doing?" she asked.

"Uh, Flik was just showing us his great safety devices," Dot said sheepishly.

"And they really work," said Flik, sighing with relief.

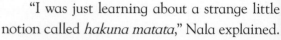

Hakuna Matata

"Why are you so sad?" Pumbaa asked Nala.

"I'm not sad," Nala said. "I'm just a little more on the serious side than the two of you."

"I think you could use a little *hakuna matata*," Pumbaa said.

"A whona mawhatta?" Nala asked.

"You really think she can handle it?" Timon whispered to Pumbaa out of the side of his mouth.

"Of course I can handle it!" Nala said, raising her voice. "I just need to know what it is first."

"Ahhhh, *hakuna matata*," Pumbaa said dreamily. "It's the problem-free way of dealing with all of life's inconveniences."

"It means, 'No worries'," Timon explained.

"Oh, I get it," Nala said. "Instead of dealing with your problems, you pretend they don't exist."

"*Hakuna matata* helps you relax," Pumbaa offered.

"It sounds like your *hakuna matata* is just another way of saying 'uninspired and lazy'," Nala continued.

"I think she might have just insulted us," Timon whispered to Pumbaa.

"There you are." Simba came walking towards them. "What are the three of you up to?"

"I was just learning about a strange little notion called *hakuna matata*," Nala explained.

"Isn't it great!" Simba said with a grin.

"Well, sure," Nala said. "If you don't ever want to get anything done."

Simba frowned. "It's not like that. *Hakuna matata* helps you get through things."

"Sure," Nala continued. "*Hakuna matata* – I don't have to worry. I don't have to try."

"I guess you could look at it that way," Simba said. "But, for me, it means, 'Don't worry about it right now. It's okay.' It gives me the strength to get through the bad times."

"Wow, I hadn't thought about it like that," Nala said.

"So, are you ready to join us now?" Timon asked.

"Absolutely!" Nala smiled.

"Bring on the crunchy beetles!" shouted Pumbaa.

"Let's go tease some elephants!" cried Timon.

"Everyone to the mudhole for a mud fight!" Simba yelled, and the three of them started off.

"Oh, dear," murmured Nala, "this isn't exactly what I had in mind." But she smiled, and ran after her carefree friends. "Last one to the mudhole is a rotten egg!" she cried.

Show Time

After Andy's toys had settled into their new home in Bonnie's room, Dolly said she had a plan to help everyone get to know one another better. "Let's have a talent show!"

All the toys were excited. But as everyone else started practising, Buzz stood by himself. His friends all seemed to know what to do, but he wasn't sure. He wanted to do something truly spectacular – something that would impress Jessie.

Buzz noticed Hamm and Buttercup working on their comedy routine. Buzz knew Jessie loved a good joke. Grabbing Woody's hat, he shouted, "Howdy partners, I'm Sheriff Woody. Did you know there's a snake in my boot?"

"I don't know about sounding like Woody," said Hamm with a smirk, "but you definitely sound wooden."

Buzz wasn't listening, though. He'd noticed that Mr Pricklepants and the Aliens were doing a play. *Jessie loves to watch plays!* Buzz thought to himself, hurrying over. The Aliens were very excited about their show, which Mr Pricklepants was directing. "There are plenty of parts," Mr Pricklepants said encouragingly. "We're doing *Romeo and Juliet*!" But Buzz wanted to change the play so it was set in space! Mr Pricklepants wasn't keen.

Then Buzz noticed Rex, who was acting out scenes from his favourite Buzz Lightyear video game with Trixie. Buzz decided there was something missing from their act – him!

The dinosaurs were thrilled. "Wait till Jessie sees me do this!" Buzz smiled to himself. But Rex and Trixie just stared – these moves weren't what Buzz did in the game.

"Hey, guys! Time to start the show!" shouted Dolly. Oh no! Buzz still hadn't decided what to do!

Then, up on the stage, Bullseye turned on the music. A lively tune filled the room … and suddenly, Buzz's whole body shook. It was as if the music was taking over his body! Unable to control himself, Buzz started dancing. He couldn't stop! He danced straight to Jessie.

Jessie grinned. She knew exactly what had happened – the music had switched Buzz into his Spanish Mode! "It's okay, Buzz," she whispered. "Just go with it!"

Buzz smiled shyly back at Jessie. "Um, well then," he said. "May I have this dance?"

When Jessie nodded, the two danced across the stage and smiled at each other. All their friends cheered. When the music ended, Buzz and Jessie took a bow together. Buzz was beaming. He'd finally impressed Jessie, and discovered a talent he never knew he had!

THE INCREDIBLES

Supers to the Rescue

Bob Parr – aka Mr Incredible – had become bored of pretending to be normal, and had secretly taken up super hero work again. He'd kept this secret from his wife, Helen, and had ended up as a prisoner on the island of Nomanisan – owned by Syndrome, who was Mr Incredible's ex-number-one fan, Buddy.

Buddy had turned himself into a Super by building machines and an Omnidroid robot, which only he could defeat. Helen had discovered where her husband was, and she knew the only way to help him was to become Elastigirl once more.

Elastigirl followed the homing signal on Mr Incredible's suit in a borrowed jet. She soon found that her Super children, Violet and Dash, had left Jack-Jack at home with a babysitter and stowed away on the jet! They had found the Super suits that Edna Mode had made for them!

As they approached the island, missiles attacked the jet. Elastigirl told Violet to create a force field around the plane. But Violet didn't think she could make one that big.

In his prison cell, Mr Incredible listened to the attack on his family with horror. "Target destroyed," came a voice from a speaker.

"You'll get over it." Syndrome sneered.

A desperate Mr Incredible grabbed Mirage. "Release me now, or I'll crush her!" he said.

"Go ahead," said Syndrome. He knew that Mr Incredible could never do such a thing. Defeated, the hero let Mirage go.

But Mr Incredible's family was still alive. Elastigirl had stretched herself around Violet and Dash to protect them, just as the missile blew the jet out of the sky. Then she had made herself into a parachute and floated, with her children, down to the water below.

Elastigirl stretched into the shape of a boat, while Dash pushed her and Violet to shore by kicking his speedy legs. They soon found safety in a cave.

"I'm going to look for your father," Elastigirl told her children. "If anything goes wrong, use your powers … when the time comes, you'll know what to do."

After Helen left, the cave suddenly filled with a huge ball of fire. Dash and Violet fled; they only just escaped! The fire was the rocket exhaust from Syndrome's base. He had launched the Omnidroid towards the city!

The Parr family were going to have to use all their Super strength to save the city, and each other, from Syndrome.

Cars TOON

Mater Private Eye

Lightning McQueen drove up to the air pump. "My tyres are going flat."

Just then, Mater popped out of nowhere. "Flat tyres, ya say? I thought I solved that crime. I was a private eye," Mater explained. Then he told his friend about his detective days. "It was a Friday night …" he began.

Mater sat behind the desk in his office reading an article about accidents caused by tyres blowing out. "I was on to something big," Mater explained. "There was a counterfeit-tyre ring."

A car named Tia drove in. "I need you to find my sister, Mia," cried Tia. "She's been carnapped! She was last seen working at Big D's club, The Carpacabana."

Big D was a sedan who had recently opened a nightclub. That night, Mater went to the club. A singer was performing. After her song, she came to Mater's table. "I'm looking for Mia. Have you seen her?" Mater asked.

"I saw her a couple of days ago with Big D. She smelled salty, like the ocean," the singer said. But before he could find out any more, Mater was thrown out of the club.

Luckily, a friendly rubbish truck gave Mater a clue that led him to the docks. There, he saw Mia on the deck of a huge cargo ship! Mater tried to sneak onto the boat to rescue her, but he was spotted! Then Big D rolled out.

A crane grabbed Mater and hoisted him up.

Just then, Tia rushed forwards. She had told Big D that Mater would be coming to the docks. Tia explained it was the only way to save her sister. The crane held Mater over the water.

Back in Radiator Springs, Lightning was on the edge of his bumper. "WHAT DID YOU DO?"

Mater laughed aloud. "Like you don't know, Lieutenant McQueen!"

Then Mater continued telling his tale. Police Lieutenant Lightning McQueen drove onto the docks with a group of squad cars. "Looks like we finally caught you, Big D," he said. But Big D's workers pushed barrels down a ramp to keep the police away. Meanwhile, Tia hit a switch on the crane and it lowered Mater to the ground. Mater threw his tow hook at another crane, which dropped its crate – right on Big D! The crate split open, and tyres spilled all over Big D.

"Aha! Just what I thought – counterfeit tyres," Mater said. Big D had been swapping good tyres for fake ones. It was his fault there had been so many car accidents lately. Now that Mater had uncovered Big D's scam, the police stepped in.

"You led us right to him, Mater," Lightning announced gratefully. "Take him away, boys!"

DISNEY
Lady and the TRAMP

Like Father, Like Son

Tramp had a whole new life. He had gone from being a stray to becoming a member of the Dear household. And now, he and Lady were proud parents.

But Tramp was finding it difficult to change some of his old ways.

"Tramp," Lady said gently, "you need to set an example for the puppies – especially Scamp."

Scamp had an adventurous side, just like his dad. So, it wasn't surprising that father and son often got carried away when they played together. They couldn't resist the urge to roll in a puddle of mud – and then chase each other across the clean kitchen floor.

Soon, Aunt Sarah and her two troublesome cats, Si and Am, were going to be visiting. Lady was worried.

"Don't worry. I promise to keep Scamp away from those troublemakers," Tramp said.

"And?" replied Lady.

"And I promise to stay away from them, too," Tramp added.

When the big day came, Lady and Tramp herded their pups into a bedroom and told them to stay put. But Scamp was curious. He slipped out of the room and hid behind the living room settee. Then he sneaked up behind the cats and swiped at their tails as they flicked back and forth. The cats turned and chased Scamp up and over the settee, under a table and into a cupboard.

Well, Tramp thought, I suppose I'm going to have to chase those nasty old cats whether I want to or not!

He enthusiastically dived into the cupboard. Seconds later, Tramp and Scamp emerged. Much to Aunt Sarah's horror, Si and Am were later found inside, tied together with a scarf. When no one was looking, Tramp and Scamp shared a victory wink.

Tramp and Scamp were banished to the garden for their antics. When Lady came out that evening, she found that they had dug up the entire garden looking for bones. Father and son saw the look on Lady's face and knew that they were about to get a lecture.

Tramp looked at Lady innocently. "You want him to get exercise, don't you?" he asked.

"Try it, Mum!" Scamp cried. "It's fun."

"What am I going to do with you two?" Lady said, laughing.

Tramp and Scamp dragged a huge bone out from behind the kennel.

"Join us for dinner?" Tramp replied.

"Well, alright," Lady said. "But, as soon as we're done, we're cleaning up this yard."

"Yes, ma'am!" chorused Tramp and Scamp, looking very pleased with themselves.

FROM THE MOVIE **DISNEY·PIXAR INSIDE OUT**

Reunited

Joy and Sadness had finally made it back to Headquarters after their long and difficult journey through Riley's Mind World. The problem was, they couldn't actually get in!

Riley's other Emotions, Anger, Fear and Disgust, ran to the window. Then Disgust had an idea. She taunted Anger until he got so mad that fire burst from his head. Then she picked him up and used the flames to cut a hole in the window! Joy and Sadness climbed inside.

"You're back!" cried Fear, feeling relieved.

While Joy and Sadness had been gone, a lot of things had gone wrong, and Anger had decided Riley should go back to Minnesota where everything had been perfect.

"Joy, you've got to fix this," Disgust pleaded. "Get up there!"

"Oh no!" Joy exclaimed, as she looked up at the screen and saw that Riley was on the bus, ready to run away. Then Joy looked at Sadness. "Sadness," Joy said, "it's up to you."

"Me?" Sadness replied. "Oh, I can't, Joy!"

"Yes you can," said Joy. "Riley needs you."

Sadness took a deep breath and stepped up to the console. Joy, Anger, Fear and Disgust watched the screen and waited.

On the bus, Riley's face changed from totally blank to very sad. She stood up. "Wait!" she called to the driver. "I want to get off!"

When the bus screeched to a standstill, Riley jumped off and started running.

At Riley's house, Mum and Dad were worried sick. Suddenly, the front door flew open and Riley burst in.

"Riley!" her mum cried.

In Headquarters, Joy handed the core memory spheres to Sadness. The spheres all turned blue, and Riley's mind was filled with memories of her old life.

Riley began to cry. "I miss Minnesota," she told her parents. "I want my old friends and my hockey team … I wanna go home. Please don't be mad."

"We're not mad," said Dad. Then Mum and Dad explained they missed Minnesota, too.

They fell into a big, warm family hug and, in Headquarters, a brand-new multi-coloured core memory was created.

After a while, Riley was back to normal – and so was her Mind World. The Islands of Personality had reappeared, with a few new ones, too. The Emotions stood in Headquarters, looking out of the window at their new view.

"Whoa!" the Emotions said, excitedly.

"We've been through a lot lately, that's for sure," said Joy. "But we still love our girl. She has great new friends, a great new house … things couldn't be better. After all, Riley's 12 now … what could possibly happen?"

DISNEY · PIXAR

TOY STORY

Wild West Showdown

A train rumbled across the desert. Suddenly, the roof exploded and the outlaw One-Eyed Bart climbed out, carrying bags of stolen money. Luckily, Sheriff Woody was there to stop him!

"You've got a date with justice, One-Eyed Bart!" cried the Sheriff.

"Ai-ai-yah!" came a cry from behind Woody. It was One-Eyed Betty, One-Eyed Bart's karate-chopping wife! She knocked Woody right off the train.

Suddenly, Jessie the cowgirl came speeding up on her trusty steed, Bullseye. They saved Woody just in time!

But One-Eyed Bart wouldn't be stopped that easily. He pulled out a detonator and blew up a bridge across a giant canyon. Bart and Betty jumped into their getaway car.

"It's me or the kiddies!" yelled One-Eyed Bart. "Take your pick!"

As the outlaws sped away, Jessie saw that the train was filled with orphans – and it was heading right towards the broken bridge! Woody had to save the orphans before going after One-Eyed Bart.

Woody rode Bullseye and leaped onto the engine. He quickly found the brake. The train came to a screeching halt – but not soon enough. It plunged into the canyon with Woody and the orphans still onboard!

Suddenly, Buzz Lightyear the space ranger appeared! He lifted the train out of the canyon.

"Glad you could catch the train, Buzz!" shouted Woody.

Jessie cheered as Buzz carried the train to safety. Next, Buzz used his laser to slice One-Eyed Bart's getaway car in two. Suddenly, a giant dog with a metal coil for a body surrounded the outlaws.

"You can't touch me, Sheriff!" shouted One-Eyed Bart. Suddenly, a giant shadow appeared overhead. A pig-shaped spaceship beamed One-Eyed Bart, One-Eyed Betty and their sidekicks to safety.

"Evil Dr Porkchop!" cried Woody.

"That's Mister Evil Dr Porkchop to you!" yelled the villain. With a wicked laugh, Dr Porkchop dropped an army of vicious monkeys onto Woody, Jessie and Buzz.

"Buzz!" shouted Woody. "Shoot your laser at my badge!"

Buzz aimed his laser beam at Woody's badge and fired. The beam bounced off the badge and hit Dr Porkchop's spaceship.

BOOM! Soon the villains were all tied up and ready to go to jail.

"Good job, deputies!" Woody shouted. The Sheriff and his friends had saved the day again!

Mickey's Spooky Night

Mickey glanced at the clock. "Oh, gosh! I need to get ready for my Halloween party. Where did I put that old pirate costume?"

As Mickey went upstairs to the dark attic, thunder crashed and lightning flashed outside.

He went over to an old trunk. He brushed off the dust, turned the key in the rusty old lock, opened the trunk … and a skeleton popped out!

"Aaaghh!" Mickey jumped back. Then he realized it was just a plastic party decoration. "Phew!"

Mickey rummaged around. "This is a lot of cool Halloween stuff! I'll take it all downstairs."

Meanwhile, Pluto was chasing a ball in the garden. As he charged under the clothesline, one of the sheets came loose and fell on him. It covered him from head to tail and he couldn't see to find his doggy door!

Suddenly, it started raining and the wet sheet stuck to Pluto like glue. He ran all over the garden, but he couldn't shake it off.

At the front of the house, Donald, Goofy, Minnie and Daisy pulled up in their car.

"Look at the lightning!" said Goofy.

Daisy giggled nervously. "It's very spooky."

Mickey's friends hurried inside. "Mickey, we're here!"

But there was no answer. Mickey was too far upstairs to hear.

Just then, the lights went out and Mickey's friends heard thumping sounds above them.

Minnie gasped. "What was that?" Something big and heavy was being dragged across the floor upstairs.

Suddenly something white ran past the window. Mickey's friends were too scared even to scream!

By now, Mickey was heading downstairs in his costume, carrying the skeleton. His friends looked up to see a horrible monster coming towards them.

Suddenly, the lights came back on. "Gosh, hiya, gang," said Mickey.

Minnie smiled. "Mickey! You scared us!"

Daisy sighed and said, "Mickey, this is the scariest, most exciting Halloween ever!"

"Yeah, Mickey, it's the best haunted house I've ever been in," Donald agreed.

"Uh – haunted house?" A puzzled Mickey looked around.

Just then, Pluto found his way in through the doggy door. He ran into the living room. Mickey and his friends looked up and saw – a ghost!

Then Mickey looked again. "Oh, Pluto! It's just you! Let's get you dried off!"

Mickey dried Pluto with a towel and smiled at his friends. "You know, with all of these ghosts, shadows and noises, this is the scariest Halloween ever!"

ᵗʰᵉ Fox ᵃⁿᵈ ᵗʰᵉ Hound

Wild Life

Tod the fox had just arrived at the nature reserve, a vast, beautiful forest where wild animals were protected from hunters. Widow Tweed had brought him there to keep him safe, since her next-door neighbour, Amos Slade, had vowed to hunt him. Amos was angry with the fox because his beloved dog, Chief, had been injured while chasing after him.

At first, Tod didn't understand why his kind owner, Widow Tweed, had left him in the middle of this strange forest, alone and afraid. But she had seemed to be as sad about leaving him as he was about being abandoned.

The first night was dreadful. It had poured with rain and, although he tried to find shelter in different hollows and caves, they were always inhabited by other animals. There was no room for the poor, wet little fox. But the next morning, things began to look up. Tod met a pretty young fox named Vixey. She showed him around the forest, which had many beautiful waterfalls and streams full of fish.

"I think I'm going to like it here, Vixey," said Tod. Having lived his whole life with the Widow Tweed, he had never met another fox before, least of all one as lovely as Vixey.

But Vixey had lived the life of a wild fox, and she knew more about the world than Tod. "You must be very careful, Tod," she warned

him. "Remember, we're foxes, and we have many enemies. You must always be on the alert for danger!"

"Come on, Vixey," scoffed Tod. "We're in a game reserve! I heard the Widow Tweed say that there's no hunting allowed in this forest. What could possibly happen to us here? We don't have a care in the world!"

Suddenly, a huge shadow fell over the two foxes. A look of great fear crossed Vixey's face. Turning around slowly and cautiously, Tod saw why. A huge bear was standing up on its hind legs. And it was staring straight at them!

"Grrrr!" the bear growled.

"Run!" yelled Vixey.

Tod didn't need to be told twice. The two foxes dashed away from the bear, scampering over hills, racing through a hollow tree and jumping over a narrow stream. When they were well away from the bear, they stopped and leaned against a rock, panting hard.

"Okay," Tod said, when he had caught his breath a bit. "I see what you mean about the dangers, Vixey. From now on, I'll be a lot more careful."

"Mmm-hmm," she replied. Then she smiled. "Come on," she said to Tod. "Let's go fishing!"

Disney · PIXAR

WALL·E
Finally Home

On the *Axiom*, the ship where all the humans now lived, little robot EVE delivered a special plant from Earth to the Captain. EVE had found it among the treasures of a robot called WALL·E.

The Captain was excited, because this plant meant he and all the humans could return to Earth. But the Captain's robot wouldn't let them. Quickly, Auto snatched the plant and dumped it down the rubbish chute.

The plant hit WALL·E. The little bot was climbing up to get to EVE! Happily he delivered the plant right back to her. But Auto electrocuted WALL·E and sent him back down the chute with EVE.

WALL·E and EVE ended up in the ship's rubbish bay. EVE rescued the injured little bot while WALL·E tried to give her the plant. He still thought she wanted it more than anything else. But WALL·E was wrong. EVE just wanted to help WALL·E now.

Soon EVE flew them up and out of the garbage bay, with the plant in hand. She wanted to get WALL·E home to Earth so she could find the right parts to fix him.

The Captain was fighting Auto for control of the ship by now. He sent a message to EVE, telling her to take the plant to a large machine called the holo-detector.

The machine would make the ship head towards Earth.

The Captain finally managed to turn off the bad robot's power. EVE fought to reach the holo-detector. At last she put the plant inside the machine. Finally they could return to Earth.

But all was not well. WALL·E had been crushed by the giant machine! Heartbroken and more determined than before, EVE wanted to take WALL·E home to his truck, where she could find the right parts to bring him back to life. As soon as the Axiom landed on Earth, EVE headed straight for WALL·E's home and repaired him. At last, he powered up ... and began cubing trash. Something was wrong. He was just another trash-cubing robot. All the love was gone. He didn't even recognize EVE!

Sadly, EVE held WALL·E's hand and leaned towards him. An electric arc passed between their heads – the robot kiss. She was saying goodbye. Then ... WALL·E's hand began to move. EVE looked into his eyes. He was coming back to life! He recognized her!

"Ee-vah?" he said. After following EVE across the universe, WALL·E had ended up right where he had started – home. But this time he had the one thing he truly wanted – EVE's hand clasped in his own.

DISNEP·PIXAR

MONSTERS
UNIVERSITY
Dig Deep!

At Monsters University, Mike and Sulley woke up early and leaped out of bed. They were heading off to practise for the annual Scare Games competition.

Their team, the Oozma Kappas, had already survived two events with two to go. Mike was determined to lead his team to victory. It was vital for him that he did, because if they lost, he'd have to leave university. His lifelong dream of becoming a Scarer for Monsters, Inc. would be over.

At practice, Mike trained his Oozma Kappa teammates in everything they would need to know for the next two events. He taught them how to sneak into a room while avoiding parents and teenagers. He taught them how to hide and not be seen. He even got them to do fast 'scary feet' on the spot, to make sure they were in tip-top shape.

The third event was called 'Don't Scare the Teen'. The OKs successfully worked their way through a maze by scaring all the child cut-outs and avoiding the teen ones. Only their biggest rivals, Roar Omega Roar, made it out of the maze before them.

That meant that there were only three teams left for the fourth event: ROR, HSS and OK.

The 'Hide and Sneak' event required all of the competitors to hide in a dark house while referees searched for them with torches.

The referees soon discovered HSS – but no one else. That meant the RORs and the OKs would compete against each other for the Scare Games trophy!

Sulley spotted Dean Hardscrabble, the head of the Scaring Programme. It had been the Dean's decision to kick Mike and Sulley off the programme.

"When we get back," Sulley said to her, "I hope there'll be no hard feelings," he said.

Dean Hardscrabble said she doubted they would win – Mike just wasn't scary enough. It made Sulley wonder if maybe Hardscrabble was right, so he decided to leave nothing to chance. He would teach Mike how to be scary.

Sulley told Mike to forget what he had read about scaring in books. He needed to stop *thinking* scary and start *feeling* it.

Mike tried a heartfelt roar.

"Let the animal out!" coached Sulley. "Dig deep!"

Mike gave it all he had. It was an improvement. Sulley just hoped it would be enough to win. And he was about to find out – the battle for the trophy was tomorrow.

The Four-legged Festival

Quasimodo was a kind young man who was always quick to offer help to anyone in need. He was especially drawn to those who were alone in the world. After spending years confined to the bell tower of the cathedral, Quasimodo knew just how terrible loneliness could feel.

It wasn't surprising, then, that Quasimodo had a growing collection of orphaned animals. First he had taken in a stray kitten, and then an abandoned puppy. Next he adopted a lamb, an old donkey, a baby bird and an ox. Esmeralda and Phoebus helped him build a pen. But they weren't sure how he could afford to continue feeding so many pets. "I'll find a way – somehow," Quasimodo told the couple. "They're counting on me!"

The Festival of Fools was coming up, and Quasimodo was a little worried about how his pets would react to all the noise and excitement. "While you're helping Clopin with his puppet show at the festival," said Esmeralda, "why don't we have Djali keep an eye on the animals?" Djali was Esmeralda's clever little goat. He was used to crowds, and often danced with Esmeralda in the village square.

"Why, thank you, Esmeralda!" replied Quasimodo. "That's a wonderful idea."

The day of the festival arrived. Esmeralda brought Djali and put him inside the pen with the other animals. The square quickly filled with people wearing costumes and masks. Delicious smells drifted through the air from the sellers' stands. The animals pushed at the sides of the pen, wanting to investigate the new smells and sounds. Djali also wanted to join the fun. He nibbled at the latch of the pen and the gate flew open.

Djali heard the tinkling of Esmeralda's tambourine on the far side of the square and ran towards the sound. The other animals followed – even as the goat crashed through a stall full of masks for sale! Everyone turned to see the animals, which were now disguised as jesters and kings, song-birds and queens. The masked animals danced right past Clopin's puppet wagon and onto Esmeralda's stage. Quasimodo watched in amazement as Djali and the others joined in the gypsy's merry dance. The crowds cheered and showered the performers with coins.

When the show ended, Esmeralda climbed down from the stage and delivered the money to Quasimodo. "This should take care of whatever food you need to buy," she said happily.

Quasimodo felt like dancing for joy – but he decided to leave that to the animals!

Bambi

First Frost

Slowly, Bambi opened his eyes. Curled next to his mother, he was toasty-warm in the thicket. Bambi blinked sleepily, peering past the brambles. Something was different. The forest did not look the same. The air was crisp and cold, and everything was frosted and sparkling.

"Jack Frost has been here," Bambi's mother explained. "He's painted the whole forest with ice crystals."

Bambi was about to ask his mother who Jack Frost was and how he painted with ice, when he heard another voice, an impatient one.

"Get up! Get up! Come look at the frost!" It was Thumper. He tapped his foot impatiently. "We haven't got all day!"

Bambi stood and looked at his mother. When she nodded approvingly, he scampered out of the thicket. Bambi looked closely at the colourful leaves on the ground. Each one was covered in an icy-white pattern. He touched his nose to a big orange oak leaf. "Ooh, it's cold!" he cried.

"Of course it is!" Thumper laughed.

"I think it's beautiful," said Faline, as she stepped into the clearing.

"Me too," Bambi agreed.

"Well, come look at this!" Thumper hopped away and the two young deer followed, admiring the way the sun sparkled on the frost-covered trees and grass.

Thumper disappeared under a bush; then Bambi heard a new noise. *Creak, crack.*

Faline pushed through the bushes with Bambi right behind her. There was Thumper, cracking the thin ice on a puddle with his feet.

Bambi had never seen ice before. He pushed on the icy thin puddle covering with his hoof. It seemed to bend. Then it shattered!

Soon the three friends were stomping on the ice-covered puddles. When all the ice was broken, Faline had an idea. "Let's go to the meadow!"

Bambi thought that was a great idea. The grass would be sparkling! They set out at a run, bounding and racing each other through the forest. But when they got to the meadow's edge, they all stopped.

They looked, sniffed and listened quietly. They did not sense danger – no, the trouble was that in the meadow, nothing was different. There was no frost.

"What happened?" Bambi asked.

"Frost never lasts long," Thumper explained. "It melts as soon as the sun hits it. But don't worry. Winter is coming, and soon we'll have something even better than frost. We'll have snow!"

A Wonderful/Terrible Day

"What a wonderful day!" Mickey Mouse said to himself. He hummed as he strolled through the outdoor market. The air was crisp. The leaves were pretty shades of red, yellow and orange. And the perfect hunk of cheese was right in front of him.

"I'll take that cheese and a loaf of bread," he told the market seller.

"You're just in time," the seller replied. "I'm about to close up shop."

Meanwhile, Donald Duck was just leaving his house. "What a terrible day!" he said in a huff. He had overslept and woken up with a crick in his neck. He hurried to cross the street, but had to stop for a red light.

When the light turned green, he stepped into the street.

H-o-n-n-k-k! A big truck roared past, just missing Donald.

"Watch where you're going!" Donald shouted. He raced ahead to the market.

"I'll take a loaf of bread," he told the seller.

"Sorry," the seller replied. "I'm sold out."

"Sold out?" Donald's eyes bulged in his head. "Sold out?"

Down the block, Mickey Mouse was having a friendly chat with Goofy. "How have you been, Goofy?" he asked.

"Fine," Goofy said as he peeled a banana. He ate the whole thing in one bite and dropped the peel on the ground.

In the market, Donald sulked. He was hungry!

"This is so unfair!" he said. Slumping his shoulders, he started off towards the park at the end of the street. But a second later he slipped on a banana peel.

"*Ooof!*" Donald fell to the ground with a thud. Scowling, he got to his feet.

Not far away, Mickey was spreading out his picnic blanket in the park. All around him, children were laughing and playing.

"Hey, kids!" he called with a friendly wave. He took a big bite of his cheese sandwich and chewed happily. "What a wonderful day," he said again.

Donald kicked a pebble on the sidewalk while his tummy growled. And then, all of a sudden – *thunk!* – a ball hit him on the head.

"Watch it, kids!" Donald shouted. He rubbed his sore head. "What a terrible day."

Just then, Donald heard a familiar voice call out, "Hey, Donald! Come have a cheese sandwich with me!"

Donald saw Mickey waving to him from under a tree. Donald wanted to stay mad. But the truth is that no duck can resist a cheese sandwich. He smiled and ambled over. Maybe it wasn't such a bad day after all!

Disney · PIXAR

TOY STORY

Sunnyside Bootcamp

Early one morning, Buzz and Rex arrived at Sunnyside Daycare. As soon as it was safe, they popped out of Bonnie's backpack. Even though they lived with Bonnie now, Buzz and Rex liked to come and visit the toys at Sunnyside.

Buzz greeted Sarge. When Andy went to college, Sarge and his last two cadets found a new home at Sunnyside. Sarge told Buzz he wished his ranks weren't so thin.

"There are recruits all around you," Buzz said. "Let's have a boot camp."

"I have lots of boots in my closet!" Ken cried. He ran off to get them before anyone could explain what a boot camp really was!

During the children's naptime, the toys snuck outside and started training.

Ken reappeared wearing some cowboy boots. When Sarge told him to run laps of the garden, Ken was horrified!

Meanwhile, the others were working hard. Sarge ordered everyone onto the bouncy trucks in the playground. Rex hopped on one and started rocking it slowly. But then Big Baby joined Rex and rocked it faster!

"Too fast!" cried Rex. "Stop!"

But when Big Baby stopped rocking, Rex went flying! He landed on top of the climbing frame! Sarge and Buzz came up with a mission: to rescue Rex.

"We're going to have to work together," Buzz told the toys.

All the toys agreed to help – except Ken. "These are vintage," he said, pointing to his boots.

The other toys made themselves into a tower, but it was too short to reach Rex! They told Ken they needed his help.

Ken thought for a moment then nodded.

"Fashion has never held me back before!"

He quickly removed his boots and climbed to the top of the tower. But he still couldn't reach Rex!

Then Ken had an idea. "Stretch," he called, "hand me my 1972 cherry-red striped platform boots!" He put them on and reached out to Rex. "Gotcha!" said Ken.

"We did it!" cheered the toys.

"Good work, troops," said Sarge. "Mission accomplished."

Then it was time for Buzz and Rex to go. They said goodbye to all the toys. But Buzz couldn't find Ken....

Buzz finally found him. "Thanks for your help today," said Buzz. "You're a great soldier!"

"Thanks, Buzz. But, great doesn't cut it," said Ken. "Once I finish designing our new army boots – we'll be fabulous!"

THE EMPEROR'S
NEW GROOVE

Kronk's Feast

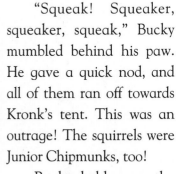

"One more time!" Kronk cried. The Junior Chipmunks looked at their leader, took deep breaths and launched into "We're Not Woodchucks" for the fourth time. "We're the ch-ch-chipmunks. We're not w-w-woodchucks," the kids sang, halfheartedly puffing out their cheeks.

The tired troop sagged on their log. Next to them, Bucky the squirrel and three of his friends sang along too – in Squirrel. "Squeak sq-sq-squeak. Sq-sq-squeak squeak, squeaker, squeak." The furry animals' tails drooped.

"I'm hungry," Tipo whispered to his sister Chaca.

"Keep singing," Chaca said behind her hand. "He's got to be done soon."

While the children began another verse, Kronk stood at the fire. He mixed, flipped and seasoned in a frenzy. He had been cooking for hours, and the smells drifting towards the tired troop were delicious.

"I'm … almost … ready." Kronk struggled to balance several plates on his arm before spinning around to present them to the troop. "Voilà." The big man grinned. "Bon appétit!"

The troop leaned forward and smiled. The food looked as good as it smelled. They began to help themselves.

Kronk stood back modestly. "I do pride myself on being a bit of a gourmet," he said.

Everyone was pleased. Everyone, that is, but Bucky and the squirrels. Where was *their* food?

"Squeak! Squeaker, squeaker, squeak," Bucky mumbled behind his paw. He gave a quick nod, and all of them ran off towards Kronk's tent. This was an outrage! The squirrels were Junior Chipmunks, too!

Bucky held open the tent flap and the squirrels ducked inside. "Squeak," Bucky commanded as he pointed at Kronk's sleeping bag. The other squirrels nodded. They knew what they were supposed to do – chew holes in Kronk's bedding! Just as the squirrels were about to get to work, they were interrupted.

"Oh, squeeeaak," Kronk's deep voice crooned from outside. "Squeaker squeeaak!"

The squirrels peeked outside the tent.

There was Kronk, holding a new plate. Balanced upon it were a golden-brown acorn soufflé and a bowl of steaming wild-berry sauce.

Bucky shrugged sheepishly at the leader.

"Thought I forgot you, huh? Would Kronk do that?" The leader set the tray down. "How about a hug?"

The four squirrels grasped the large man's legs and squeezed. All was forgiven. Together all the Junior Chipmunks enjoyed their meal.

315

Mater in Paris

One lazy afternoon, Mater was listening to music. Suddenly the music stopped and a voice spoke to Mater through the radio. It was British secret agent, Holley Shiftwell!

"Hello Mater!" she said. "Sorry to startle you. I'm contacting you because Finn and I need your help. We're in Paris tracking several Lemons who escaped from the World Grand Prix. Will you help?"

"Sure thing!" Mater said. "Love to!"

Suddenly, Siddeley the spy plane landed in the middle of Main Street! Mater's best friend, Lightning McQueen drove up. "Mater, what's going on?" he asked.

"I'm going on a secret mission to Paris," whispered Mater. "You wanna come, too?"

"Paris? Um ... well ... sure," said Lightning.

Once in Paris, Mater and Lightning met up with Holley and Finn.

"We've been tailing these Lemons for a while, but they keep getting away," said Finn.

"Them Lemons are tricky," said Mater. "You just gotta learn how to think like them. If I was a Lemon, I'd make sure I had plenty of spare parts."

"Brilliant," said Finn. "You and Lightning can visit the spare parts dealer at the marketplace. Holley and I will head to the markets on the west side of Paris."

When Lightning and Mater got to the spare parts dealer, he had been robbed!

"Them Lemons was here already," said Mater. Then he spotted a trail of spare parts on the ground. The pair followed the trail all the way to a nearby café where Mater noticed two odd-looking cars. One of them backfired and his grille fell off. It was a disguise!

"Lemons!" cried Mater. "Their old exhausts make 'em backfire!"

The Lemons quickly fled the café. Lightning and Mater followed them through the city. But suddenly, there were not two, but six Lemons surrounding them!

"We're gonna get rid of you once and for all, tow truck, and your race car friend, too!" yelled one of the Lemons. Then he sprayed knock-out gas at Mater and Lightning.

But Mater quickly spun his tow hook! It blew the gas back at the Hugos. The thugs instantly passed out.

Some more Lemons arrived, but Mater had an idea....

Lightning and Mater led the Lemons on a chase, all the way to the top of the Eiffel Tower. The Lemons were so exhausted, they tipped over. Finn and Holley arrived just in time to capture them. Another great mission completed by secret agent Mater!

Blade to the Rescue

Dusty and Blade got into position to fight the forest fire that was heading towards Fusel Lodge. The lodge was full of guests after the grand reopening party and they were all now at risk from this raging fire.

Blade radioed the mechanic, Maru, and ordered an evacuation.

Maru got in touch with Cad Spinner, the park superintendent, at the lodge.

"Blade insists on an evacuation," he told Cad. "To be safe, you've got to get everyone out."

"Absolutely not!" Cad replied. He wasn't about to let a little fire spoil his big celebration.

As they approached the fire, Blade ordered Dusty to only drop half of his fire retardant. But Dusty wasn't paying attention. He was watching the warning light on his control panel. It was blinking red, indicating his gearbox was about to fail, and without a new gearbox, Dusty would never race again.

With his mind elsewhere, Dusty watched Blade drop his fire retardant on to the fire. Then he accidentally dumped his, too. All of it! Blade was furious. Why had he let this irresponsible rookie on the attack team?

"Return to base!" he yelled.

But Dusty didn't return to base. He wanted to make up for his stupid mistake. He flew down to the surface of Anchor Lake and tried to reload his pontoons with water. It was a tricky manoeuvre and one he hadn't yet mastered. The lake was too choppy and Dusty's nose hit the water's surface.

"My engine stalled!" he yelled to Blade. Suddenly he found himself drifting downstream towards an outlet from the lake and into the rapids!

"Stalled? Oh for …" Blade grumbled. He had to go and rescue him.

Blade threw down a line, but it fell short. "You need to start your engine!" he cried. "You can take off before the falls!"

Dusty tried and tried. Eventually he got the engine going and gave it full throttle. Just as he started to lift off, the warning light flashed again. He knew that meant trouble. His gearbox wouldn't take it, so Dusty slowed down.

"Why are you holding back?" Blade yelled. Then he watched Dusty going over the falls!

Blade swooped in and snagged Dusty in mid-air. It took all of the rescue helicopter's strength to swing Dusty to safety and put him down on the ground.

But there was no time to rest. The fire was closing in … fast!

THE **JUNGLE Book**

Dawn Patrol

One day, Mowgli went to the jungle to visit his old friend Baloo the bear.

"Why so sad, Mowgli?" asked Baloo.

"It's the dry season, and the river is getting low," said Mowgli. "My friends in the village are worried about running out of water."

"Oh," said Baloo. He scratched his head. "But what about the spring in the jungle? It never goes dry."

Mowgli shook his head. "The spring is much too far inside the jungle. It would take all day to get there from the village."

Just then, Bagheera the panther padded over. "Mowgli, I have an idea – Dawn Patrol."

The next morning, Bagheera, Baloo and Mowgli all waited by the spring. Before long, the ground shook with the approach of Colonel Hathi and his elephants.

"Hup, two, three, four. Hup, two, three, four," chanted the Colonel as the herd marched behind him.

"Here they come," said Bagheera. "Dawn Patrol."

Quickly, Bagheera, Baloo and Mowgli hid in the bushes. They waited for the elephants to stop at the spring and take a long drink.

"Ready to try my plan?" Bagheera whispered to Mowgli. The boy nodded, then the two sprang from the bushes crying, "To the river! Quick! Everyone, as fast as you can!"

The elephants looked up in alarm.

"W-what's the m-meaning of this?" stammered the Colonel.

"Shere Khan is coming! Run for the river!" called Mowgli.

"Company … RUN!" cried the Colonel, and the elephants stampeded through the jungle.

Bagheera and Mowgli watched the herd knock down every tree between the spring and the river. When Mowgli reached the river, he turned around and saw a clear, easy path straight to the big spring!

Now it was time for Baloo to play his part.

"Hey, whoa!" cried Baloo, running up to the herd. "False alarm!"

"What's that?" asked Colonel Hathi.

"Shere Khan isn't coming after all," said Baloo. "Human hunters are after him, so he's heading far away. We're all safe!"

The Dawn Patrol sighed with relief. Then Colonel Hathi called, "Forward, march!"

As the elephants marched off, Mowgli grinned. "With this new path to the spring, my friends will never run out of water."

Bagheera nodded. "Good work," he said.

"Yes, it was," said Baloo with a laugh. "And you know what was good about it? Somebody else did the work for us!"

Pinocchio
Slugger

Pinocchio, as you know, was not always a real boy. Once, he was a puppet. And before that, he was a log. And before that, he was the trunk of a tall, shady tree. But that's of no great importance to our story ... it's simply to remind you that Pinocchio was not always a boy – and that to him, being a real boy was indeed a dream come true.

Our story, in fact, takes place some time later, when Pinocchio was walking home from school one day. He had just been thinking to himself of what real-boy play he would enjoy that afternoon – climbing trees, or skimming stones, or maybe just stomping in the mud – when suddenly he spied a whole group of real boys gathered in a field just down the road.

"What are you doing?" asked Pinocchio.

"Playing baseball," said a red-haired boy.

"Baseball?" Pinocchio hadn't heard of that game before. But it sounded like fun.

"Can I play?" he asked.

The boys nodded.

"Did you bring a glove?" one boy asked.

"A glove?" said Pinocchio.

"That's okay," said the boy. "You can use mine while I bat." He tossed a big, brown leather glove into Pinocchio's hands. "You can play first base."

Pinocchio grinned. First base! That sounded important! This game was going to be fun. Now, if he could just work out which base was first....

Luckily, the other boys ran off to their bases, leaving just one empty. Pinocchio trotted out to the dusty square. Then he waited to see what came next.

"Batter up!"

Whoosh!

Crack!

It didn't take long. One fast pitch, and before Pinocchio knew it, a ball was sailing over his head, and a tall boy was running full speed at him!

"*Ahhhhh!*" Pinocchio screamed, covering his face with his big glove. The boy was safe. And Pinocchio moved to right field. But on the very next pitch, where should the ball fly, but up ... up ... up ... and down to right field. This time, Pinocchio tried to catch it – but it landed with a *plop* on the grass behind him.

But Pinocchio never gave up and, when it was finally his turn to bat, he stepped into the batter's box and held his head high. To Pinocchio's surprise, the bat felt strangely natural in his hands ... almost like a part of his old, *wooden* self. He watched the pitcher carefully ... and on the first pitch – *crack!* – he sent the ball high and away, into the sky.

"Hooray!" the boys cheered. A slugger had been born! And a real boy had learned a new game.

319

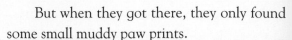

The Kitten Sitters

"We're going to look after Minnie's kitten, Figaro, tonight," Mickey Mouse said to his nephews, Morty and Ferdie.

As Minnie and Figaro arrived at Mickey's house, Pluto came racing across the lawn, an angry chicken behind him!

"Pluto! Have you been chasing chickens again? Maybe Figaro can teach you some manners!" Minnie said as she stomped off, leaving Figaro sitting in Mickey's arms.

Minnie was hardly out of sight when Figaro leaped down and scampered into the kitchen. He jumped on to the table, knocking over a jug of milk.

Pluto growled, but Mickey just cleaned up the mess. "Be nice, Pluto," he said.

Later, Pluto ate all his food. But Figaro refused to touch the food Minnie had left.

At bedtime, Morty called out "Uncle Mickey, did you close the kitchen window?"

"Oh, no!" cried Mickey. The window was open and Figaro was nowhere to be seen.

Mickey and the boys searched the house but couldn't find Figaro. So they went to Minnie's house, but Figaro wasn't there either.

"Have you seen a little black-and-white kitten?" Mickey asked a policeman in the street.

"I certainly have!" he answered. "He was teasing the ducks by the pond!"

But when they got there, they only found some small muddy paw prints.

The group followed the trail to another street, where they met a lorry driver.

"Have you seen a kitten?" Mickey asked.

"Yes!" cried the driver. "He knocked over my eggs!"

Mickey groaned as he paid for the broken eggs.

They searched the whole town, but there was no sign of the kitten. When they returned home, the sun was starting to rise.

Soon, Minnie drove up. "Where's Figaro?" she asked.

Just then, there was a loud clucking. A dozen hens came flapping over the garden fence, with Figaro close behind.

"There's your sweet kitten!" exclaimed Mickey. "He ran away, teased the ducks in the park. Then he broke the eggs and –"

"I had hoped Figaro would teach Pluto some manners," Minnie said, "instead, Pluto has been teaching him to misbehave!" She picked up Figaro and drove away.

"We'll tell her the whole story later, when she's not so upset," said Mickey to the boys.

"Don't tell her too soon," begged Morty. "As long as Aunt Minnie thinks Pluto is a bad dog, we won't have to kitten-sit Figaro."

Mickey smiled. "Maybe you're right. We could all use some peace and quiet."

Disney · PIXAR
MONSTERS UNIVERSITY

The Final

At Monsters University it was the final event of the Scare Games. It was a battle for the trophy between Mike and Sulley's team, the Oozma Kappas, and their biggest rivals, the Roar Omega Roars.

The RORs and the OKs entered the packed stadium. The OKs got huge cheers from the crowd. They were the unexpected finalists, so everyone was rooting for them.

"It's time to see how terrifying you really are in the scare simulators," said the VP of the Greek Council, the sponsors of the games. "Be warned. Each simulated scare has been set to the highest difficulty level."

One member from each team – Reggie from ROR and Don from OK – took their places at the starting line. The RORs laughed at Don and called him 'Grandpa' – until he beat Reggie!

Terri and Terry from OK went against Chet from ROR, followed by Squishy against Chip, and then Art against Javier.

After those four rounds, the RORs had a significant lead over the OKs. It was up to Sulley and Mike to win it for the team!

Sulley went up against Randy, Mike's old roommate. Sulley entered the simulator. It was like a child's bedroom, with a robot-child asleep in the bed.

Sulley successfully dodged every obstacle in the room, creeped up to the bed, and let out a thunderous roar. It was so loud, it shook Randy's simulator and Sulley easily won the challenge. Now the RORs and the OKs were tied in the games!

The last two team members to compete were Mike and Johnny.

"Don't take the loss too hard," Johnny sneered at Mike. "You never belonged here anyway."

Mike ignored him. He couldn't let anything distract him from doing his best. Johnny entered his scare simulator and got a huge scream from his robot-child. He was certain he had won it for the RORs.

Next Mike entered his room. He ruffled the scare simulator curtains and creeped along the side of the bed. Then he closed his eyes and concentrated. This was it. He took a deep breath, jumped and let out his most explosive roar! The robot-child sat bolt upright – and filled Mike's scream can all the way up to the top. The OKs had won the Scare Games!

The stadium cheered wildly as Mike walked out of the simulator. The Roar Omega Roars were stunned. They never imagined that they would lose the Scare Games – especially to the Oozma Kappas!

But had the OKs won fairly...?

Disney · PIXAR

TOY STORY

Buzz's Space Adventure

One day, after a long playtime, the Peas-in-a-Pod were feeling tired. They asked Buzz to tell them a story about space!

"Once upon a time," Buzz began, "the evil Emperor Zurg stole a top-secret Space Ranger Turbo Suit. Star Command knew I was the only one who could get it back!"

"Wow," said Woody. "I wonder how it feels to be a space hero."

"Me, too," said Rex. "Hey, Buzz! Can I be in your story? But with big arms?"

"Sure, why not?" said Buzz, as he continued.

"I was heading into dangerous space, so I brought a special crew: First Lieutenant Woody and Second Lieutenant Rex!

As we touched down on Planet Zurg, a loud humming noise filled the air. We needed to investigate.

Suddenly, we spotted an army – hundreds of Emperor Zurg's loyal Zurgbots, and all of them were humming. Woody and Rex had it covered, so I went off to find Zurg's headquarters … and that Turbo Suit!

But I hadn't gone far when I saw one Zurgbot. It was strange. Usually, they never travelled alone. His humming sounded odd, almost like a melody.

"Hold your fire!" the Zurgbot cried. "I'm not like the others! My name is Zenny, and I don't want to hum – I want to sing. But the emperor will not allow it."

Apparently this Zurgbot also opposed Zurg! But with the entire galaxy at stake, how could I trust him?

"I will take you to the Turbo Suit," Zenny promised.

True to his word, Zenny quickly led me into the heart of Zurg's lair – and to the Turbo Suit.

But as I reached for the suit, a band of Zurgbots attacked. And they had my lieutenants!

Then Zurg appeared and our doom seemed near.…

"Not so fast, Zurg," a voice called out.

It was Zenny!

"Quiet, Zurgbot!" ordered the emperor.

"No," said Zenny. "I may look like other Zurgbots, but I don't have to act like them!"

And with that, he began to sing! As Zenny's voice grew louder, stalactites fell from the cave's ceiling. They dropped to the floor, trapping Zurg. Zenny untied our bonds and set us free! Quickly, I climbed into the Turbo Suit and, with the help of my lieutenants, defeated the Zurgbot army! Zenny helped!

As we headed home, we could see Zenny below, teaching the other Zurgbots to sing. Planet Zurg would be a happier place from then onwards. The End."

101 DALMATIANS
Having a Ball!

"Ten days until Santa!" the spotted puppies barked, bouncing into one another as they tumbled down the hall.

"Ten days until presents!" Penny barked.

"And 10 days until Christmas dinner!" Rolly added.

"Ten days to stay out of trouble!" Pongo said with a smile.

"Do you puppies know what comes before Santa and dinner and presents?" Perdita asked.

"Umm … stockings?" Lucky asked.

"No, before that," she said.

Patch wasn't sure. He sat down on the hall rug to think.

"We have to decorate and sing carols," Perdita said, wagging her tail. At that very moment, Roger and Anita threw open the door to the study and invited all the dogs inside.

Patch blinked. He couldn't believe his eyes. "What's a tree doing in the house?"

"Just watch." Perdy gave Patch a quick lick.

While the dogs looked on, Roger and Anita began to decorate the tree. They hung lights and angels, snowmen and tinsel. Of all the decorations, Patch liked the glittering glass balls best. Balls were one of his favourite things! He could not take his eyes off them.

When the tree was ready, Anita brought in cocoa and dog biscuits. Munching on a biscuit in front of the fire, Patch didn't think the evening could get any better. Then Roger sat down at the piano, and everyone began to sing.

Patch howled along with the others, but he could not stop looking at the balls on the tree. A large red one was hanging near the floor.

Patch reached over and gave the ball a pat with his front paw. It swung merrily above him. Looking at his reflection, Patch started to laugh. His nose looked huge!

"What are you doing?" Penny stopped singing to see what was so funny. Then Freckles joined them, then Lucky. The puppies took turns knocking the ball and watching it sway, then – *crash!* – it fell to the floor, shattering.

The singing stopped. Poor Patch was sure the special evening was ruined.

"Oh, dear." Anita scooped the puppies out from under the tree. "Careful, now," she said. "Those balls aren't for playing with."

While Roger swept up the glass, Patch cowered. He knew he was in trouble.

"Maybe I should give you all one gift early," Anita said with a grin. Patch couldn't believe his luck. Instead of a firm talking-to, each puppy got to rip open a small package. Patch tore off the paper. Inside was a brand-new red rubber ball!

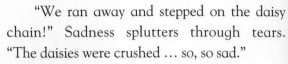

Disney · PIXAR
FROM THE MOVIE **INSIDE OUT**

Sadly Ever After

Anger, Disgust, Fear, Sadness and Joy all work together in Headquarters and watch after their girl, Riley.

"Sadness, cheer up! We're ice-skating! We love ice-skating!" Joy says.

"I'm too sad to skate." Sadness whimpers

"You know what you need? A happy memory! Pick one," Joy replies.

"Maybe that time we went to the park and had a picnic?" Sadness suggests.

"That is a great memory," Joy says excitedly. "We did lots of things that day. Mum and Dad surprised us with a cupcake! Riley was about to take a big bite when –"

"A ladybird landed on the frosting and got stuck," Sadness continued. "Poor ladybird."

"Sadness!" Joy pleads.

"That picnic was just peachy until that dog ran in and ruined everything!" shouts Anger. "That must make you angry, right, Sadness?"

"Mum and Dad wouldn't let us take the dog home," Sadness moans.

"You left out the most gruesome part of that day," says Disgust. "We slipped in the mud and disgusting gloop went everywhere. Doesn't that completely gross you out?"

Sadness sighs. "No, it's sad. That jumper was our favourite. We ruined it."

"Um, remember when we made a daisy chain?" says Fear. "A giant bee nearly stung us!"

"We ran away and stepped on the daisy chain!" Sadness splutters through tears. "The daisies were crushed … so, so sad."

"This clearly isn't working. Choose a sad memory," suggests Joy.

"There was that time we missed the school bus," Sadness begins.

"That was sad, but how does it make the three of you feel?" Joy asks the team.

"Furious!" Anger screams. "That bus driver left three seconds early!"

"And we nearly choked on the exhaust fumes! So beyond gross," Disgust adds.

"And we were going to get in trouble for being late to school!" Fear explains.

"Do you want to know how I remember that day?" Joy asks. "It was the best day ever! Mum ended up driving us to school. We sang out loud to the radio and stopped for a hot chocolate!"

"You're right, Joy," Anger says calmly. "Maybe that wasn't so bad."

"Nothing gross about that," says Disgust.

"I feel all warm and safe now," Fear says.

Sadness thinks for a moment. "I feel …"

"Great, right? You're happy! We're all happy," says Joy. But then….

"I feel sad!" Sadness cries. "When we took a sip of the hot chocolate, we burned our tongue."

Anger, Disgust, Fear and Joy just sigh.

DISNEY
PLANES
2

Wildfires Rage On

After saving Dusty from being washed over a waterfall, Blade decided they needed to get to safety. "Follow me," he shouted to Dusty as the wildfire raged around them. When they reached the entrance to an old mine, Blade turned on Dusty. He was angry with him for not following orders. He had risked both their lives.

But Dusty was angry, too. He had never wanted to be a firefighter.

"My gearbox is bust," Dusty admitted. "I'm never going to race again."

Blade sighed. "Life doesn't always go the way you expect it," he said. And Blade knew what he was talking about. He had once been a famous television star – a patrol helicopter in the popular TV show *CHoPS*.

Blade and Dusty entered the mine just before the firestorm reached them. Flaming embers and hot smoke swirled around the firefighters. Blade used his body to shield Dusty from the heat.

When the fire had burned past, the two slowly emerged.

Back at Fusel Lodge, Piston Peak's impressive hotel, the park superintendent was unveiling a commemorative plaque ... with his face on it! Suddenly someone screamed. One of the fires was racing towards the lodge! The guests panicked and raced for the exits.

Out on the runway, Pulaski, the lodge's fire truck, tried to keep the evacuation orderly. When a swanky jet pulled to the front, Pulaski stopped him and sent him to the back. He wasn't letting anyone jump the queue.

Meanwhile, back in the forest, Blade and Dusty rolled out of the mine and into a meadow after the fire had moved on. But Blade was so badly damaged from the fire that he crashed on take-off.

Dusty was alarmed. Blade had saved his life – twice. He needed to get help. "Blade is down!" he radioed urgently. "I repeat: Blade is down!"

Windlifter, a heavy-lift helicopter, responded to Dusty's call. As soon as he arrived, he quickly put a harness round Blade, lifted him up and carried him back to base.

When they arrived at the air-attack base, Maru the mechanic got right to work, fixing Blade's broken parts.

While the rescue helicopter rested, Maru told Dusty that Blade's partner on the TV show crashed while doing a stunt. Blade was there, but he didn't know how to help him and his friend had never recovered. That was why Blade had left the show and ended up at Piston Peak.

"Blade ... he used to pretend to save lives," said Maru. "Now he saves 'em for real."

THE INCREDIBLES

Mr Incredible's Greatest Adventure

Syndrome – previously named Buddy – had just launched a deadly robot towards the city. Syndrome had once been Mr Incredible's number one fan, but when Mr Incredible told him, "Supers are born, not made," the boy had decided to prove his hero wrong.

Syndrome had lured Mr Incredible to his island and held him prisoner. Mr Incredible's wife, Elastigirl, had discovered where her husband had gone and set off to save him. Their two Super children, Violet and Dash, stowed away on the jet.

At headquarters, Mirage – who was working for Syndrome – had decided to set Mr Incredible free. She was angry that Syndrome had challenged the hero to hurt her. She wanted Mr Incredible to know that his family was still alive.

Mr Incredible was so happy to hear this news that he hugged Mirage. But just then Elastigirl burst in! *THUMP!* She punched Mirage from across the room. Mr Incredible tried to explain, but Elastigirl was too angry.

"Where are the kids?" asked Mr Incredible.

"They might've triggered the alert," said Mirage. "Security's been sent into the jungle!"

Syndrome's guards had indeed found Violet and Dash. They chased the two young Supers. Vi protected herself and Dash with a force field. Then Dash began to run. They raced through the jungle. Mr Incredible and Elastigirl eventually found them.

Together, the family fought off Syndrome's guards. But suddenly Syndrome arrived and locked the Incredibles in his immobiray! "Looks like I've hit the jackpot!" Syndrome gloated."

Then he took them to his base and suspended them in an immobi-ray cell. The family was helpless as Syndrome described his evil plan. "The robot will emerge dramatically, do some damage, and just when all hope is lost …" the villain explained. "Syndrome will save the day!" He sneered at Mr Incredible. "I'll be a bigger hero than you ever were!"

"You killed off real heroes so that you could pretend to be one!" said Mr Incredible.

Syndrome cackled and took off for the mainland.

"I'm sorry," Mr Incredible told his family. "I've been a lousy father. So obsessed with being undervalued that I undervalued all of you. You are my greatest adventure."

As he spoke, Vi was creating a force field, allowing her to escape the energy beams and set her family free. Soon the Incredibles were back in action! It was up to them to stop the Omnidroid before it attacked the city.

DUMBO
A Talented Mouse

"Look, Dumbo," Timothy Mouse said, pointing to the newspaper. "There's another article about us in here!"

That wasn't unusual. Ever since Dumbo had become famous for being able to fly, everyone was interested in him.

Mrs Jumbo, Dumbo's mother, peered over Timothy's shoulder. "What a nice story," she cooed. "Too bad the picture isn't better – why, I can hardly see you, Timothy!"

Timothy peered at the paper. "Hey," he said, scanning the story. "This article doesn't mention me at all!"

"It's all right," Mrs Jumbo said soothingly. "Everyone knows how important you are."

Timothy puffed out his chest proudly. After all, he had taught Dumbo to fly!

Then he sagged again. "Am I really that important?" he said. "It's Dumbo who has the talent – not me."

Mrs Jumbo and Dumbo tried to comfort him, but he wandered away sadly. He was so smart, so talented – he should be famous too!

"I have to figure out a way to get famous on my own," he muttered. "But how?"

Suddenly he snapped his fingers.

"I've got it!" he cried. "I'll learn to fly too! That way Dumbo and I can be famous together!"

He quickly climbed to the top of the tallest circus tent. Dumbo had learned to fly by jumping off things. Timothy just hoped it would work for him too. He rubbed his hands together.

"Here goes nothing…." he muttered.

He leaped off the tent and looked down. The ground seemed very far away.

"Uh-oh!" Timothy gulped. What had he done? The ground got closer and closer. Timothy squeezed his eyes shut….

Suddenly, Timothy felt himself being whisked upwards. Opening his eyes, he saw that he was clutched in Dumbo's trunk.

"Whew!" he gasped. "Thanks, chum!"

Dumbo smiled at his little friend. He set Timothy in his cap.

Timothy settled into the familiar spot. Flying was much more fun when Dumbo's ears did all the work!

Soon they landed beside Mrs Jumbo.

"Oh, Timothy!" she cried. "You're safe! When I saw you fall, I was so worried … Dumbo and I don't know what we'd do without you."

Timothy blinked. "Never thought of it that way," he mused. "Maybe I'm not front-page news every day. But who cares? I know I'm important, and my friends know it too. That's what matters!"

He smiled. He had plenty of his own talent, and that was good enough for him!

Disney·PIXAR

The Real Adventure

Russell was a Junior Wilderness Explorer, and he had knocked on Carl Fredricksen's door to see if he needed help. Carl had been in a bad mood – he was being forced to move out of his home. He told Russell to find an imaginary bird called a Snipe, just to get rid of him.

Carl and his wife, Ellie, had both dreamed of being explorers and Carl had promised her they'd visit Paradise Falls in South America. But they had never managed to save enough money to go. When Ellie passed away, Carl missed her very much.

Then Carl decided he had to keep his promise and go to Paradise Falls. He tied thousands of balloons to his house and it lifted into the air. But he didn't realize that Russell was still on the porch, looking for the Snipe!

Soon the pair landed in South America. They pulled the house along as they walked towards Paradise Falls. Before long, they met a strange bird called Kevin (who was actually female) and a talking dog called Dug. There was also a pack of dogs controlled by the great explorer Charles Muntz – he wanted to capture Kevin.

Russell and Carl managed to escape with Kevin, but then Charles set Carl's house on fire! Carl couldn't let all his memories of Ellie go up in flames, so he gave up Kevin.

Russell was very upset because Carl had promised to protect Kevin. They wanted to help her to get back to her babies.

Carl told Russell he no longer needed his help, then he towed the house the rest of the way to Paradise Falls by himself. He placed the house exactly where it appeared in one of Ellie's drawings of Paradise Falls.

Russell was still angry with Carl. "Here," he said, throwing his Wilderness Explorer sash on the ground. "I don't want this anymore."

With a sigh, Carl picked up Russell's sash and went into his house. Carl found Ellie's adventure book. He had kept his promise to her, but he still felt sad. He wished Ellie was here.

Carl started to close the book, but something caught his eye. It was a photograph of their wedding day. Carl turned the page. He had never looked through the whole book before. To his astonishment, it was filled with photographs of the two of them over the years. On the last page, there was a message from Ellie:

Thanks for the adventure. Now go and have one of your own.

Carl smiled, realizing that Ellie had got her wish after all. Their life together had been the real adventure.

A Real Sleeper!

"Time for bed, Nemo," said Marlin. "It's a school day tomorrow," he added. "You need to get your rest."

"Okay," said Nemo. "But can you tell me a story? How about one from when you were younger?"

"Well, just one then," said Marlin, swimming back over to his only child. He thought for a moment, then smiled broadly. "Did you know that when I was younger – much younger, actually – did you know that I wanted to be a comedian?"

Nemo's eyes widened with surprise. "*You*? A comedian? Aren't comedians supposed to be … funny?"

"Well, you see, son," said Marlin, "life is not easy for a clownfish. You may as well realize that right now. See, when you're a clownfish, everyone you meet assumes that you are funny. It's a common mistake. Anyway, years ago, I figured that as long as everyone expected me to be funny, I would try being funny for a living."

"But Dad," said Nemo, "you aren't funny at all."

"Hey now! Wait just a minute!" Marlin said, a bit huffily. "In my day, I was known as quite the crack-up! Let me see. I'm sure I can remember some of my old routine, if I just think about it for a minute." He thought for a moment. "All right, it's all coming back!"

He cleared his throat. "Good evening, ladies and jellyfish! The ocean sure is looking *swell* tonight. Would you like me to give you a coral report about the latest happenings on the reef? Get it?" he said, looking down at Nemo. "You see, there's something called an oral report, and the words coral and oral sound quite a bit alike."

Nemo gave his father a pained look.

"So, the other day my appendix nearly burst," Marlin went on. "So I decided I'd better go to a sturgeon!"

Nemo blinked. "Dad, these really aren't that funny," he said with a yawn.

"A *sturgeon*. Get it? Rather than a surgeon?" Marlin sighed and continued his routine. "A funny thing happened on the way to the show tonight. I met a guy, nice fish and all, but he seemed to be a bit down on his luck. He told me he was living on squid row."

Nemo's eyes were starting to droop sleepily.

"Do you know why the whale crossed the ocean?" Marlin continued. "Now, don't try to guess. I'll tell you: the whale crossed the ocean to get to the other tide. The other *tide*."

Nemo's eyes were now completely closed, and a tiny snore escaped from him. Marlin smiled at his sleeping son.

"Works every time," he said with a chuckle.

Mater's Jukebox

"Yeee-ha! Ready or not, Radiator Springs! My jukebox is ready!" Mater hollered. He had made a fantastic jukebox and he couldn't wait to show all of his friends.

He hooked it up to his towline and off he went. The first car he saw was Ramone, but Ramone didn't have time to listen to the jukebox. Little tractors were messing up his body paint shop!

"I've got to clean up this place!" Ramone cried.

"Gee, I see what you mean," Mater said.

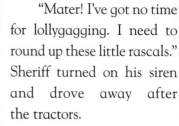

Next, Mater passed by his best friend, Lightning.

"Sorry, Mater!" Lightning called. "I've got to round up these little tractors." Lightning zoomed after another little tractor as it darted away.

Dadgum! Them little tractors sure is fast. I can help, but it's hard to move fast with my brand-new jukebox, Mater thought.

At Casa Della Tyres, Luigi had no time to hear Mater's junkyard jukebox either.

"No-no-no-no!" Luigi cried. "Look at Luigi's Leaning Tower of Tyres! Now she is just Luigi's Pile of Tyres!"

Mater knew he had to help, but how?

In front of the fire station, Red was sobbing over his trampled flowers!

"Did the little tractors do this?" asked Mater. "Hey, you know what? Maybe a little

music would –" But Red was too sad to listen.

Mater rounded the corner and found Sheriff. "Hey, Sheriff, you'll never guess what I made…."

"Mater! I've got no time for lollygagging. I need to round up these little rascals." Sheriff turned on his siren and drove away after the tractors.

For such cute little fellas, these tractors sure are causing a load of trouble! Mater thought. *I gotta put away my jukebox so I can help my friends.*

As Mater continued his way back to his scrapyard, he cranked up his jukebox and began to sing along with the music. A tractor followed him shyly.

Soon, other tractors started following Mater and his jukebox! To his surprise, Mater noticed the music was attracting all of the little tractors. He turned up the sound and started a little tractor round-up.

"Well, lookee here!" Mater shouted. "These little fellas like my music!"

"Mater rounded up the tractors!" cried Sally.

The whole town cheered. "Hip hip hooray for Mater!"

"That's music to my ears!" Sheriff sighed.

Everyone was happy. The tractors were out of trouble, and the music was great!

Dawson Takes the Case

"M y little boy is missing!" a sobbing Mrs Mousington cried to Basil, the Great Mouse Detective. "Can you help me find him?"

"I'm terribly sorry," said Basil. He was examining a brick wall very closely, looking for clues. "But I'm working on an important case for the Queen. I don't have time."

"No, wait!" cried Dr Dawson, Basil's partner. "Madam, if the Great Mouse Detective is too busy, then perhaps I can offer you my services."

"A splendid idea!" said Basil.

Before Dawson left with Mrs Mousington, Basil stopped him. "Don't forget this," he said, handing Dawson an umbrella.

"But it's a sunny day," said Dawson, puzzled. "Why would I need an umbrella?"

"A sunny day can turn dark quicker than you think," advised Basil. "Remember that, Dawson, and you'll do fine."

Dawson shrugged and took the umbrella. Then he turned to Mrs Mousington and said, "Show me where you last saw your son."

Mrs Mousington took him to a shop with a tall tree in front of it. Dawson searched the area and found a long, white hair. But a closer look told him this was not just any hair. It was a cat's whisker!

Calling to a nearby bird, Dawson asked for a lift up. On the shop's roof, Dawson saw a cat dozing, and beneath its paw was a tiny mouse's tail.

The bird set Dawson down on the roof, and he wondered how he was going to lift the cat's heavy paw. Then he remembered the umbrella!

Using one end as a lever, he heaved. Beneath it he found Mrs Mousington's terrified son.

"The cat was saving me for dinner!" the little boy mouse cried.

Dawson pulled the little mouse free. With relief, he waved at the boy's mother, who was waiting on the pavement below. But before Dawson could signal another bird for a ride down, the cat woke up.

Dawson saw only one escape – he opened his umbrella and jumped with the little boy mouse in his arms.

Mrs Mousington let out a terrified scream. But the umbrella filled with air and slowed their fall until they landed gently on the pavement.

Mrs Mousington hugged her little boy close. "Oh, Dr Dawson, thank you!" she cried.

Back at the Great Mouse Detective's house, Basil was delighted to hear how Dawson had saved the little boy.

"It was easy," Dawson told Basil. "Thanks to your umbrella, I'd call it an open-and-shut case!"

Disney·PIXAR

MONSTERS
UNIVERSITY

Just Like Everyone Else

There was wild cheering in the stadium at Monsters University. The Scare Games were over and there had been the biggest upset in the Games' history. The losers' team, the Oozma Kappas, had won!

The OKs hoisted Mike Wazowski, their team leader, up into the air. He had been the last one to go into the scare simulator, and to everyone's surprise, he got the loudest scream out of his robot-child!

Mike was delighted, but he was also relieved. It meant he could rejoin the university's Scaring Programme. Dean Hardscrabble had kicked out Mike and Sulley, but she had agreed to let the whole team join if they won the Scare Games. And they had done it!

For Mike, this was a special moment – he had proved to everyone who teased him and told him he wasn't scary that he had what it takes to be a top Scarer. He went back into the simulator to relive the moment. He turned to the child robot and said, "Boo!"

Just as before, the robot screamed loudly, as if it was really scared! Sulley was watching from the doorway.

"I knew I was scary, I didn't know I was that scary," said Mike. He checked the settings on the simulator. Someone had changed them from 'hard' to 'easy'! It was Sulley.

Mike was hurt and angry.

"You said you believed in me, but you're just like everyone else!" he yelled at Sulley and stormed away.

The other Oozma Kappas heard everything. They were devastated. None of them wanted to win by cheating.

Sulley wandered across campus. Students congratulated him on his win. Even the best club at the university wanted him to rejoin. Sulley felt awful. He knew he didn't deserve their praise.

Meanwhile, Mike was in the Door Tech department. He stole a key to the lab where students tested doors to the human world. He was going to prove to everyone that he was scary, once and for all!

Back in the university, Sulley spotted Dean Hardscrabble heading up the steps to the School of Scaring. He went up to her and confessed everything.

"You did what?" she exclaimed. "I expect you off campus by tomorrow!"

Suddenly, the alarm went off in the Door Tech Lab. Dean Hardscrabble flew off to investigate. Sulley's heart sank. He knew that it would have been Mike that set off the alarm, and that it meant serious trouble.

Sulley knew he had to help his friend.

The Last Portal

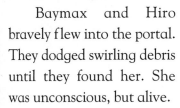

Finally, Hiro and his friends were starting to solve the mystery of the masked man, Yokai. They had discovered that Yokai was really Professor Callaghan – the man who had abandoned Tadashi in the fire, and who'd used Hiro's microbots to save himself. Hiro also realized that Callaghan's daughter, Abigail, had been lost in Alistair Krei's teleportation experiment. Krei, the billionaire owner of Krei Tech, was now in danger, because Callaghan wanted revenge.

Across the city, Krei was about to demonstrate the one remaining teleportation device when, suddenly, Callaghan appeared.

"You took everything from me when you sent Abigail into that machine!" he yelled. "Now I'll take everything from you."

"No! You can't!" Krei screamed, as microbots scooped up him and the portal.

"Professor Callaghan!" Hiro shouted, as he and the others arrived. "Let him go! Is this what Abigail would have wanted?"

"Abigail is gone!" Callaghan replied.

"Go for the mask," Hiro told the team, as Callaghan sent a wave of microbots towards them. Baymax snatched Callaghan's mask and the microbots fell. The portal crashed to the ground, but it didn't deactivate. Then Baymax made a discovery. "My sensor is detecting signs of life," he reported, pointing towards the portal. "The life signs are female," Baymax continued.

Hiro realized it must be Abigail!

Baymax and Hiro bravely flew into the portal. They dodged swirling debris until they found her. She was unconscious, but alive.

Hiro latched on to Abigail, and Baymax used his thrusters to fly them all towards the exit. But a large chunk of debris hit Baymax, damaging his thrusters. Baymax couldn't get out of the portal without them!

"There is still a way I can get you both to safety," Baymax said. He planned to release his rocket fist to propel Hiro and Abigail out of the portal.

"No! I can't lose you, too!" Hiro shouted.

"Tadashi is not gone," Baymax said, touching Hiro's chest. "Tadashi is here."

"Baymax is here, too," Hiro cried. Then, reluctantly, he said, "I am satisfied with my care."

He hugged his best friend one last time. Then Baymax's rocket fist sprang out and carried Hiro and Abigail towards the exit of the portal. As Hiro jetted away, he watched Baymax becoming smaller and smaller, until he was gone.

Hiro would never, ever forget him.

The Rust Bucket Derby

"Yee-haw!" hollered Mater as he and Lightning McQueen pulled in to the Rust Bucket Stadium. Mater owned the stadium and he loved it.

Bubba, a big tow truck twice the size of Mater, drove up. Two smaller trucks pulled in close behind. "You were right, Bubba!" said one. "This is perfect for our headquarters!"

Mater and Lightning stared in surprise.

"You heard right," said Bubba. "Tater and Tater Jr here own the Po' Tater Towing Company. And they're gonna set up an office right here in Rust Bucket Stadium. You challenged me to a racing derby, Mater. Remember? The winner gets your stadium!" Bubba sneered.

"Well, if you say so, Bubba," said Mater. "You know how I forget things!"

"Tater and Tater Jr will be the judges," Bubba declared.

"That's not fair!" Lightning exclaimed.

"Go Bubba!" shouted Tater and Tater Jr as they took the judges' seats. "Let the tyre snaggin' begin!"

Guido threw tyres into the air. Both tow trucks sent their hooks whipping up and caught four tyres, but Bubba knocked one out of Mater's grip.

"Whoo-oo, I win!" Bubba shouted.

"Bubba didn't play fair," Tater Jr whispered to Tater.

"What does it matter?" Tater replied.

The next event was cone dodging. Mater raced backwards and Bubba couldn't keep up. Mater won! Now it was the last event, a one-lap race. Whoever won would be champion!

"Say goodbye to your stadium," Bubba snarled as he roared into the lead. Mater was catching up when Bubba dropped his tow hook onto the track!

"Bubba stop, that's dangerous!" Lightning yelled. Bubba sneered, but then his hook snagged in the road!

"Help!" Bubba cried, flipping onto his side. Mater screeched to a stop. Whipping his tow cable in the air like a cowboy, he hooked on to Bubba's window.

"You want to help Bubba even though he's trying to take your stadium?" asked Tater.

"He's in trouble," said Mater. "C'mon! We can pull him up if we work together!"

They pulled with all their might and Bubba was saved. After this, Bubba decided that Mater could keep his stadium.

"Mr Mater, will you teach us how to snag tyres?" asked Tater Jr.

"Sure thing, Taters," Mater said. "Always glad to help friends."

Disney
Aladdin
Monkey See, Monkey Do

"Come on, Abu!" Aladdin called across the busy Agrabah marketplace.

From his perch on top of the basket-seller's cart, Abu barely heard the call. He was captivated by the monkey he had just spotted peeking out at him from behind the fruit seller's cart. Abu jumped off the basket cart and darted over to say hello.

But the other monkey scurried away and hid behind a wheel. From his new hiding place, he peeked out at Abu.

Abu looked around, trying to think of a way to draw out the monkey. The fruit seller was distracted, talking to a customer, so Abu hopped up onto the cart and picked up an apple. He balanced it on top of his head. Then he scurried over to the edge of the cart and peered down, hoping to attract the monkey's attention.

But he was gone.

Abu heard monkey chatter behind him. He turned around to find the monkey standing at the other end of the fruit cart, balancing an apple on *his* head, just like Abu.

Abu laughed and picked up a pear and an orange. He began juggling them in the air, hoping to amuse the other monkey.

But the other monkey didn't look amused. He looked annoyed! He thought Abu was trying to show him up. Not to be outdone, the monkey also picked up a pear and an orange and began to juggle them, just like Abu.

Abu put the fruit down. He did a handstand on the cart railing.

The other monkey did a handstand too.

Abu grabbed hold of the cart awning, then flipped over and swung from the awning by his tail.

The other monkey did the same.

Abu laughed again. He thought this game was fun. But now he wanted to find a stunt that the other monkey couldn't copy. Abu looked around. He spotted Aladdin coming his way.

Abu had an idea. He jumped off the fruit cart, darted over to Aladdin and scrambled up the length of his friend's body until he was lounging comfortably on top of Aladdin's head.

The other monkey stared in amazement. He didn't know that Aladdin was Abu's friend. How could he copy that stunt? He looked around. The closest human was the fruit seller. Throwing caution to the wind, the other monkey scurried over to him – but he'd only climbed as high as the fruit seller's shoulder before the man chased him away.

Then, from behind the basket cart, the other monkey crossed his arms, pouted and watched that sneaky Abu laugh and wave goodbye as he was carried away on top of Aladdin's head.

Deputy Mater

The morning air in Radiator Springs felt wonderful as Sally looked out from her motel. Suddenly, a noisy blur whizzed by. It was Boost, Wingo and DJ playing loud, thumpy music.

"Slow down!" Sally called out, but the speeding pranksters were long gone. Sally rolled over to Flo's V8 Café for breakfast, where she saw Fillmore talking with Sheriff.

"Good morning, fellas," said Sally. She told Sheriff about the speeders.

"I know, Sally," said Sheriff, "but I'm having a hard time keeping up with them."

"Why don't we get you some help, man?" Fillmore suggested.

"What a terrific idea!" exclaimed Sally. Just then, Mater came down Main Street. There was something different about him.

"Hi there, Mater. What did you do with your door? It's painted white!" exclaimed Sally.

"Oh shoot, I was asking Ramone if he could cover my rustiest spot and he had the wrong colour paint in the sprayer thing."

Sally looked thoughtfully at Mater's white door. "How do you feel about helping out Sheriff – and all of us?" she asked.

That afternoon, Sheriff proclaimed Mater an honorary Radiator Springs deputy! Mater read out a list of helpers. He chose Sarge, Lizzie, Sally and Lightning McQueen. The new recruits went to Ramone's body shop where they were given an official Radiator Springs shield symbol. Then they headed to Main Street.

Lizzie heard something in the distance. "Heads up, deputies!" she cried out.

Mater rolled into the middle of the road just as a familiar, noisy blur came to a halt inches away.

"Hello, pranksters," said Mater sternly. Facing him were Boost, Wingo, DJ and Snot Rod, all puffing from racing so fast. "We're glad you like our town. But would you please respect our rules? The speed limit here is much lower than you're goin'."

"We saw a sign that said 66, sir, and we thought we were going the right speed," Wingo explained. Mater gestured to a blinking yellow light hanging over the intersection.

"What's that for?" asked DJ.

"I'm deciding here 'n' now to make it the slow-down light," said Mater. "When you see it you keep it cool on the accelerator. Okay?"

The pranksters all nodded.

"I bet you guys could use some oil," said Flo as she passed around fresh cans.

So all the cars, from the slowest cars in town to the rushing visitors, all settled down to enjoy the beautiful day in Radiator Springs.

THE JUNGLE Book

"Hey, Hey, We're the Vultures!"

"Nothing exciting ever happens around here," Buzzie complained to his vulture singing buddies.

"That's not true," said Flaps. "What about that fight we had with the tiger Shere Khan last week?"

"Blimey, you're right," said Ziggy. "That was pretty exciting."

"But what are we gonna do now?" asked Buzzie.

"Let's sing," suggested Ziggy.

"Hey, good idea!" said the other three vultures.

"Only one problem," said Dizzy. "We need a tenor."

"Awww, you're right," said Ziggy. "That little Man-cub fellow, Mowgli, would have been a great tenor. Too bad he left the jungle."

"So, what are we gonna do?" asked Buzzie.

"How 'bout we hold an audition?" suggested Ziggy.

"Good thinking," said Flaps.

So the vultures put the word out in the jungle and, a week later, there was a line of animals ready to try out for the group.

"Name?" Buzzie asked the first applicant.

"Coconut," the monkey replied.

"Alright, Coconut, let's hear ya sing," said Flaps.

Coconut shrieked for a few minutes, and the four vultures huddled together.

"He's not very good," said Buzzie.

"And he's a monkey," added Flaps.

"Next!" said Dizzy.

The vultures auditioned a lemur, two sloths, a wolf, a hippo, a toad and an elephant. None seemed like the right fit. Finally, the last animal stepped up.

"Name?" asked Buzzie.

"Name's Lucky," said the vulture. "Hey, aren't you the four fellows that helped that little man-cub scare away that tiger Shere Khan?"

"Yeah," said Buzzie. "We are."

"Then I guess you four might be called 'lucky' yourselves!" cried Lucky. He began to laugh at his own joke.

"Go ahead and sing," said Ziggy, rolling his eyes.

Lucky sang for a few minutes and the four vultures huddled together.

"He's not bad," said Dizzy.

"Plus, he's a vulture," said Ziggy.

"And he's the last one left," pointed out Flaps. That settled it.

"You're hired!" the vultures sang.

"See, told you I was Lucky!" cried the vulture.

"But only with auditions," said Dizzy.

"Yeah," said Buzzie. "When we meet Shere Khan again, we'll see how lucky you really are!"

New Friends

In South America, Carl was sitting inside his house. He had flown it there with thousands of balloons tied to it. He had promised his wife, Ellie, that he would take her to Paradise Falls one day, but sadly she had passed away. Carl kept his promise but he felt sad. That is, until he looked through Ellie's adventure book. It was full of pictures of their life together. Carl had realized their life had been the true adventure.

A boy named Russell had accidentally come along for the ride. They'd met a strange, big bird called Kevin and a talking dog named Dug. A pack of dogs were trying to catch Kevin. Their leader, the explorer Charles Muntz, wanted to capture the bird. Russell was angry at Carl. Carl had promised to protect Kevin, but he had let the bird go in order to save his house from a fire.

Suddenly, Carl heard something. He hurried outside and saw Russell gripping a bunch of balloons. "I'm gonna help Kevin, even if you won't!" Russell cried.

"No!" Carl shouted. He had to help Russell, but the house wouldn't move. The balloons had lost too much air. He had an idea. He began throwing things out of the house to make it lighter. Carl realized he didn't need the things – Russell was more important!

Carl was on his way, but then he heard a knock at the door. It was Dug. Together they set out to rescue Russell. Then they saw the boy being lowered out of Charles' airship! Carl grabbed the garden hose and, using it like a rope, he swung over to the airship and saved Russell.

Once Russell was safe, Carl and Dug went back for Kevin. They set the bird free, but suddenly Muntz appeared with a sword! Carl fought him and finally escaped. He made it back to the house when *BANG!* The balloons began to pop.

The house plunged downwards and landed on top of Charles' airship. As Carl fell out of the house, Muntz ran inside to grab Kevin. Carl knew he had to save his friends – the house was about to fall off the edge of the airship. Carl told Russell and Dug to hold onto Kevin, then he waved a big bar of chocolate – Kevin loved chocolate. The big bird jumped onto the airship, saving Russell and Dug at the same time. Muntz's foot got caught in some balloons, and he drifted away.

"Sorry about your house," Russell told Carl as they watched it disappear into the clouds.

"You know," said Carl, "it's just a house."

It didn't seem as important to him, now that he had friends. They climbed aboard the airship – it was time to go home.

Disney · PIXAR

MONSTERS
UNIVERSITY

You Look Funny

Mike Wazowski was a monster on a mission. He was about to prove that he deserved a place on the Scaring Programme at Monsters University.

All he'd ever wanted was to become a Scarer for Monsters, Inc. When he'd got a place on the Scaring Programme, it was the first step to fulfilling his dream. That was a year ago. Since then he'd been kicked off the Programme; forced into joining the losers' fraternity, Oozma Kappa; had won the Scare Games against all odds ... only to realize that his teammate, Sulley, had cheated, because he didn't think Mike could be scary enough to win.

No one believed Mike was scary enough, but he was about to prove that he could scare the wits out of any child!

Mike broke in to the Door Tech Lab at the university. He grabbed a door and placed it in the docking station – the portal to the human world. All he had to do now was walk through it and perform a real Scare on a human child.

Mike quietly entered the room. He rolled across the floor and ruffled the curtains. Then he creeped closer to the child's bed. He could hear her stirring. Mike leaped up. "ROAR!" he cried as ferociously as he could.

The child just looked at Mike and smiled. "You look funny," she said.

Mike couldn't believe it. His Scare hadn't worked. Everyone was right. He really wasn't scary! Then he suddenly became aware that he wasn't in a child's bedroom at all. He was in a big room ... and it was full of kids ... and they were all looking at him. Mike had walked into a cabin full of campers!

Back in the Door Tech Lab, Hardscrabble and her guards were holding back a crowd.

"No one goes through that door until the authorities arrive," she announced.

Sulley arrived at the lab and told the OKs that it was Mike who had entered the human world without authority.

They all panicked. "But he could die out there!" cried Squishy. Sulley told him he wasn't going to let that happen. He would rescue Mike – but he needed the OKs' help to lure the guards away from the door. Don created a distraction, and while the guards were dealing with Don, Sulley charged towards the door. Hardscrabble spotted him at the last minute.

"Sullivan, don't go in there! It's extremely dangerous!" she cried.

Sulley knew the dangers, but he had to save his friend.

Bambi
The Winter Trail

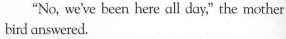

One winter morning, Bambi was dozing in the wood when he heard a thumping sound nearby. "C'mon, Bambi!" his bunny friend Thumper cried. "It's a perfect day for playing."

Bambi followed Thumper through the forest. The sky was blue and the ground was covered in a blanket of new snow.

"Look at these tracks!" Thumper said excitedly. He pointed to a line of footprints in the snow. "Who do you suppose they belong to?" Bambi didn't know, so they decided to follow the trail. They soon came to a tree.

"Wake up, Friend Owl!" called Thumper.

"Have you been out walking?" Bambi asked.

"Now why would I do that?" Friend Owl replied. "My wings take me everywhere."

Bambi and Thumper continued on. Next, they spotted a raccoon sitting next to a tree, his mouth full of red berries. "Hello, Mr Raccoon," Bambi said shyly. "Did you happen to see who made these tracks in the snow?"

The raccoon shook his head and began tapping the tree. "I know!" Thumper cried. "He thinks we should ask the woodpeckers."

Soon, Bambi and Thumper found the woodpecker family. "Did you make the tracks in the snow?" Thumper called up to the birds.

"No, we've been here all day," the mother bird answered.

"If the tracks don't belong to the woodpeckers or the raccoon and they don't belong to Friend Owl, whose can they be?" Bambi asked.

"I don't know," Thumper replied.

They soon reached the end of the trail, and the tracks led all the way to a snowy bush, where a family of quail were resting.

"Did you make these tracks?" Thumper asked.

"Why, yes," Mrs Quail answered. "Friend Owl told me about this wonderful bush. So this morning, my babies and I walked all the way over here."

Thumper and Bambi happily joined the quail family for a snack. Soon, it was time for the friends to go home. They'd spent all day following the trail. When they turned to leave, a big surprise was waiting for them – their mothers! Bambi bounded over to his mother and stretched his nose up for a kiss.

"How'd ya find us?" Thumper asked.

Thumper's mother looked down at the tracks in the snow.

"You followed our trail!" Bambi cried. His mother nodded.

"Now, let's follow it back home," Bambi's mother said. So that's just what they did.

Disney·PIXAR

TOY STORY TOONS

Small Fry

One evening, at Poultry Palace, Bonnie was excited to see which toy would come with her Fun Meal.

She looked over at the display case, where she saw a mini Buzz Lightyear. "Can I have a Buzz Lightyear?"

The cashier shook his head. "I'm sorry. Those are for display only."

"Come on, Bonnie," said her mum.

Mini Buzz watched Bonnie playing in the ball pit with the real Buzz Lightyear and Rex, then he leaped out of the display case and ran to the ball pit.

When Bonnie wasn't looking, he pulled the real Buzz deep beneath the colourful balls. Then Mini Buzz popped up next to Rex.

Soon, Bonnie's mum put them in Bonnie's backpack. Mini Buzz was thrilled. Bonnie's mum hadn't noticed that he wasn't the real Buzz!

Later that night, the real Buzz Lightyear crawled out of the ball pit. He was trapped inside Poultry Palace! As he tried to escape, he met some strange toys.

"Well, hello!" said a mermaid toy. "Welcome to the support group for discarded Fun Meal toys."

Buzz knew he needed to get back to his friends … but how would he escape?

In Bonnie's bedroom, Mini Buzz hopped out of the backpack.

He greeted the other toys. "I'm Buzz Lightyear. I come in peace!"

"He says the plastic in the ball pit made him shrink," said Rex.

"No way. Where's the real Buzz?" Woody asked.

But Mini Buzz was having too much fun! He grabbed Woody's hat and ran around the room!

"It's playtime! I'll be the cowboy!" he yelled.

That was the last straw. The toys tackled Mini Buzz and tied him up. The little toy confessed that he had left Buzz in the ball pit!

The toys started planning a rescue mission. Hamm suggested picking the lock of Poultry Palace. One of the toys wanted to drive a truck through the front door!

"Or you could use the drive-thru," came a new voice.

It was Buzz! He was back!

Buzz glared at Mini Buzz. "So, what do you have to say for yourself, Space Ranger?"

Mini Buzz just gulped.

Later at Poultry Palace, Mini Buzz apologized to Buzz with the help of the unwanted toys. "I know now that the real prize is inside each and every one of us!"

The other toys applauded. It looked like Mini Buzz had found a place where he belonged.

ROBIN HOOD

Robin Lends a Hand

It was a hot day in Sherwood Forest – a very hot day! So hot that the Sheriff of Nottingham had decided not to collect taxes, for fear the coins would burn his greedy hands!

As for himself, Robin Hood was trying to keep cool in the shade of Sherwood's oaks. Taking off his hat, he stretched out under the tallest, broadest tree, closed his eyes, and waited for a breeze.

"Halt! Who goes there?" he shouted suddenly. "Oh!" His eyes rested on a startled little bunny with a load of twigs scattered about his feet. "Skippy, my good man. Forgive me. I didn't mean to scare you."

Quickly, Robin helped to load up Skippy's arms once again. "Now, then," he said, patting the bunny on the shoulder. "That's better." But Skippy didn't seem to agree. Robin didn't think he had ever seen him look so unhappy.

"Why so glum, old chum?" Robin couldn't help but ask.

"Oh, Robin," Skippy sighed. "It's so very hot, and all the other children have gone to the swimming hole. But Mother has so many chores for me to do, I don't think I'll ever be able to join them."

"I see," said Robin, nodding. "That could get a fellow down, now, couldn't it?"

"I'll say," said Skippy.

"Unless …" Robin went on with a big grin, "… a fellow had a friend to help him out!"

Skippy's sorrowful face grew brighter. "Do you mean…?"

"Indeed!" Robin answered, bending to pick up a handful of sticks. "I have no other pressing engagements this sultry day. Allow me to assist you, my boy, and I dare say we shall have your chores done in half the time, at least."

"Hooray for Robin Hood!" Skippy cheered, nearly dropping his sticks once again. "Hip, hip, hooray!"

And so, working together, Robin Hood and Skippy gathered firewood. They wrung out the laundry and hung it out to dry. They picked some juicy plums and a basketful of lettuce, weeded the garden and built a scarecrow. By lunchtime, in fact, not only was every one of Skippy's chores done, but he and Robin had washed all the windows and swept Skippy's cottage floor.

"Robin Hood, how can I ever thank you? I'd still be hard at work if it wasn't for you!" Skippy asked when they were through.

Robin scratched his head and thought for a moment. "I have it!" he declared at last. "Take me swimming with you!"

"You betcha!" Skippy said happily. "C'mon, let's go! Last one in is a rotten sheriff!"

The Journey Begins

Bernard couldn't believe this was really happening. Even though he was a caretaker, he had been selected by the Rescue Aid Society to come to the aid of a little girl named Penny, who appeared to be in grave danger. And what's more, he, Bernard, had been selected over all the other mice to be partners with the very beautiful and clever Miss Bianca. It was Bernard's first rescue mission ever and, even though he was very nervous, he was excited to get started.

Bernard had got himself packed and ready to go in minutes, and now he had arrived to pick up Miss Bianca.

"I'll just be a few more moments, darling!" she called to him as he waited outside her door.

"Uh, okay, Miss Bianca!" he called back, glancing quickly at his watch.

Just as soon as Miss Bianca had finished packing, they'd be on their way....

"Uh, Miss Bianca?" called Bernard after a while. "We really ought to be going, I think. We don't want to miss our flight!"

"All right, darling!" said Miss Bianca. "Come give me a hand with this suitcase, please!"

Bernard found Miss Bianca trying to close her overstuffed suitcase. She had already packed several boxes as well. "Are you quite sure you'll be needing all those evening gowns,

Miss Bianca?" Bernard panted as he sat on the bag and tried to zip it up. "And that tea set? And 14 pairs of shoes?"

"A lady must be prepared for anything, darling," she crooned. "Now, I'll just put on my hat and we'll be off."

Bernard gave a final bounce on the suitcase and was able to snap it closed. After what seemed like hours, Miss Bianca appeared at last in a cloud of dizzying perfume. She was wearing a beautifully cut travelling cape and a stunning little hat.

"I'll take that!" said Bernard as Miss Bianca reached for the suitcase. It felt as though it was full of bricks, but Bernard managed to manoeuvre it through the door, where he grabbed his much lighter bag in his other hand.

"Darling," Miss Bianca said sweetly as they headed to the airport, "please don't fret. Everyone knows that flights are always delayed!"

Even when the plane is an albatross? Bernard wondered to himself. Yes, Miss Bianca and Bernard certainly made an unusual team. But he was sure now that they would get the rescue job done.

Just as long as he didn't drop her suitcase on his toe!

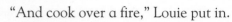

Scrooge's Nature

"Would you look at that!" Huey pointed to a picture of a Junior Woodchuck relaxing in a hammock, while another camper fished in a nearby lake.

"And that!" Dewey's eyes widened. He pointed at a picture of a star-filled sky in the same brochure.

"Camping at Faraway Lake sure looks fun," Louie agreed. "Do you think Unca Scrooge would…?"

"You never know. He might pay for us to go," Huey said. The three boys looked at one another.

"Nah!" they said in unison. Uncle Scrooge may have been the richest duck in the world, but he did not part with his money easily.

"Let's show him, anyway," Huey said. "It's worth a shot."

The other boys followed Huey into their uncle's study.

Dewey nudged Huey forward. "Look at this, Unca Scrooge." Huey thrust the brochure into his uncle's lap.

"Humph." Uncle Scrooge scowled at the glossy photos. "What have we got here, lads?"

"It's a camp, Unca Scrooge. It's educational," Huey stammered.

"Looks like a waste of my hard-earned money," the old duck said.

"But … but we could camp out under the stars," Dewey said.

"And cook over a fire," Louie put in.

"And see nature," Huey added.

Uncle Scrooge's eyes narrowed. He looked from the brochure to his nephews' hopeful faces and back to the brochure. So, they wanted to learn about nature, did they?

"Here you are, boys," said Uncle Scrooge a short time later. He smiled from the safety of the screened-in back porch. "You have tents …" He indicated the three small leaky tents set up in the garden. "You can see the stars …" In fact, only one or two stars were visible through the branches of the tree the tents were under. "And you're cooking over a fire," Scrooge finished, pointing at the tiny, smoky little flame.

Huey slapped at a mosquito on his arm. Dewey shook his head to chase away a cloud of gnats. Louie yelped as he was dive-bombed by a bat. Who knew the garden had so much nature in it!

"This is much better than that Junior Woodchuck nonsense, isn't it, boys?" Uncle Scrooge asked, with the smile of a duck who has saved himself a penny.

"Yes, Unca Scrooge," Huey, Dewey, and Louie said. Then they turned back to the fire.

"I think …" said Huey.

"… next time," continued Dewey.

"… we ask Unca Donald!" finished Louie.

Dĩsnep · PIXAR
MONSTERS UNIVERSITY
Start Being You!

How Mike and Sulley ended up in the human world was a long story. Neither of them were trained Scarers. Worse still, neither had permission to be there. But Mike went through the portal in Door Tech Lab at Monsters University to prove to everyone, and to himself, that he could scare human children. Sulley went to get Mike back.

When Sulley slipped through door into the human world, he found he was in an empty cabin. Where had Mike gone? He went to the window and saw a group of rangers gathered in the dark outside. Deciding Mike must have fled to the nearby forest, Sulley made a break from the cabin. The rangers shined their flashlights on him as he disappeared into the trees. They thought they'd seen a bear.

Sulley found Mike sitting by a lake.

"You were right," said Mike sadly. "The children weren't scared of me. I thought I could show everybody I was something special … but I'm just not."

Sulley said he wasn't much different. He had messed things up his entire life. "You're not the only 'failure' here," he said.

Just then the rangers arrived. The pair made it back to the cabin, but when they opened the door through which they had come, they found it was just a cupboard. It no longer led back to the monster world! Dean Hardscrabble, head of the Scaring Programme at the university, had shut it down from the other side!

The rangers were getting closer. Mike had an idea. "If we scare them, we could make enough scream power to activate the door from this side."

He jumped up to the rafters and looked down at Sulley. "Are you ready?" he asked.

"Mike, I can't," Sulley replied. He could never live up to his dad's reputation – he was Bill Sullivan, one of the best Scarers of all time.

"Yes, you can. Stop being a Sullivan, and start being you!"

As the rangers entered the cabin, Mike and Sulley turned on a fan, shook the shutters and fluttered the curtains. This unnerved the rangers. Then Mike slammed the door, which made them jump. Next came clawing on the walls and the bunk beds toppling over like dominoes!

"Aaaahhhh!" screamed the rangers.

Next, Mike gave Sulley the signal and the big blue monster rose up menacingly and let out a deafening, ferocious roar.

The petrified rangers screamed … and screamed … and screamed! It had worked!

Sledging

Lady stood on the porch as Jim Dear and Darling walked up the front path. Jim pulled a sledge and Darling held their son. They were all covered in snow, rosy cheeked and smiling from ear to ear.

"That was fun! Wasn't it Darling?" Jim asked.

"I don't know the last time I had so much fun," Darling agreed, patting Lady on the head.

"But we should get out of these wet clothes before one of us catches a cold," Jim said, leaning the sledge against the side of the house.

"I agree," Darling said. And the three of them hurried inside.

Just then, Tramp came walking up the front path. "Hey, Pidge," he said to Lady. "What do you say we take this old thing for a spin?"

"What is it, anyway?" Lady wanted to know.

"A sledge!" Tramp told her.

"What do you do with it?" she asked.

"You ride down hills," Tramp explained.

"That sounds dangerous," Lady said hesitantly.

"Nah, it's fun!" Tramp cried. "So, what do you say?"

"It's awfully cold out here," Lady said. She wasn't convinced at all.

"Oh, come on," Tramp said. "It'll be great! You saw how much fun Jim Dear and Darling had." Tramp grabbed the rope in his teeth and pulled the sledge across the porch and down the steps.

Lady took off after him. "Wait for me!" she cried anxiously.

"Come on, Pidge!" Tramp encouraged her. "Jump on!"

Lady jumped onto the sledge, and Tramp pulled her down the snow-covered street and up to the top of a nearby hill. "What a view, huh?" he said.

"What a view indeed," Lady agreed. "What now?"

"Now, we ride," Tramp said. He pushed the sledge forward and took a running leap onto it, sending them racing down the hill.

"Oh, dear!" Lady yelped as they went down the hill, the wind blowing her ears back.

"Just hold on!" Tramp instructed.

Lady squeezed her eyes shut, and Tramp barked with excitement. But suddenly they hit a patch of ice, the sledge spun, and they went flying – right into a snowbank!

Tramp jumped to his feet. "Pidge, are you okay?" he asked anxiously.

"Okay?" Lady asked. She was already pulling the sledge back up the hill. "Hurry up, Tramp! Let's do it again!"

346

Air-attack Action!

The wildfires were spreading in Piston Peak National Park. They were threatening to engulf the Fusel Lodge. A mass evacuation was underway. Cars were jammed along the road and planes were fleeing the orange smoke-filled skies.

Park superintendent, Cad Spinner, was panicking. He had spent too much of his time – and the park's money – on this lodge. He wasn't about to see it burn to the ground. Plus, he was up for promotion and this wretched fire could ruin it all!

Cad ordered André, the concierge, to send more water to the rooftop sprinklers.

"No!" said André. "The firefighters need that water to make the retardant to put out the fires!"

But Cad only cared about his lodge so he redirected the water himself.

Meanwhile, outside, Cad's boss was working with Pulaski the fire engine and Ol' Jammer, a park employee, to get all the vehicles to safety.

Suddenly, a gust of wind sent the fire roaring down the ridge. Debris blocked the only road and burning trees fell across the train tracks. The train came to a screeching halt.

"We're gonna have to find another way out," the secretary shouted.

"There is no other way out," Ol' Jammer responded. "We're trapped!"

Back at the air base, Windlifter took command. It was after dark – a dangerous time to fly – but he knew what the team had to do. "Load up," he ordered.

Maru tried to fill them with fire retardant, but the hoses were dry. "Problem!" he cried. "There's no water pressure!"

"All we have left is what's in our tanks," said Windlifter. "Let's make it count!"

After flying through the fire, the air-attack team took aim at the flames that blocked the road. Windlifter and Dipper dived down and made precision drops.

Dusty lined up and released his retardant on the other side of the blaze. They had done it. The fire was out! Dusty was pleased he'd got something right at last.

The guests cheered as the smokejumpers cleared the road. The little utility vehicles pushed the debris out of the way and lifted the scorched and fallen branches over the cliff.

The secretary of the interior and Ol' Jammer then led the guests to safety. But not all the guests had escaped. There were two RVs trapped in Augerin Canyon. It was Harvey and Winnie, the lovely couple the air-attack team had met at the reopening party of Fusel Lodge! Dusty had to help them!

Pinocchio

The Greatest Gift

Pinocchio was the luckiest boy in the world – and he knew it. No longer a wooden puppet, at last he was a real, live boy! And Pinocchio knew he owed it all to Geppetto for believing in him.

"I wish I could give Papa something in return," Pinocchio said to himself one day.

Pinocchio didn't have any money, so he decided to make a gift for Geppetto.

"Perhaps I should use Papa's tools and carve a present for him out of wood!" said Pinocchio.

So, one day while Geppetto was out, Pinocchio sat down at the woodworking bench. The problem was, Pinocchio didn't know how to woodwork.

"That looks dangerous," said Pinocchio, eyeing a chisel. "I don't think Papa would want me to use that on my own." He decided he needed another gift idea. "I know!" he said. "Maybe I can cook something for Papa!"

Pinocchio went over to the hearth, where Geppetto did all of the cooking.

But he soon realized that he didn't know how to cook either. "And Papa is always telling me to stay a safe distance away from the fire," he reminded himself.

Pinocchio looked around the little house and spotted Geppetto's accordion sitting on the table.

"Of course!" cried Pinocchio. "Papa loves music. I could write him a song as a gift and then perform it for him!"

So Pinocchio picked up the accordion and began to play. But it sounded … well … awful!

"Hmph," Pinocchio said in frustration. "I don't know how to play the accordion *or* write a song." He put the accordion down and stood in the middle of the room. Tears were welling up in poor little Pinocchio's eyes when Geppetto came in through the front door.

"My boy," Geppetto said, "what is the matter?"

Through his tears, Pinocchio explained how he had wanted to make a gift to show Geppetto how much he appreciated everything his father had done for him.

As Geppetto listened, his look of worry softened into a smile, and then *his* eyes welled up with tears. "My son," he said, "don't you know that you, and you alone, are the greatest gift a father could ever want?"

"I am?" Pinocchio asked.

"You are," replied Geppetto.

"Well, in that case," said Pinocchio with a sly grin as he hugged his papa, "you're welcome!"

Then Geppetto picked up the accordion and they sang and danced all evening!

Rematch!

Lightning McQueen and Francesco Bernoulli had challenged each other to a race in Monza, Italy – Francesco's hometown.

"*Benvenuto!*" said Francesco. "Your plane was late, but this is no surprise. You will be late crossing the finish line, too."

Lightning smiled. Then he whispered to Mater, "I am so beating him – right here on his own turf!"

As they left the airport, the cars were surrounded by photographers.

"Everyone loves Francesco. He has too many fans," said Francesco.

"Nobody has more fans than Lightning!" Mater piped up. He showed Francesco some bags overflowing with fan letters.

"Francesco has much, much more fan mail!" said Francesco.

Lightning cruised over to Francesco. "How about a warm up before the big race – just you and me?" he asked.

Francesco nodded. "Ah, good idea, Lightning! Try to keep up, if you...."

Before Francesco could finish, Lightning was a red streak down the road! "Ka-ciao, Francesco!" yelled Lightning.

Francesco was just about to catch up when he nearly spun out on a left turn.

"How do you make those left turns so well?" Francesco asked Lightning.

"Get equipped with some treaded tyres," said Lightning. "Then turn right to go left. A very good friend taught me that once."

They finally stopped. Francesco sighed. "Ahh, Italia is beautiful, no? Just like Francesco!"

Lightning chuckled. "Do you always think about yourself?" he asked.

"Of course," said Francesco. "On the racetrack, Francesco only thinks about himself and doing his best. This is why he always wins!"

The next day was the big race. Francesco came out of the first left turn ahead. He showed off his new treaded tyres. "Perhaps Lightning has taught Francesco too well!"

As Lightning zoomed out of the pits, he got distracted by the camera flashes and the screaming fans. Suddenly Lightning remembered what Francesco had said about focusing on himself and doing his best. Lightning looked straight ahead and took the lead!

As the two cars crossed the finish line, the crowd gasped. The race was ... a TIE!!!

The cars tried to figure out what to do. Then Francesco shouted, "No more talk! Talk is slow. What do we do? We race!"

Then the two fastest cars in the world zoomed away together!

DISNEY · PIXAR

THE INCREDIBLES

The Supers Work Together

Bob and Helen Parr – Mr Incredible and Elastigirl – and their children, had been trying to live normal lives. Since all Supers were banned from using their powers, Bob had been working at an insurance company. But he soon got bored of ordinary life and started doing super-hero work in secret – without telling his wife. He'd ended up being lured into a trap by Syndrome, a self-made Super who had created a robot that only he could defeat.

Syndrome had killed off real heroes so that he could be one himself!

The Incredibles were trapped on Syndrome's island. Syndrome had launched his deadly robot to the city, and had just left to 'save the day'. Luckily, Violet – Mr Incredible's daughter – had created a force field, allowing her to set her family free. The Incredibles were back in action!

The family escaped from the island in a rocket and flew towards the city where the robot was already destroying everything it could find. The people of the city were terrified.

"Someone needs to teach this hunk of metal a few manners!" Syndrome told the crowd. Sneakily he worked the robot's remote control and removed the Omnidroid's arm. The crowd cheered, and Syndrome loved it.

But the Omnidroid was a learning robot, and it realized Syndrome was controlling it. It knocked Syndrome out!

The Incredibles crash-landed in a van that Elastigirl had attached to the rocket. Then Mr Incredible announced he would fight the robot alone. When Elastigirl objected, Mr Incredible begged her, "I can't lose you again," he said. "I'm not strong enough."

Elastigirl smiled. "If we work together, you won't have to be."

The Supers fought as a team. Mr Incredible's old pal Frozone helped them too. Still, the Omnidroid proved to be quite strong – that is, until Mr Incredible remembered that the only thing that could defeat the Omnidroid was itself. He grabbed an arm that had fallen from the robot. Elastigirl, Frozone and the children pushed buttons on the remote while Mr Incredible aimed the arm so it pointed at the Omnidroid. Just then Elastigirl found the right button….

The rocket on the robot arm ripped the robot apart. The city was saved!

Syndrome recovered to find everyone cheering the Supers! No one cared about him! Furious, he creeped away … determined to get revenge on The Incredibles.

Disney · PIXAR

TOY STORY TOONS

Partysaurus Rex!

One day, Mr. Potato Head and the other toys were having a bubble party. Everyone was having fun until Rex ran towards a bubble and *pop!* it burst. The other toys were annoyed and called him "Party-pooper Rex!" Rex was embarrassed.

Just then his owner, Bonnie, grabbed him and hurried to the bathroom. "Bath time!" she called.

Rex was a little anxious – he'd never been in a bath tub before!

"Do you want to flood the house?" Bonnie's mum joked when she saw how full the tub was. She pulled the plug and helped Bonnie out, leaving Rex behind.

"Welcome aboard!" called Cap'n, a tugboat toy, after Bonnie and her mum had left. "What do they call ye, sailor?"

"Partysaurus Rex!" Rex exclaimed. He wanted these toys to think he was fun.

Just then, the last of the water gurgled down the drain and the toys fell on to their sides at the bottom of the bath. Without water, they couldn't move!

Rex wanted to help the bath toys. *Maybe I could turn the water on?* he thought. So he turned on the tap, pushed the plug into place and the bath began to fill. Then he pressed a button on a toy with flashing lights and music!

"Partysaurus, you rock!" said Ducky.

The toys tossed beads round Rex's neck.

A toy squid jumped on his head, and Helga the soap dispenser put her Viking hat on top of the squid. Rex was really starting to look like a partysaurus!

But Rex was also nervous. The tub was full of toys now! Fearful that the water would overflow, Rex tried to turn the tap off, but the knob broke! So he pulled the stopper on top of the tap, instead.

Everything was silent … then the shower came on, filling the bathtub even faster!

Rex could see water creeping over the edge of the tub. "Overflow!" he cried.

Helpless, Rex screamed as the water swept everyone over the edge!

Meanwhile, when Rex hadn't returned, Buzz, Woody and the rest of the gang had gone to the bathroom to look for him.

"I'm a partysaurus!" said Rex proudly, when his friends asked what he was doing.

"You?" scoffed Mr. Potato Head.

Just then, a voice came through the window. "Psst! Partysaurus!"

Outside, water toys surrounded Bonnie's swimming pool.

"Rex! Rex! Rex!" they chanted.

Rex's friends were stunned.

"Duty calls!" said Rex, jumping out of the window. Partysaurus Rex was back!

Thunderbolt Patch

Every evening, Pongo, Perdita and their 15 Dalmatian puppies would gather around the television to watch the heroic adventures of Thunderbolt the dog. The puppies would stare wide-eyed as Thunderbolt saved the day from all sorts of thieves and villains. Patch wanted to be just like Thunderbolt!

After the programme, it was time for the puppies to go to sleep so Pongo and Perdita could go for a walk with their humans.

But one night, Patch had other ideas. "Can't we stay up a bit longer?" he pleaded.

"It's time for sleep now," Perdita replied, as she and Pongo left for their walk.

But Patch didn't want to go to sleep. He wanted to go on a great adventure, just like Thunderbolt! And when the puppies heard a strange scurrying sound, Patch saw his chance.

"Look!" whispered Patch, pointing to a small mouse sitting near the puppies' basket. "It's a big bad bandit! We've got to catch him!"

The puppies all wanted to play pretend, so they scampered out of bed and sneaked upstairs after the fearsome outlaw.

"Follow me," Patch whispered, pretending to be Thunderbolt. "That nasty scoundrel is heading towards the music room."

Before the puppies could catch the bandit, they heard someone coming up the stairs. It was Nanny! If she caught the pups, they would be in big trouble.

"Hide," whispered Patch. The pups quickly scampered into the music room and found hiding places.

"Now, what's all this noise?" asked Nanny, looking around the apparently empty room.

As the pups held their breath, Patch spied the scoundrel slipping back downstairs. When the coast was clear, the puppies resumed their chase.

"That sly burglar must be in here somewhere," said Patch as the puppies searched the empty kitchen.

"There he is!" shouted Rolly, suddenly.

Rolly darted towards the bandit ... but he knocked over a bag of flour. The flour covered Rolly, turning him white!

"That pup doesn't have any spots," Patch said, pointing to his brother. "He must be the REAL intruder!" Patch pretended.

The puppies all pounced on Rolly, but soon Pepper saw Pongo and Perdita outside.

"Mother and Father are coming!" Pepper exclaimed. "Everyone back to bed!"

"Come along, chaps!" shouted the leader of the pack. "Thunderbolt Patch will save the day!"

When Pongo and Perdita peeked in on their precious puppies, they found them ... curled up in bed – just as they had left them!

a bug's life

Red Alert!

"Nice work with the wheat husker," Flik said. He smiled with satisfaction as he watched a troop of ants lower the contraption that lightly smashed the wheat kernels. How had the colony got along without his clever inventions? Flik wondered.

"How's it going with the berry masher?" called a voice. It was Atta, the colony's Queen.

"I was just heading over to take a look," Flik said, smiling at Queen Atta. "Care to join me?"

"Sure," Atta said as she led the way to the berry-mashing area. Mashing berries was messy, so the ants did it in a special part of the anthill.

"Cowabunga!" called a large ant. Ten dozen ants leaped off a rock onto a giant lever. The lever lowered, pressing a flat rock onto a pile of berries. Sweet red juice squirted out from the sides and dripped into carved wooden bowls.

When all the juice was squeezed out of the berries, Atta dipped her finger into a bowl for a taste.

"Delicious," she said. Red juice stained her mouth and chin.

"The berries were especially sweet this year," Flik said modestly.

"And with your new invention we should have plenty of juice for this year's feast," Atta said. "As long as Dot and the Blueberries don't drink it all first," she added.

Flik laughed. Dot and her Blueberry friends loved berry juice and were always trying to dip into it before the feast. They had been shooed away from the berry masher more than once in the last week. Three times, in fact!

"Good work, masher ants!" Flik called to the horde that was climbing back up to their jumping rock. Another group was making a pile of fresh berries.

They had nearly finished piling a huge mound of berries, when suddenly the alarm sounded.

"Alert, alert!" a guard ant called through a megaphone made from a rolled-up leaf. "Red fire ants are storming the colony!"

Flik, Atta and the masher ants fled the food area as fast as their legs could carry them. Sure enough, they soon ran into half-a-dozen red ants. Flik was about to charge when he heard a familiar voice.

"Flik, it's me!" it said. The voice sounded like ... Dot's.

"Hold on!" Flik shouted. The ants stopped. Flik quickly wiped the first red ant's sticky face. "These aren't fire ants," Flik explained. "They're Blueberries – covered in berry juice!" He smiled at Atta. "Maybe we should call them Redberries, instead!"

Racing for Good

Early one morning in Radiator Springs, Lightning was showing around a special guest – racing superstar Jeff Gorvette.

"Thanks for helping me out with this charity race for Antique Auto Aid," Jeff said. "I hope we raise a lot of money to help older cars."

They headed towards the Speedway.

"And it will be good to see some of our old racing buddies," said Jeff.

"You're right," said Lightning. "In fact, I think I hear one now. Ciao, Francesco!"

"Francesco is happy to race for charity," said the Italian racing car. "Francesco is so generous and wonderful!"

Lightning laughed. "Ah, Francesco, you haven't changed."

Then more racers arrived. Shu Todoroki revved his motor. Carla Veloso showed off some quick turns and Nigel Gearsley, the suave English gentlecar, greeted friends with a wink.

Then a familiar green car pulled up. Chick Hicks! Lightning was suspicious.

"I guess my invitation got lost in the mail," said Chick.

"Well, Chick, we didn't think this type of race was your thing," said Jeff.

"You afraid I'll beat you guys?" Chick exclaimed.

Lightning sighed. "Fine, Chick. But you better be on your best behaviour."

But during the race, Chick was up to his usual dirty tricks. He smashed into Nigel and then made Carla and Shu spin out. "Ha, ha, ha … OW!" Chick realized he had dented his side.

Chick tried to ram Francesco, but he swerved out of the way and Chick scraped up against the wall. "Yeooow!" he cried.

Chick caught up with Jeff and Lightning. The two friends winked at each other and slowed down, letting Chick pull out in front.

"Who's the big winner here today? It's … AHHHHH!" Chick went into a tailspin – right over the finish line!

Chick hobbled up onto the winner's podium. "Well? Give me the money and trophy already!" he yelled.

Lightning presented a giant cheque to Chick. Then Lizzie, the charity spokescar, took the cheque straight back from him.

"Hey! What's going on?" exclaimed Chick.

"Chick, thanks for helping us raise so much money for charity," said Jeff.

Chick was stunned. "I did WHAT?"

Lightning laughed. "That's right, Chick. You actually raced for a good cause. Next time, just don't beat yourself up over it!"

DUMBO

The Show Must Go On

The wind whistled around the Big Top, pulling the canvas tent that Dumbo was holding out of reach of his small trunk. "I'll get it," Dumbo's mother said as the tent flapped over their heads.

If the weather hadn't been so terrible, Dumbo thought, he could have flown up to grab the edge of the tent. But the whipping wind was too much, even for Dumbo's wing-like ears.

At last, standing on her back legs, Mrs Jumbo caught the canvas in her trunk. She pulled it taut and let the roustabouts tie it off. But Dumbo noticed several new rips in the fabric.

"Quit your clowning!" the Ringmaster barked at the clowns. He noticed the rips too. He ordered the clowns to sew them up. "The repairs must be finished by showtime!"

Dumbo felt terrible. All the circus performers, animals and roustabouts were working hard in the storm. He had gone and made even more work, by letting the canvas get torn. And now the Ringmaster's mood was as foul as the weather!

Just then, Dumbo noticed another blast of cold air whirl the Ringmaster's black top hat off his head.

"That does it!" the Ringmaster shouted. "There will be no show tonight!"

Dumbo could not believe his ears. The announcement was even enough to wake Timothy Q. Mouse from his nap in a nearby bale of hay.

"No show? I can't believe it!" Timothy cried. The rest of the circus folk couldn't believe it either. They silently continued to set up.

"What a fuss over a hat." Timothy shook his head. "The show must go on."

Dumbo nodded. Then something caught his eye. The Ringmaster's hat was caught on the flagpole, high over the Big Top. Perhaps he could get it for him?

Bravely, Dumbo took off. The wind was strong, but he tucked his head down and flapped his ears hard. When the wind calmed for a moment, the small elephant saw his chance. He grabbed the top hat and flew quickly to the ground.

Shyly, Dumbo held out the hat to the Ringmaster.

"Thank you, Dumbo." The Ringmaster took his hat gratefully. He looked around at all the people and animals still hard at work. He looked a little embarrassed. Then, as he placed the hat on his head, he shouted, "The show must go on!"

Everyone cheered.

"What'd I tell ya?" Timothy asked, winking at Dumbo.

Disney · PIXAR
FINDING
NEMO

Old Man Octopus

"You're it!" Nemo tagged Sheldon, who was hiding next to a mollusc.

"Aw, man!" Sheldon swished his tail. "I'm going to get you next time, Nemo."

"Only if you can find me," Nemo teased. Then he called louder, "Ollie, ollie, all swim free!" The rest of the fish, who were playing hide-and-seek, returned to the giant barnacle they were using as base. When they were all there, Sheldon began to count again.

Nemo swam away, scanning the reef for a good hiding spot. Sheldon would be out to get him for sure. Nemo swam past a large empty abalone shell. "Too easy," he muttered. He darted into an anemone. "Way too obvious." Finally he came to a dark cave in the coral. "Too dark," he shivered, looking into the spooky opening. "It'll be perfect."

Mustering his courage, Nemo swam inside. At first he couldn't see anything. Then, as his eyes adjusted to the dark, Nemo saw a large eye open on the cave wall. What could it be?

Another eye opened. Then the entire wall began to move.

"O-O-Old Man Octopus!" Nemo stammered as eight long arms oozed off the cave wall. Nemo and his friends told stories about Old Man Octopus at sleepovers. In the stories, Old Man Octopus sneaked up on little fish and gave them a terrible scare.

"S-sorry to disturb you, sir." Nemo swam towards the cave entrance. Then he noticed something amazing. The octopus's arms were changing colour … and texture! Instead of matching the brown bumpy cave wall, now they looked more like the reddish coral at the bottom of the cave.

"You didn't disturb me, boy. Tell me what brings you to this corner of the reef?" The octopus's voice was slow and kind, and Nemo's fear melted away.

"Hide-and-seek, sir," Nemo answered politely. "But I wouldn't need a cave if I could camouflage myself like you!"

Old Man Octopus laughed. "Hide-and-seek, eh? One of my favourites. The camouflage does come in handy, but nothing beats a cloud of ink when you want to make a break for the base!"

"You can shoot ink clouds too?" Nemo was so excited, he forgot to be quiet.

"I hear you, Nemo!" Sheldon shouted.

"Are you ready to swim for it?" Old Man Octopus whispered with a wink.

Nemo nodded. He high-fived one of Old Man Octopus' tentacles. Then, in a burst of inky blackness, he darted out of the cave, past Sheldon, and all the way back to the barnacle base. Safe!

Tod's Homecoming

Tod the fox wanted to show his fox friend Vixey where he grew up. He took her to the top of a hill where they could look down on a beautiful valley.

"I grew up on Widow Tweed's farm," said Tod, pointing with his paw at a farm nestled in the valley. "She took care of me when I was just a cub.

"And that's my best friend Copper," Tod said, pointing to a handsome hound. "Copper lives at Amos Slade's farm. His house is right next door to Mrs Tweed's."

As the two foxes watched, Widow Tweed, Amos Slade, and Amos's cranky old dog, Chief, climbed into an old banger. With a puff of smoke, they drove off.

But Copper was still at home. He was near the fence, snoozing under an old barrel.

"Let's go visit Copper," said Tod.

"Not me!" Vixey declared. "I'm a fox, and I'm not fond of hounds. I'll catch some fish for our dinner. See you later."

Alone, Tod scampered down the hill, excited about seeing his old pal. But, when he got there, he spotted a strange man sneaking into Amos Slade's hen house.

"Wake up, Copper!" yelled Tod. "A chicken thief is raiding the hen house!"

Copper woke with a start and leaped into action. But the rope around his neck held him back.

"You'll have to stop that chicken thief yourself!" cried Copper.

"But I can't stop him alone!" Tod replied.

"We'll help," someone chirped. Tod looked up and saw Dinky the Sparrow and Boomer the Woodpecker sitting on the fence.

"Let's go!" said Tod.

Tod burst into the hen-house first. The thief was there, holding a squawking chicken in either hand.

Tod bit the man in the ankle.

"Ouch!" howled the thief.

Boomer flew through the window and pecked at the chicken snatcher's head. The thief dropped the chickens and covered his head.

Meanwhile, Dinky untied the knot that held Copper. Now, Copper was free – and angry too! Barking, he charged at the burglar.

Eggs flying, the chicken snatcher screamed and ran. As he raced down the road, Dinky and Boomer flitted around his head, pecking him until he was out of sight. The fox and the hound trotted back to the farm.

"Good to see you, Tod," said Copper, wagging his tail. "What brings you here?"

"I just stopped by for a quiet visit," Tod replied.

"It was real quiet, all right!" said Copper.

Disney
THE
LION KING
All Wet

Timon pounded his tiny chest and gave a mighty yell as he swung out over the lagoon. He let go of a vine and threw his arms out wide, hitting the water with a small but very satisfying smack. He popped to the surface, shouting: "Ta-da!"

Pumbaa was next. "Look out below!" he called. He backed up on the rock ledge, then charged. The warthog's splash sent water flying high into the air. The lagoon was still rippling when he surfaced.

"Not bad," Simba said. "But I bet Nala could do better." The Lion King looked up at Nala, who was sunning herself on a rock as far from the water as possible.

"Ha!" Nala laughed. "You know I don't like to get wet."

"Oh, come on, Nala. Give it a try. The water's fine!" Simba said.

"The water *is* fine …" Nala replied slowly, rolling over and licking her paw "… for drinking."

Pumbaa and Timon sniggered. Simba frowned. Nala was making him look silly in front of his friends. Was he King of the Pride Lands or not?

Using his most commanding voice, Simba gave Nala an order. "You will come swimming with us right now, or else!"

Nala did not even lift her head. She closed her eyes. "Or else what, Your Mightiness?"

Simba couldn't come up with anything, so the argument was over. And Nala, as usual, had won.

Accepting his defeat, Simba ran to the edge of the rocky ledge, sprang high in the air and tucked his paws in for a royal cannonball.

Pumbaa and Timon were drenched. Slinking slowly out of the water, Simba signalled to them. He pointed at his dripping mane and then up at Nala's rock.

Timon winked, and he and Pumbaa began a noisy mock water fight to distract Nala. While they hollered and splashed, Simba climbed up to Nala's warm spot in the sun. He walked quickly but silently. Drawing closer, he crouched, his legs coiled to pounce. Nala did not move.

Then, with a triumphant roar, Simba jumped onto Nala's rock and gave his sopping mane a mighty shake. Nala was drenched.

Nala leaped to her feet with a snarl. Simba rolled onto his back, laughing.

"You're all wet, Nala!" Timon guffawed. Pumbaa was laughing so hard, he could barely breathe.

Nala tried to glare fiercely at Simba, but she couldn't. She had to laugh too. "King of the practical jokers," she said.

Bambi

Night-time is for Exploring!

As the moon rose above the forest, Bambi snuggled close to his sleeping mother. What a day it had been! Exploring new places, learning new words and meeting new friends. Bambi yawned and closed his eyes....

"Bambi! Oh, Bambi!"

Bambi slowly opened his eyes. "Thumper?" he whispered. "Why aren't you asleep?"

"Asleep? Come on!" cried Thumper. "Sleep is for the birds! How can you sleep when there's so much to see and do at night?"

"But everybody knows that night-time is for sleeping," Bambi said.

"Oh, brother," Thumper said. "Do you have a lot to learn! Follow me, Bambi, and I'll show you how the night is a whole new day!"

And suddenly, at the prospect of a new adventure, Bambi's sleepiness disappeared. Quietly, he stood up and let Thumper lead the way.

Thumper was right – the forest was as busy at night as it was during the day, but with a whole new group of animals. Owls, opossums, raccoons and badgers – all those animals that Bambi thought spent most of their lives asleep – were now as lively as could be.

"Wh-wh-what's that?" Bambi exclaimed, as a dot of light landed on his nose.

"Don't worry, Bambi, it's just a firefly," Thumper said with a giggle.

"'Firefly'," Bambi said. Then suddenly, the little light disappeared. "Hey, where'd it go?"

"There it is!" cried Thumper, pointing to Bambi's tail. "No, wait. It's over there."

Happily, Thumper and Bambi chased the firefly as it flitted from one friend to the other. "I think he likes us!" Thumper cried.

But their game was soon interrupted by a flurry of sound. Thousands of leathery wings were suddenly beating overhead.

"Duck, Bambi!" hollered Thumper, just as the whole group swooped around their heads.

"Boy, that was close!" said Thumper.

"Were those fireflies too?" Bambi asked.

"Naw," Thumper laughed. "They didn't light up! Those were bats."

"'Bats'," repeated Bambi. "They're really busy at night."

"You can say that again," agreed Thumper, trying to stifle a yawn. And, since yawns are contagious, Bambi's own yawn was not far behind.

"This was fun," Bambi told his friend. "But what do you say we go home and go to bed?"

But there was no answer ... for Thumper was already fast asleep!

THE INCREDIBLES

A Job for the Incredibles!

Mr Incredible, his wife Elastigirl and their children Violet and Dash had just defeated a deadly robot created by Syndrome.

Syndrome's real name was Buddy, and as a boy he'd wanted to be Mr Incredible's sidekick. When Mr Incredible told Buddy that Supers were born, not made, Buddy had vowed to prove him wrong.

Syndrome had created an Omnidroid robot that only he could defeat. He sent the robot to the city and turned up at the last moment to 'save the day' – but his plan had gone wrong. The robot had turned against him, and the Incredibles had saved the city instead. Syndrome was angry.

Later, when the Incredibles went home, they found a new sitter had come for their youngest child, Jack-Jack – it was Syndrome!

"You stole my future," said Syndrome. "I'm returning the favour! Don't worry, I'll be a good mentor … and in time, who knows? He might make a good sidekick!"

Syndrome blasted a hole in the roof and flew off with Jack-Jack towards his waiting jet. But Jack-Jack was upset. He began to cry and wail. Then he began to transform using Super powers! Suddenly Syndrome was no longer holding a sweet baby, but a flaming monster! Jack-Jack tore through Syndrome's rocket boots. Syndrome quickly dropped him and raced for his nearby jet.

Mr Incredible and Elastigirl were shocked. Until now, they thought Jack-Jack didn't have any Super powers!

Mr Incredible used his strength to throw Elastigirl into the air. She caught Jack-Jack and then stretched out into a parachute to bring him safely back to the ground.

"This isn't the end of it!" Syndrome raged. But he was wrong. Mr Incredible picked up a car and threw it at the jet. Syndrome's cape got caught in one of the engines and with one last yell, he was gone. As the jet exploded, Vi protected her family with a force field – the Incredibles were safe.

"That's my girl," said Elastigirl.

The Incredibles returned to their undercover life. But fitting in was just a little easier now. Vi was more confident and Dash was allowed to use a little of his Super speed by running on the school team.

But as the Super family left school sports day, the ground began to rumble. A monstrous machine broke out of the earth, with a menacing figure riding on top of it. It was time for the family to put on their masks and change into their Super suits. This was a job for the Incredibles.

Mickey's Night Before Christmas

Twas the night before Christmas, and all through the town, most creatures were stirring and scurrying 'round.

The stockings were hung by the chimney with care, while Mickey sat back in his big comfy chair.

When out on the lawn there arose such a clatter, Mickey sprang from his chair to see what was the matter. Away to the door Mickey flew in a flash. Had Goofy arrived with his usual crash?

Then what to his wondering eyes should appear, but a jingle-bell sleigh – were those really reindeer? And a little old driver so cheerful and bright, could this be Uncle Scrooge? Yes, it was! What a sight!

"Yoo-hoo!" called out Minnie. "May we join the fun?" And Morty and Ferdie showed up on the run.

"Hiya, pal!" came a voice from a Pluto-led sleigh.

"It's Goofy!" cried Huey. "Grab snowballs! Let's play!"

Just then, "Time for dinner!" rang out through the house. Every creature was stirring – each dog, duck and mouse!

Pass the turkey and stuffing and cranberries, please! Mashed potatoes, gravy, carrots and peas! Seconds for anyone? Now, don't be shy. Did you get enough food? Did you save room for pie?

When they'd filled themselves up from their heads to their shoes, they all settled down for a short winter snooze. Each found a spot and soon dozed in their beds, while visions of Christmas treats danced in their heads.

Then out of the sky flew a wonderful sight: it was jolly St. Nick on his Christmas Eve flight! St. Nick crossed the roof with a leap and a bound, and sprang to the chimney, not making a sound.

On the hearth down below, Pluto thought, *What is this?* as a clump of wet snow doused the fire with a hiss. Then all of a sudden, a man all in red, plopped right down that chimney ... and patted his head!

"Merry Christmas!" he said, giving Pluto a hug. Then he left a big sack on the living room rug. And laying a finger aside of his nose, and giving a nod – up the chimney he rose.

The clock chimed at midnight and on the last stroke.... "It's Christmas!" yawned Grandma. Those nappers awoke!

"Let's open the presents!" the kids called with glee.

"What's this?" Mickey asked. "There's a sack by the tree! Now we all have our gifts, so let's give a big cheer! Merry Christmas to all, and a Happy New Year!"

A Merry Christmas

"Merry Christmas!" Ebenezer Scrooge crowed as he watched the Cratchit children open the gifts he'd brought.

"A teddy bear!" Tiny Tim exclaimed. His sister had a new doll, and his brother was busy playing with a new train set.

"And there's another present too," Scrooge said with a twinkle in his eye. "I'll be right back." A moment later, he reappeared, carrying a big package wrapped in red paper and tied with a giant green bow.

The children ripped off the paper and squealed in delight.

"Father, it's a sledge!" they cheered.

"I can see that," Bob Cratchit replied, looking up from the turkey he was carving. Scrooge had brought the turkey over that very morning.

"Can we go sledging? Can we? Can we?" the children chorused.

"Of course," Cratchit replied. "But not until after dinner."

"And dinner is ready right now," Mrs Cratchit said.

"Dinner!" the children shouted as they scrambled to their seats at the table.

Mrs Cratchit sat down at the table. "I can't remember when we've had such a feast, Mr Scrooge," she said happily. "Thank you."

Scrooge raised his glass in the air. "That's what Christmas is all about," he said warmly. "Happiness and goodwill."

Everyone clinked glasses, then got busy eating.

"Now, how about that sledging?" Mr Cratchit said when they had eaten.

Minutes later, everyone was wrapped up. Scrooge pulled the children through town, singing Christmas carols at the top of his lungs.

"Why is everyone staring at Mr Scrooge?" Tiny Tim whispered to his father.

Mr Cratchit smiled down at his son. "Because they like him," he said.

"I like him too," Tiny Tim said, as Scrooge pulled the sledge to the top of a hill. Everyone climbed off to look at the steep slope.

Scrooge picked up the sledge and walked several paces away from the top of the hill. Then, taking a running start, he jumped onto the sledge and raced to the bottom.

"Whoopeeee!" he cried.

Then Scrooge pulled the sledge back up the hill. "Who's next?" he asked, panting.

"Me!" Tiny Tim shouted. Everyone else got a few turns too.

Later, as he pulled the children back to their house, Scrooge felt warm despite the chill in the air. This was the merriest Christmas he could remember.

Peter Pan
Return from Never Land

After Captain Hook had brought Wendy's daughter, Jane, to Never Land, she had met Peter Pan, Tink and the Lost Boys. Her mother's stories were true! But even though she'd seen them all with her own eyes, Jane still refused to believe in the magic. And she especially refused to believe in fairies.

"If Jane doesn't believe in fairies, Tink's light will go out forever!" said Peter, after Jane had stormed off.

Peter and the Lost Boys set out to find Jane, but Hook found her first.

"That pesky Pan stole my treasure. Help me get it back and I'll take you straight home," he said, handing Jane a whistle to blow when she found the treasure. Jane wanted to go home, so she agreed and headed back to find Peter.

The Lost Boys were happy to see Jane again. They took her on an exciting adventure through Never Land.

"Why don't we go on a treasure hunt?" Jane suggested. The others thought it was a good idea, so the search began and soon, Jane found herself in Dead Man's Cave with Hook's treasure! Peter was so impressed that he made Jane the very first Lost Girl. Jane was so honoured that she threw the whistle away and decided to never tell Hook about the treasure.

But one of the Lost Boys picked it up and gave it a good blow. Moments later, Hook and his pirates entered the cave and captured Peter and his gang.

Peter thought Jane had betrayed them. "Because you don't believe in fairies, Tink's light is going out!" he cried.

Jane felt terrible and left to find the fairy. When Jane found Tink, her light had faded to almost nothing. "I'm so sorry, Tink!" Jane sobbed.

Tinker Bell's light began to flicker back to life. Jane had started to believe!

On the pirate ship, Hook had tied the Lost Boys to the mast and was about to make Peter walk the plank.

"Not so fast!" someone shouted. It was Jane – and Tinker Bell was at her side! Hook was so surprised that Jane managed to snatch the key from him and free Peter and the Lost Boys, while Hook's crew stood gaping in shock.

An angry Captain Hook chased Jane up the mast. "Give up, girl!" he snarled.

"Never!" cried Jane. And thanks to a little pixie dust, she jumped off the mast and flew out of Hook's reach! When Hook tried to grab her, he tumbled overboard and into the ocean!

Before long, Jane was back home in London. When it was time for Peter and Tink to leave, Jane ran to the open window.

"I'll always believe in you," she promised Peter and Tink. And she kept her promise.

Disney · PIXAR

MONSTERS
UNIVERSITY
Team Wazowski and Sullivan

Only the bravest of brave monsters enter the human world from Monstropolis. The Scarers of Monsters, Inc. risk their lives daily, gathering screams from human children to power their world.

So when Mike Wazowski and James P. Sullivan, students at Monsters University, entered the human world without permission and found themselves stuck, they needed to think fast!

Dean Hardscrabble, the head of the Scaring Programme at the university, had turned off the power to the door, so there was only one thing for it. Mike and Sulley needed to generate enough scream power to activate the door from the human side.

Now, Mike had discovered that he wasn't scary at all, and Sulley didn't have any confidence … but with Mike's brains and Sulley's fearsome roar, they made the adults chasing them scream and scream and scream!

The light above the door in the Door Tech Lab at the university powered back up. The adults' screams filled the scream can to the brim. In fact, all the other scream cans in the room filled up, too!

"Impossible!" said Dean Hardscrabble, just as Mike and Sulley exploded through the door.

"How did you do this?" asked Dean Hardscrabble in disbelief, but they didn't have a chance to answer. CDA agents burst in and led Mike and Sulley away.

They were expelled from the university. But there was good news too – their Oozma Kappa team-mates were in the Scaring Programme! Dean Hardscrabble had let them in as she was so impressed by their performance in the Scare Games.

"You're the scariest bunch of monsters I've ever met," said Mike. "Don't let anyone tell you different."

Everyone hugged. Then Mike and Sulley were on their way.

"So what now?" Sulley asked Mike.

Mike thought for a moment. "For the first time in my life, I don't really have a plan," he said.

Just then Hardscrabble appeared with a copy of the school newspaper. They were on the front page. "You surprised me," she admitted.

Mike looked at the newspaper. Next to their photo was an ad for mailroom workers at Monsters, Inc. Suddenly Mike had a new plan!

The friends got jobs working in the mailroom at Monsters, Inc. They knew that with hard work, there was nothing Team Wazowski and Sullivan couldn't do….

The Best Corn Festival, Ever!

The evacuation of Piston Peak was almost complete. The air-attack team was trying to douse the last of the wildfire flames and keep the exits clear.

Dusty had heard that two cars were still trapped in Augerin Canyon. It was his new friends Harvey and Winnie! Dusty went to help.

When he arrived, Blade, the head of the air-attack team, was already there, fully repaired and back in action.

Alone on the burning bridge, the couple trembled in fear. The bridge started to collapse and Harvey began to slip off it – until Blade threw him a line to hold him in place.

Dusty flew under the bridge with his engine screaming. His warning light flashed red, but Dusty couldn't slow down now, even if it meant destroying his precious gearbox. He had to keep going. Harvey and Winnie's lives depended on it.

He pulled straight up and skimmed the face of Whitewall Falls, filling his pontoons with water! It was a skilled and heroic manoeuvre.

With his warning light still flashing, Dusty turned back to the bridge and doused the flames surrounding Harvey and Winnie. They rushed to safety as the bridge collapsed behind them.

"Good move, partner," said Blade.

Dusty smiled. But then … *KA-CHUNK!*

Dusty's gearbox failed. His propeller stopped turning and Dusty Crophopper, racing legend, crashed into the forest far below.

Days later, Dusty, rolled out of Maru the mechanic's hangar. His firefighting friends were there to greet him. Maru had good news for Dusty: not only had he patched up Dusty's injuries, he'd used spare parts to build him a custom-made gearbox!

"I'd say you've earned that firefighters certification," said Blade.

Dusty cranked the engine and his propeller sprang to life! He was fixed and, best of all, he could now go home – as fast as he liked!

While he was away, Dottie had completely updated Mayday, Propwash Junction's only fire engine. But now Propwash had two certified firefighters – Mayday and Dusty – and the airport was open for business again.

The Corn Festival that Dusty had almost ruined got into full swing.

Chug got on the loudspeaker. "Ladies and gentleplanes, the Corn Fest is proud to present the Piston Peak Air Attack Team and our very own … Dusty Crophopper!"

Everyone cheered as the firefighters flew by. Then Dusty, with his engine pushed to the max, came in low and soaked everyone.

BULL'S-EYE!

BIG HERO 6

Big Heroes

While battling the evil Professor Callaghan, Baymax had sensed life coming from inside a teleportation portal. Baymax and Hiro had entered the portal and found Callaghan's daughter, Abigail, who had been lost there when Krei's experiment had gone wrong.

Abigail and Hiro had managed to escape, but Baymax had been damaged inside the portal and was gone forever.

As Hiro came crashing out of the portal, his friends rushed over to him.

"Baymax?" Wasabi asked, worried.

Hiro just shook his head. They all saw the rocket fist Baymax had used to propel Hiro and Abigail to safety. Baymax had been a carer and a hero until the very end.

Paramedics arrived and began treating Abigail at once. She had been rescued just in time and was going to be okay. Callaghan stared sadly at his daughter as the police led him away.

Not long afterwards, the news channels covered the story of a mysterious explosion: "Reports are still flooding in about a group of unidentified individuals who prevented what could have been a major catastrophe. The whole city of San Fransokyo is asking, 'Who are these heroes and where are they now?'"

Hiro and his friends had never really thought of themselves as heroes. But if people wanted to call them that, it was fine by them! With Callaghan defeated, things finally began to return to normal. Hiro started classes at uni with his friends by his side.

Hiro was even assigned Tadashi's old workspace at the university's robotics lab. As he moved his things into the room, Hiro unpacked Baymax's rocket fist. It was the one piece of Baymax that Hiro had been able to save. With a gentle smile, Hiro gave it a fist bump.

Suddenly, the fingers uncurled and Hiro gasped. There, in Baymax's fist, was his green nurse chip! The robot must have held on to it, knowing Hiro would find it one day. This crucial chip contained all of Baymax's program and with it, Hiro could rebuild him!

And that's exactly what he did....

Before long, Baymax was back, and he was every bit as caring and cuddly as before. Of course, Hiro built him the same suit of armour and gave him the same skills, but Hiro knew now that those skills would only ever be used the way Tadashi had intended them to: for the greater good.

The team was reunited. If San Fransokyo needed them, they would be ready.

After all, they were Big Hero 6!

Disney · PIXAR

Cars

Rally to the Finish!

German racing superstar Max Schnell invited Lightning McQueen to the Black Forest Rally Race Invitational. Lightning was thrilled! He asked Mater, Luigi and Guido to come along as his race crew.

When Team Lightning arrived in Germany, they were greeted at the airport by Max then whisked off to a pre-race party. Lightning was happy to see two more World Grand Prix buddies there: Spanish racer Miguel Camino and French rally car Raoul ÇaRoule.

Later, Lightning told Mater he wanted to head to the Black Forest to practise on the racetrack.

An old gentlecar overheard their plans. "Black Forest at night, eh? Just beware of that Waldgeister Monster."

"A m-m-monster?" said Mater.

"I'm sure that 'monster' is just a legend," said Lightning. He and Mater drove out to the forest. They revved their engines and took off.

"Whee-hoo!" yelled Mater, as he raced down a tree-lined path. "This here's fun!"

The buddies drifted down roads and across bridges until ... Mater got lost.

"Lightning? Hellooooo?" yelled Mater.

Suddenly, Mater felt something snag his tow hook. "Who's there?" he gasped as he spun around. A huge figure loomed over him.

"AAAAAHHHHHH!" Mater screamed,

taking off backwards. "The monster's REAL!"

But no one believed him. The next day was race day. Lightning and the other racers pulled up to the starting line.

Mater drove out onto the track. "You guys aren't still gonna race, are you? There's a MONSTER!"

"There's nothing to worry about, buddy," Lightning said.

The green start flag dropped. Lightning sped around a tricky curve with Max, Raoul and Miguel right on his bumper.

Suddenly, the racers heard a low grumbling sound that shook the forest floor. It grew until a roar echoed everywhere! They stopped in their tracks, panic-stricken.

"It's the Waldgeister Monster!" yelled Lightning. "HE'S REAL!"

The cars raced for their lives! They sped down a rocky slope and skidded around turns. They raced full speed towards a river and leaped over it! The audience couldn't believe what they were seeing. All four racers crossed the finish line at the same time and they had all broken the rally record for the fastest time!

"What motivated all of you to race your best today?" asked a reporter later.

"Well, we couldn't have done it without the Waldgeister Monster," said Lightning.

Goofy's Sledging Contest

One chilly morning, Goofy wakes up to find snow outside his window.

"Yahoo!" he yells, jumping out of bed. "Winter is here!"

Goofy loves winter: getting bundled up in his warmest clothes, building snowmen and the crunch of snow. But Goofy's favourite thing is sledging!

Goofy has lots of sledges, but he wonders if there is a faster way down the hill. He looks for something that could work and finds just the thing … his surfboard!

Goofy runs outside and up a hill. He puts the surfboard down, jumps on it and … sinks!

"Gosh," says Goofy. "I guess I need something lighter."

Then he gets two bananas and puts the peels on his feet. He takes a step forward and … *BAM!* Goofy slips and falls into the snow.

"Ouch!" he says. "I guess I slip on banana peels, but they don't slip on snow."

Just then, Mickey comes along. "Why are you lying in the snow?" he asks.

"I'm trying to find the fastest way down the hill," Goofy explains. "Any ideas?"

"Hmmm," Mickey says. "I have a racing sledge that is very fast. You could try that."

"I wonder if it is faster than my sledges? We should all have a race!" says Goofy.

He calls Minnie, who calls Daisy, who calls Donald. Everyone is very excited!

Goofy's friends look for things to race on. Mickey takes out his sledge, Donald finds a blow-up raft and Minnie and Daisy choose a sledge with two seats.

Maybe a sledge is best, after all, Goofy thinks.

But which one should he use? Goofy can't decide. So he piles his sledges into a washing basket and drags them all to the hill.

The friends head to the top of the hill and get ready to race. Goofy takes out all the sledges, but he still can't decide!

"Everybody ready?" Mickey asks. "On your marks, get set …"

But Goofy isn't ready! He turns … and accidentally falls right into his washing basket!

"GO!" yells Mickey.

The race has started without Goofy! But then the basket starts to slip down the hill. It moves faster and faster until Goofy slides past his friends!

"Yahoo!" he yells, as he races to the bottom of the hill. Goofy has won!

"You were so fast!" Mickey says.

"What made you use the wash basket?" asks Minnie.

Goofy smiles. "I guess you could say I just fell into it!"